SLIM

SLIM

A Reporter's Own Story
of AIDS *in East Africa*

Ed Hooper

THE BODLEY HEAD
LONDON

First published 1990
© Ed Hooper 1990
The Bodley Head Ltd, 20 Vauxhall Bridge Road, London SW1V 2SA

Maps © Malcolm Porter 1990

A CIP catalogue record for this book
is available from the British Library

ISBN 0-370-31342-9

Printed in Great Britain by
Mackays of Chatham PLC

To Sue, Eileen and Eric,
for being patient

We started burying people from last Sunday – until now we are burying, we are burying, no resting, no resting.

Charles Sserwanga,
Gwanda parish, Uganda

The epidemic cannot be stopped in one country until it is stopped in all.

AIDS has the potential to bring us together, if we can thwart those who would use it to drive us apart.

Jonathan Mann,
Director of the WHO's
Global Programme on AIDS

CONTENTS

ILLUSTRATIONS

ACKNOWLEDGMENTS

I would like to thank the following people, all of whom have contributed, through their help or kindness, and in most cases both, to the completion of this book: Michael Anders, Jan Boxshall, Margaret Carswell, Wilson Carswell, Richard Carver, Jeff Crisp, Bert Dammers, Cory Dean, Chuck Elliott, Sandy Eriksson, Sally Fegan-Wyles, Alan Fleming, Chris Glaser, Rick Goodgame, Gill Gordon, Teresa Guerreiro, Bill Hamilton, Graham Hill, Lindsey Hilsum, Hilary Hughes, Sharon Kingman, Tobias Landau, Koert Lindyer, Sue Lucas, Nick Moon, Roland Neveu, Gerry O'Kane, Graham Peterson, Anthony Pinching, Tom Rayner, Ulrike Seibel, Arthur Stern, Nick Stockton, Mons Swartling, Helge Timmerberg, Andrew Timpson, Paul Upton, Jonathan Vickers, Ros Widy-Wirski, Mike Wilson and Jonathan Wright.

I would like particularly to thank Derek Johns, who from the outset has provided good humour and encouragement; it is only regrettable that circumstances prevented his continued involvement up to the day of publication.

A number of organisations have also offered considerable assistance, notably ActionAid, AHRTAG, Amnesty International, the Bureau of Hygiene and Tropical Diseases, Cafod, *Der Spiegel*, IPPF, the Panos Institute, Save the Children Fund, UNHCR, UNICEF, and the World Health Organisation, especially those involved in its Global Programme on AIDS.

In addition to the above named individuals there are very many people, mostly African, but all resident in Africa, who cannot be mentioned by name because to do so might conceivably cause them problems. Some of these people appear under pseudonyms in the text of this book; others do not. To these persons – and I am confident that those alluded to will know who they are – I offer sincere thanks for their assistance and kindness, which often went well above and beyond any conceivable call of duty. As a token of gratitude, The

Bodley Head and I have agreed to donate a percentage of the profits from this book to the indigenous Ugandan relief agency TASO – The AIDS Support Organisation – which is providing remarkable care and support for Ugandans with HIV and AIDS.

AUTHOR'S NOTE

Insomuch as any one person's recollection of events can be deemed to be accurate, I hereby declare that the events portrayed in this book took place as described in Africa and Europe between 1986 and 1989. In fact, in most cases the protagonists of *Slim* speak with their own voices, as transcribed from the sixty hours of recordings which I made; only occasionally, for reasons of comprehension, grammar or economy of space, have editorial changes been made, and then only to the words; not, it is hoped, to their sense.

In cases where the narrative relies on memory (as is the case, for instance, with the conversations involving Mike Rukeba, Sam Okware, Commander Katsigazi and Sue), I have done my best to be accurate and fair, but freely acknowledge that memory is something of a playwright, that recall tends to be coloured by self-interest. I hope that the recollections of others will not differ too markedly from my own.

In several cases, particularly with African sources, names have been changed to protect identities. Sometimes a person's profession has also been obscured, and in three instances the circumstances under which a conversation took place have been somewhat altered, always for the same reason.

ED HOOPER
1989

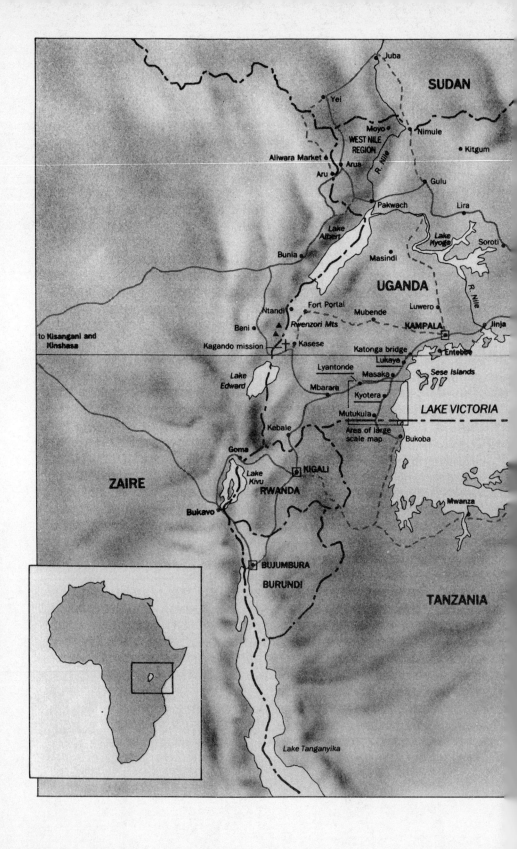

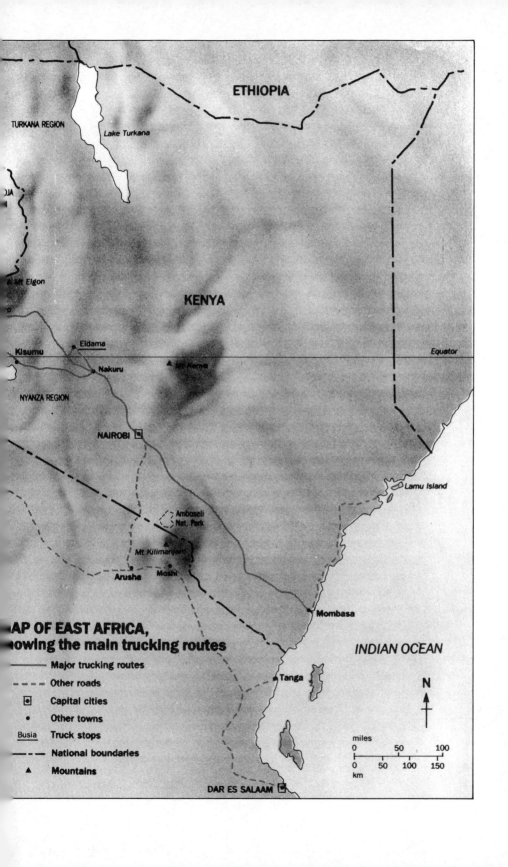

ETHIOPIA

TURKANA REGION

Lake Turkana

JIA

Mt. Elgon

KENYA

Kisumu   Eldama

Nakuru   ▲ Mt. Kenya   Equator

NYANZA REGION

NAIROBI ◉

Lamu Island

Amboseli
Nat. Park

▲
Mt Kilimanjaro

Arusha   Moshi

Mombasa

AP OF EAST AFRICA,
owing the main trucking routes

INDIAN OCEAN

————— Major trucking routes

– – – – Other roads   Tanga

◉ Capital cities   N
                                           ↑
• Other towns

Busia   Truck stops

—••— National boundaries

▲ Mountains

miles
0   50   100
0   50   100   150
km

DAR ES SALAAM ◉

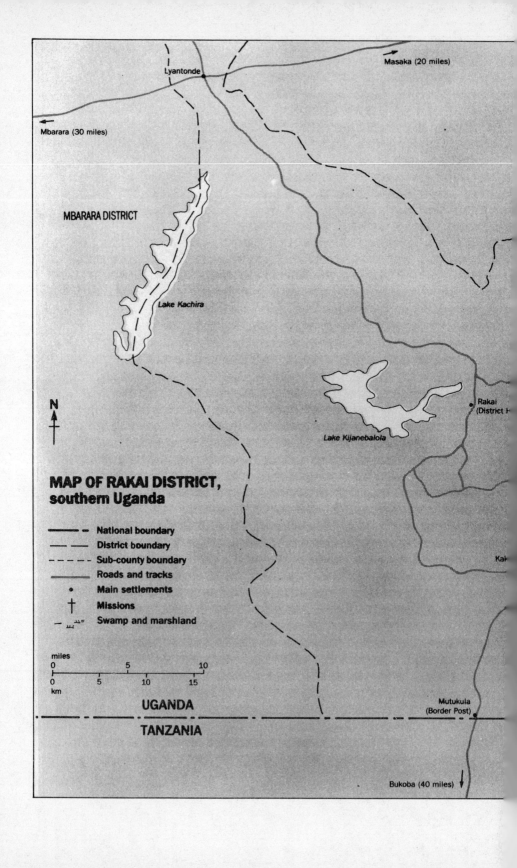

Lyantonde

Masaka (20 miles)

Mbarara (30 miles)

MBARARA DISTRICT

Lake Kachira

N

Lake Kijanebalola

Rakai
(District H

MAP OF RAKAI DISTRICT, southern Uganda

——— — National boundary
——— — District boundary
– – – – – – Sub-county boundary
———— Roads and tracks
• Main settlements
† Missions
Swamp and marshland

Kak

miles
0   5   10
0   5   10   15
km

UGANDA

TANZANIA

Mutukula
(Border Post)

Bukoba (40 miles)

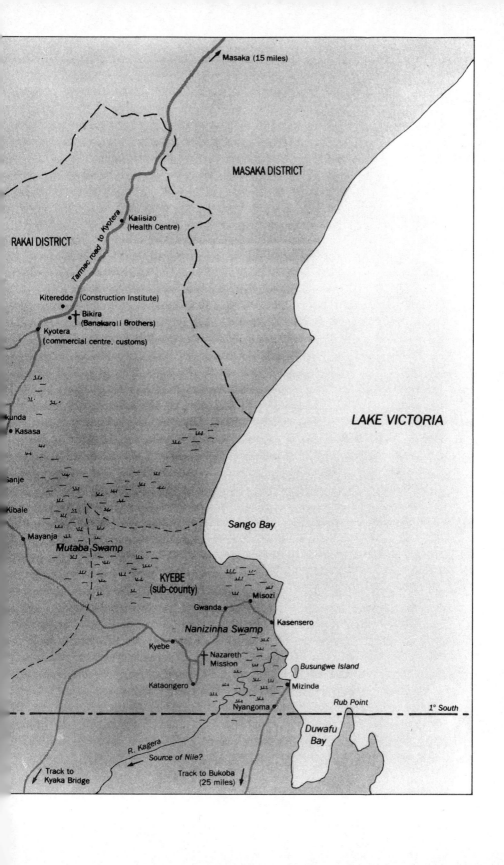

PROLOGUE

Early in September 1980 I crossed the border from Kenya into Uganda, and straight away began a love affair. As in most love affairs, we were not always happy together – in fact there were times when we loathed the very sight of each other, so much so that on two occasions I was sent packing most cruelly, without even a chance to put my side of the argument. And yet, although I sit here now a little more wisely, and say 'never again', and lick my wounds, were the object of my affections to let me know that I was welcome to return, that we could start again from scratch, that it was all a big mistake, can I really say that I would refuse without a second thought? I fancy not.

My love affair, I must now confess, was with a country and a people: the country and the people of Uganda, Winston Churchill's one-time 'Pearl of Africa' (though how his well-turned phrase has since come back to haunt the place!) By the end of that first evening, with my sleeping bag laid out on the roof of the Tourist Lodge in Kampala's main street, and with a tableful of new friends provided by the Canton Bar and Restaurant around the corner, I was already infatuated. And who could fail to be in this country of wit, of charm, of unbowed victims? These were the people who, less than eighteen months before, had thrown off the yoke of that most infamous dictator of the 1970s, Field Marshal Idi Amin Dada, Conqueror of the British Empire and anti-hero of the British gutter press. And I was not alone in my sentiments, for the other travellers who arrived in Uganda in late 1980, during what might be called the interregnum between Amin and Milton Obote – travellers like Tom the American (soon to become Kampala correspondent for the *Guardian*), David the Australian teacher, and Jean-François the crazy French motor-cyclist – all, without doubt, felt the same. All were smitten.

As for me, the honeymoon period was not over in a day, or a month, or even three months. It took much longer before I realised that my love was fickle, that she cared for me less than I for her. For long I persisted in bringing her tokens of my affection, gifts to prove my worth. Within a few days I had shaved off the beard which had adorned my chin for the previous eleven years. And my love glowed, for she honoured those who were smartly turned out. Then, before the end of the first month, I had embarked on a financial venture with some solicitous and charming and only-temporarily-strapped-for-cash local partners. We opened an import–export company together, I and they, I who had no business experience or acumen whatsoever, and they who were similarly qualified with the readies. And we exported one very small parcel of handicrafts, none of which were ever sold back in London, and we imported one very small parcel of Christmas cards, which went like hot cakes, being the only Christmas cards in Kampala over the festive period. Unfortunately, my partners neglected ever to hand over any of the resulting profit, due to their persistent problems of liquidity. In the end I got off very lightly, losing only 200 pounds in sterling and a couple more in sweat . . .

What other love tokens did I foolishly offer? Well, in order to convince my love that I was serious, I sought employment, a steady job – at least then, I thought, I could provide security. And within two months I, who had arrived with a rucksack and two spare shirts, had procured a post with the United Nations, as transport officer for the World Food Programme. At that point, WFP had just taken over responsibility for helping the pastoralists of Karamoja, who were suffering one of their periodic famines. As it turned out, my job was far from onerous: the office was run by a hard-working boss who found it almost impossible to delegate, and who was anyway loath to send me up to the famine areas, lest I run up too many juicy per diem allowances in foreign currency, and upset his budget. Looking back now, of course, I should have put the plight of the starving above the principle of fair pay, and offered to travel up to Karamoja for nothing – instead of sitting twiddling my thumbs in the under-ventilated UN building. I did not, however, and to my discredit instead got drawn into the greedy games of money and allowance-grabbing which preoccupied many of the expatriates in the office. All this while the local employees were receiving a thirtieth of my salary, and a hundredth of those of the international staff.

I offered other proofs of my affections also, proofs which it is now better that I refrain from mentioning. Suffice it to say that, from the start, Uganda knew that I was hooked.

By this time, in 1981, great changes had taken place in the political arena. The former president, Apolo Milton Obote, had returned to power in a bitterly-disputed election victory which had somehow received the blessing of a visiting 'Commonwealth Observer Group'. (It is depressing to find that Britain, in this case through the offices of the Commonwealth Secretariat, still frequently exerts a very negative influence on Uganda.) The victory was effected by a variety of different ruses. Several candidates for Obote's party, the Uganda People's Congress, were declared 'elected unopposed' after rival candidates were forcibly prevented from registering; the Chief Justice, who would investigate cases of alleged malpractice, was replaced by a UPC functionary, as were the district commissioners who served as returning officers; and, at the death, the job of vetting and announcing the results was taken over from the Electoral Commission by Obote's vice-president-to-be, Paulo Muwanga. This hollow victory was then celebrated by two hours of orchestrated gunfire in the streets of Kampala by the so-called Uganda National Liberation Army. It was this army, the UNLA, which in early 1979 had aided the Tanzanian army, the TPDF, in the ousting of Idi Amin. And it was the same UNLA that now kept Obote and his cronies in power for the next five years, and in so doing probably caused more death and destruction than even the thugs in dark glasses whom it had earlier chased across the Sudanese border.

It is worth noting that one Yoweri Museveni stood in the elections, and was defeated, probably quite legitimately, and that his political party, the Uganda Patriotic Movement, succeeded in picking up only one seat. Nevertheless, two months after the elections, in February 1981, Museveni and his supporters went to the bush in protest at the fraudulent vote, and subsequently attacked Kabamba, an important army barracks in the west. By 1982, his group had renamed itself the National Resistance Army, or NRA, with a political 'parent' known as the National Resistance Movement. It quickly became the leading guerilla opposition to the UPC government, the most politically-motivated and the most militarily effective of three or four such rebel organisations.

And there was much to oppose. Already, even before the elections, the UNLA had flattened a large part of West Nile region, the former power base of Idi Amin. In the years that followed, the 'treacherous' Banyarwanda and Bahima (who were presumed to be supporters of Museveni), the 'arrogant' Baganda (Uganda's most populous and influential tribe, who inhabit the region of Buganda, the country's heartland) and the 'ungovernable' Karamojong in the north-east, all found themselves victims of the UNLA's heavy-handed terror tactics. The nights around Kampala and other major towns were punctuated by the regular sounds of gunfire, known laconically by the locals as 'popcorn'; in the mornings there were always looted homes, always bodies. The roadblocks which were arbitrarily set up around the country became established venues for extortion and murder. The Obote government constantly cited the presence of 'bandits' (as it was wont to refer to guerillas) as the reason why the civilian population had to be 'controlled'. The common man was on a hiding to nothing.

Nowhere more so than in Luwero district. It was from here, in the lush and densely-populated northern part of Buganda region, that Museveni and the NRA decided to mount their early operations. The region quickly became a war-zone, with each guerilla attack being followed by army reprisals on the local villagers. The young UNLA soldiers, predominantly drawn from the Nilotic north of Uganda, presumably lived in constant fear of ambush as they travelled along the narrow murram roads, hemmed in on every side by swaying grasses as tall as a tank. And as their terror mounted, they became ever more violent in their dealings with the local Bantu population. 'The only good Muganda is a dead one' was scrawled across the walls of many a ruined trading centre. Eventually, in 1983, the remaining civilians were rounded up into 'refugee camps', and Obote's government petitioned international assistance for those 'displaced due to banditry activities'. In fact, the camps were little better than concentration camps, set up to deprive the NRA of its moral and material support base. The infamous 'Luwero Triangle' was well and truly born.

At this stage I had finished my contract with WFP, as well as another short-term contract with UNHCR, the United Nations High Commissioner for Refugees, but I was happy to stay on in Uganda. By then I was living rent-free in a beautiful house on Mutungo Hill, overlooking Lake Victoria – my part of the bargain being to renovate the place. Since, during the previous two years, it had been looted down to its toilet and electrical fittings, this was a job which kept me busy for some time. I still had most of my UN wages, so money was not a problem – and somehow, the days seemed always to fill themselves pleasantly enough. I spent time picking up bits of second-hand furniture, locating spare parts for the Honda 90 I had bought, exploring the small villages around Kampala and the lake shore, jotting down vignettes in my notebooks . . .

Some time during late 1982, I dusted off my rucksack, and set off on a short safari to eastern Zaire. I spent two weeks there, speaking halting French, dancing to the sounds of Lingala, and drinking tall bottles of 'Primus', the excellent Zairean beer. When it was time to return, I decided to go via West Nile region, the destruction of which I had detailed in a confidential report for the UN nearly two years before. In Arua, the main town, I found that all the Kampala flights were full, so I had to head back home by lorry.

Towards the end of the two-day, 300-mile journey, the road passed through the Luwero Triangle. As soon as we reached the area, it was clear that something was very wrong. The roadblocks were even tougher and more brutal than usual, and the homesteads that we drove past seemed quite deserted. Many of the houses had their doors, window-frames and roofs ripped out. At one point on the road, about a dozen drunken soldiers flagged us down, and then forced their way on to the back of the lorry. Although I could not understand their language, their general tone of abuse and intimidation was unmistakable. Soon they began to demand money from the thirty or so people on board, which all but myself agreed to give. On several occasions they shouted to the driver to stop, so that they could loot something – a bag of charcoal, a bunch of bananas, a goat – from the houses by the roadside. Everything was done quite openly; for once, I was also treated to the sort of casual thuggery which Ugandan citizens were forced to suffer on a daily basis. Normally, for better or worse, the presence of a *muzungu*, a white person, tended to inhibit the process.

When I returned exhausted to Kampala, I went straight to visit my then-girlfriend, Grace, at her flat in the centre of town. Just before dark, some friends of hers, also Langi (the northern tribe of Obote, and of 'the man behind the throne', UNLA Chief of Staff David Oyite-Ojok) called by to say hello. They were three sisters, all tall and beautiful, and before long one of them had gone off to fetch some *waragi* (the local liquor, made from cassava or bananas). What with my tiredness, and the alcohol, and the attentive, flirtatious company, I got careless. Abandoning all restraint, not bothering to hide my disgust, I told the tale of the soldiers in Luwero. Later, as the eldest sister took her leave, she whispered to Grace: 'What are you doing with this man? You are going out with a spy.'

She told Grace that she was a friend of Oyite-Ojok, and would be informing him of the conversation. Grace and I did not waste time debating whether or not the threat was serious; after a long, sleepless night, we fled to Kenya. While there, the strain began to tell, and we decided to end our relationship of fifteen months. But once back in Kampala, I thought it best that we resolve the situation by visiting the eldest sister to confront her with her threats. This attempt to call her bluff misfired, however, when several 'UPC youth-wingers' (the title bestowed upon semi-official party hacks and security boys) walked in, and then disappeared again into the night with Grace in tow. I spent the following day visiting the various official and semi-official security headquarters around town, demanding to be told where she was being held. Nobody knew a thing.

Eventually, at four o'clock in the afternoon, Grace reappeared in tears. She had been taken to Nile Mansions, the former luxury hotel which Oyite-Ojok and his fellows had converted into their private living quarters and torture centre. Fortunately, being 'of the right tribe', she was quickly released, but early the following morning she was rearrested, and taken to UPC headquarters where, for seven hours, she was questioned about her relationship with me. Eventually she was dispatched to bring me in for questioning. The interrogation turned out to be courteous and proper, but I was required to write down all my activities since entering Uganda, and details of the conversation of that evening a fortnight before. During the questioning, it became clear that the eldest sister had considerably embellished her story, to give it more weight.

The significance of all this was simply that I was now known to the authorities, having been officially interrogated, and a file on me now existed, even if it had not done so before. That file was to grow over the next two months. First the UPC boys who had taken Grace that night wanted to buy me drinks, to be my friend. Then others began harassing me on the street. One, observing that I still had a British number plate on the Honda, told me, 'You have a file this thick just sitting on my desk. I can pick you up any time I like.' Like his colleagues he was, of course, looking for *chai* (tea, or a bribe). But I was stubborn. I told him to fetch the police if he had charges he wished to make.

The next major incident was the shooting of my nearest neighbour, an Asian businessman. I heard the shots, at about eight o'clock one evening, but such sounds had become so commonplace by then that I thought little more of it. Until the morning that is – by which time the whole hill was abuzz with the news. I walked down to his house, which was about 200 yards away, and someone told me the full story. It seems that he had returned from Mbarara, in western Uganda, after dark the night before. He had just completed a business deal, and was carrying about 3 million Ugandan shillings which, even in those days of hyper-inflation, was a lot of money. Someone, a disgruntled employee perhaps, must have informed on him, because a few minutes after his return some military police from Luzira barracks, a couple of miles away, burst in through the front door. They instructed everyone present – some six people – to lie face-down on the living-room floor. Then they ransacked the house. It did not take long to find the money. As they were leaving, one of them casually walked up behind the businessman, and machine-gunned him in the back of the head. When I left, they were still trying to wash the blood from the walls.

I have never been sure why the incident had such an effect on me. It was partly of course the fact that I knew the man. It was partly the proximity to my own home, although robberies and shootings were endemic in the area, and, a few weeks before, I had had to remove the better part of a truckload of soldiers from my garden, while their commander weakly explained that they were on a 'night exercise'. (The night exercise proceeded anyway, amidst much shooting, and ten homes on the hill were looted clean.) But finally it was, I think, the casual nature of the violence which impressed me. The protectors of the people were killing the people, the authorities were busily grabbing what they could, and nobody was safe any more. The whole edifice of society was crumbling, and it was no longer the fence that kept out the bad guys; it was one's own willpower. As a cathartic exercise, I got out a notebook, and wrote it all down.

And this was the notebook they found when they arrested me three months later. Of course I should have expected it. I'd had the warnings, I knew I was 'on the books'. I knew that I was someone they couldn't place easily. (A traveller? A United Nations official? Unemployed, without visible means of support, and always arriving in sensitive places – West Nile, Ankole, Luwero – at sensitive times.) But I'd survived being held up, having guns shoved in my ribs, attempts to rob my house. And I believed, quite simply, that I could cope with anything that came along. Then, out of the blue, came the hand on the shoulder. And I discovered that I could do absolutely nothing about it.

It happened at about lunch-time, one Saturday in March 1983. I was driving down the hill into town on the Honda, and two policemen were standing by the edge of the murram road. For some reason I stopped to talk to them, and even got out some cigarettes to offer around, something which I never normally did in such circumstances. Then another man in plain clothes emerged from behind a hedge, and ordered me to get off the bike. I thought he was joking at first, and laughed at him, but then he made to grab me, and I quickly dismounted. That was it. Suddenly I was entirely helpless, in the grip of circumstances quite beyond my control.

The arresting party, gathered at a junction slightly further down the hill, comprised the head of Special Branch, and about twenty assorted men from the police, the army, CID, and other, more shadowy, free-lance security groups. It all started very low-key (... Could I come down to the police station to help with some enquiries? ... I could leave my bike here, it would be looked after ...) and ended with my being hustled into the back of a Mercedes, and driven off flanked by armed soldiers. Someone informed the British High Commission, and the Deputy High Commissioner drove out to the police station where I was being held, and drove away again, having been told that nothing was known of my whereabouts.

About ten weeks before, with cash getting a bit low, I had joined three young British friends who were operating a small, independent construction company. I was taken on as a commission agent, going around ministries, embassies and aid agencies in a three-piece suit, showing photographs of completed jobs and touting for more work. The response was very good: the orders fairly rolled in. Then, at the beginning of that particular week, the firm was suddenly invited to become sub-contractor for a large and lucrative construction job at Bombo barracks, the largest military enclave in up-country Uganda, situated on the edge of Luwero district. I counselled against becoming involved: apart from the obvious dangers to life and limb from both UNLA and NRA, there was the untenable moral position of doing a job for the 'bad guys'. The general manager disagreed, and on the Friday travelled up with an engineer to view the site.

At the same time, it so happened that these three friends were looking after, for another friend, the house below mine on Mutungo Hill – the same one where the Asian businessman had been shot in December. And later on the Saturday afternoon, they too were arrested. Both the houses were searched exhaustively, and various innocuous items (T-shirts, quarter-inch maps, grinding stones and the like) were removed for examination. But then, as the afternoon drew to a close, we were driven off and dumped at four different police stations around Kampala. Our possessions, even our socks and shoes, were taken from us, and we were bundled into overcrowded cells for the rest of the weekend. No explanations were given, but it seemed clear that the Bombo contract was somehow involved. Perhaps we were viewed as a security risk – or perhaps as unwelcome business rivals.

On the Monday, we were taken back to the two houses, which were searched a second time. This time, however, items were found. In the house my friends were looking after – a gun, some fuse-wire, and a home-made aerosol bomb. In mine – drugs. However, my friends were luckier than I. The authorities made such a mess of depositing the 'evidence' at their place – planting a gun which was standard army issue, and leaving behind footmarks on the walls where they had climbed in – that my alleged co-conspirators had to be hustled out of the country on the next London-bound plane. I, meanwhile, was hauled off to court, charged with possession of Indian hemp, and after being granted bail (which might have allowed me to flee the country), also issued with a detention order. Twice they spelt my name wrong, and twice I refused to accept the document. But it was only delaying tactics; shortly afterwards I was driven off to Luzira Maximum Security Prison, officially under suspicion of 'acting, having acted, or being about to act in a manner detrimental to the peace and security of the state of Uganda'. It was here, in Luzira, that I first met Mike Rukeba, together with several other characters, from crooks to cabinet ministers, who appear later in this book.

The prison experience, which had a long-lasting (and, strangely, a largely positive) effect on me, is another story. And, as it happened, the ordeal didn't last very long. I discovered that most cases like mine dragged on for months without evidence being offered by the prosecution: the defendants were merely brought into court every fortnight for 'mention'. So, after two weeks, I took a gamble and pleaded guilty to the charge of possession: I was promptly let off with a fine. After a further two weeks, the detention order was without explanation rescinded, and I was released from gaol and driven to the border with two apologetic detectives and a couple of bags of clothes. I never did recover the rest of my possessions – I placed them in the care of a British plumber living nearby, who, instead of shipping them back to me in Britain as promised, sold some of them and kept the rest. But then Uganda's that sort of country.

The point of this long preamble is to give some historical perspective to the story which follows. Uganda, over the last twenty years of civil war and internal upheaval, has had a history as tragic as that of any other country in the world, Mozambique and Cambodia included. A series of dictators and power-grabbers have milked the country dry, leaving it one of the poorest in the world, and allegedly killing off as many as a million Ugandans in the process. The response of the Ugandan people (and of many of the resident foreigners) has been to survive no matter what. This they have managed to do only at the cost of a few moral compromises. Put bluntly, many people have had to learn to lie and cheat in order to stay alive. On the other hand, some tremendously positive qualities, notably a cork-like buoyancy and a wickedly sly brand of humour, have been added to an already exceptional national character.

After Luzira, it was small wonder that my love affair with Uganda didn't last in its original form. It became, instead, a case of love-hate. I had tasted the best, and also the worst (albeit that the worst for me

bore no resemblance to the worst for those in West Nile or Luwero).
Anyway, I still found the taste addictive. I couldn't leave it alone.

Seven months after I returned to England, UNLA Chief of Staff
David Oyite-Ojok was killed when his helicopter crashed on take-off
from an army camp in the Luwero Triangle. I had learnt a lot about
Uganda's political jungle during my month in Luzira, and I realised that
the death of the hard man had tremendous implications for Uganda's
future. I wrote an extremely lengthy piece on the subject, and touted
it round Fleet Street. Although no one printed that first feature, this
was my beginning in journalism. Soon I was getting articles into the
African magazines, and doing the odd news story for the *Guardian*.

Then, early in 1984, I was asked to write a booklet about Uganda
for the Minority Rights Group. I eventually spent seven months on
the research and writing, and during that time, I interviewed over fifty
people, including two past Ugandan presidents. The report, which was
published anonymously to protect friends and contacts back in Uganda,
comprised the first attempt at a comprehensive account of the human
rights abuses being perpetrated by Obote's regime and the UNLA.
When it was issued, in December that year, it attracted a fair amount
of attention, including much criticism by defenders of the President.

Early in 1985, I left for Sudan. As chance would have it, my
timing was good, for within the next two months, President Nimeiri
was ousted in a bloodless coup after sixteen years in power, and shortly
afterwards the terrible sub-Saharan famine became, to most people's
surprise, perhaps the major news story of 1985. I got some *Guardian*
front pages, I placed stories in several other magazines and newspapers,
and the BBC took me on as their (unsalaried) stringer in Khartoum.
Then in July came the news that Obote had been toppled in Uganda.

I waited until November 1985 before going back in, and then I
kept my head very close to the ground. The July coup was basically a
transfer of power within the UNLA from the Langi to another northern
tribe, the Acholi. But too many of the same people were still in powerful
positions for me to feel comfortable, even when surrounded by the BBC
'ring of confidence'. I was known as a man with a past history in Uganda,
whatever the rights and wrongs of that history. I felt a lot happier back
in Nairobi where the Kenyan President, Daniel Arap Moi, was hosting
peace talks between the official Kampala government, headed by General Tito Okello, and Museveni's NRM, which had by that stage set up
an interim administration in the south-west of the country.

I returned to England for Christmas, and was advised by NRM

contacts that, despite the peace agreement, a final move would be made on Kampala during late February, 1986. I made plans to return to Uganda by the middle of that month, so as to be in place in good time. But then, on 23 January, just as I was about to fly out of Khartoum to spend two weeks in Ethiopia, news came through on the BBC that Kampala was being attacked on nine fronts. The NRA had gone early. The next day I flew straight down to Nairobi, but already the flights into Uganda had been cancelled, and the land route was clearly unsafe, given the large number of UNLA soldiers who were fleeing eastwards. The NRA moved into Kampala on the 25th, and officially took over the government the following day. And on 29 January, the day Yoweri Museveni was installed as President, I flew in to take up my post as news stringer for the BBC, and a number of other print and radio outlets. The old feelings were all still there.

Many observers claimed that it was the first time that an indigenous guerilla movement had overthrown an African government without substantial external assistance (though others recalled FROLINAT in Chad). On a more local level, it was certainly the first time in post-independence Uganda that real power had passed from the hands of the Nilotic or Sudanic northerners, whom the British had left in charge of the army and police force, to the Bantu peoples from the south of the country, where the capital city and most of the business wealth was located.

The new regime promptly announced that it would rule according to a ten-point programme, the main tenets of which were the establishment of a popular 'grass-roots' democracy, the restoration of security, the rejection of religious bigotry and tribalism, and economic development based on both socialist principles and a mixed economy. The new emphasis on human rights had immediate and dramatic effects. The gaols were opened, roadblocks virtually disappeared, and the rule of law obtained for the first time in many years. No longer afraid of being illegally arrested, tortured or killed, Uganda's citizens even began to venture out on the streets at night once again. And soon, the 300,000-odd Ugandan refugees in southern Sudan and north-eastern Zaire started to return home in large numbers.

Thus, in those first few months of the Museveni presidency, there was a great deal about which journalists could write and broadcast. The war against the former army (now the rebels) in the north was not really won until early April, and there was much Western concern (some of it spurious) about the NRA's use of child soldiers, many of whom were the orphans of those killed by the UNLA. There were also the horrific discoveries to be made in the torture rooms of Nile Mansions, and in the deserted countryside of Luwero district. There, as the displaced began to trickle back into an area that had once supported three-quarters of a million people, the piles of human bones found around so many villages finally confirmed the opposition claims that Uganda had its own 'killing fields'.

By the middle of the year, most of us reporters were just about ready for a breather. But it was not to be. For we kept hearing stories about a mysterious killer epidemic that was sweeping through the south-west of the country. The culprit, apparently, was something called 'Slim' . . .

PART ONE

The Problem

1 · STORM CLOUDS

I still have the photograph. The young man, brown-skinned and hollow-cheeked, slender, not quite good-looking, is pictured on a straight road running through the swamp. Behind him, above the reeds and papyrus, is a steely grey sky, with clouds rushing in fast towards the camera. But the man himself, who stares off to the right, to where the lake should be, stands bathed in a golden light that seems to have crept in beneath the gathering gloom, singling him out for its particular attention.

Apart from its atmosphere of foreboding, the picture is interesting for two reasons. First because of the man. His name is Mike Rukeba, a local journalist whom I had first met three years before when we were both inmates of Luzira Prison. Rukeba, whose appearances long before the end were to become as welcome as those of the albatross.

And secondly because of the location, just a few miles south of the equator. For this has not always been a place of eery calm. These are the swamps that surround Katonga bridge where, eight months before the taking of the photograph, was fought the crucial battle of the civil war that brought Yoweri Museveni and his National Resistance Army to power in Uganda. Here, at the end of 1985, the two sides (the NRA and the ill-named Uganda National Liberation Army) faced off for several weeks. They peppered each other's lines with mortar shells and automatic fire as the fight for control of the bridge ebbed and flowed. Rukeba, in the photo, might even have been peering through the rushes in an attempt to make out the battle-dressed corpses which were said to lie rotting in the brackish water.

Legend has it that the NRA eventually won the day by crossing the swamps at night by dug-out canoe, and then cutting back behind the opposing lines. The Tanzanian army, the TPDF, is said to have done much the same thing during the ousting of Idi Amin in 1979. Whatever actually happened, Museveni's forces advanced quickly from Katonga to the capital Kampala, which they took with surprising ease at the end of January 1986. The ousted soldiers of the UNLA, like Amin's troops seven years earlier, took what loot they could carry and headed off northwards, or else slipped into civilian clothes and disappeared into Kampala's unlit back-alleys, hoping to avoid the vengeance of the mob. When it came down to it, neither of these armies of oppression was prepared to fight to hold on to power. The bullies were finally shown up for what they really were: more bombast than bomb-shell.

For several days after Museveni's takeover, the capital throbbed through the night to the sound of the victory drums. Long lines of celebrants wound their way through the streets, dancing and singing; every few minutes came the high-pitched ululating cries of women – that special, intense sound that denotes extreme joy over much of the African continent. In those heady days, most Ugandans – certainly most of those who came from the south of the country – believed that Museveni's victory marked an end to the corruption, misrule and tribally-motivated genocide which had characterised the previous regimes of Milton Obote, Idi Amin and Tito Okello.

Six months after Museveni's takeover, in the south of the country at least, little of this enthusiasm for the NRA and its political parent, the National Resistance Movement, had waned. Foreign journalists, like the two other passengers in the car that day – Jonathan Wright, the Nairobi-based Reuters correspondent, and myself, as Kampala-based stringer for the BBC and various magazines – privately agreed that the advent of President Museveni was a good thing for Uganda. The man had fought for his beliefs, he was a charismatic leader, and he, together with those who had accompanied him in from the bush, apparently had every intention of ruling fairly and wisely. He had pledged, for instance, that the NRM would provide an interim government which would hold power for a maximum of four years, after which free elections would be held. And only that month, in an unprecedentedly forthright speech at the Organisation of African Unity summit, he had attacked his fellow heads of state for their failure to speak out and publicly condemn the past human rights abuses that had taken place in his country. He had gone on to pledge that, in contrast to previous regimes, the NRM would make human rights a cornerstone of its policy.

Mike Rukeba, whom Wright had invited along that day for his local knowledge, was also quite clearly one of the converted. When I had first come across him in prison three years before, it had appeared that the authorities had suspicions that he was a guerilla sympathiser, a secret supporter of the NRA which was just then stepping up its operations in the Luwero Triangle. Be that as it may, Rukeba was certainly a member of the same ethnic group – the pastoralist Bahima/Batutsi – as Museveni and most of the NRA's military commanders. And that, in the mad days of 1983, was quite enough to get you put inside. In my own case, pressure from the British Foreign Office had led to release after just four weeks, but Rukeba was kept inside for over two years, until Obote's own overthrow in July 1985. There was little doubt that he too welcomed the arrival of the new regime.

But this was mid-1986; the revolution and its dramas had come and gone. Reporters like ourselves had begun to provide some rather less hectic background coverage of topics such as the rehabilitation of the war-ravaged areas. There were certain issues which raised political question-marks about the new regime, to be sure, such as the continued existence of a tribal élite in the NRA and NRM, and the banning of rallies and speeches and flag-waving by the old, largely moribund, political parties. But these were not yet perceived as being of very much importance. And indeed, the story we were following that day was not – overtly at least – a political story at all.

The three of us were on the track of the latest of the killer diseases which Uganda seems to spawn with monotonous and cynical regularity. During that same year of 1986, for instance, there were also serious outbreaks of sleeping sickness and bubonic plague. Normally such epidemics, even when they caused tens or hundreds of deaths, were dismissed by most foreign reporters as being of only limited news interest when viewed in the general African context of famine, disease and civil war. This epidemic, however, was different.

In Kampala's offices, bars and night clubs, it had become the latest topic of conversation. Whether people spoke in English, in the East African lingua franca of Kiswahili, or in Luganda, the language of the country's heartland, there was one word which kept cropping up, an incessant sibilance, a persistent whisper on everyone's lips. The word was 'Slim'. It made a dead, rustling sound, that of something which slips unnoticed into your home when you're not looking. Slim was Uganda's latest horror. Its victims seemed simply to waste away to nothingness.

Over the last twenty years Ugandans have become experts in coping with violence and suffering. They have developed a special love for euphemism and *double entendre*, knowing as they do the power of humour to debunk, to soothe and to heal. Thus the word 'Slim' – the shape of Western models, and the fit of fashionable men's shirts – was readily adopted as the nickname for this new and terrible phenomenon.

In Kampala, where the boundaries between fact and fantasy, information and disinformation, have been steadily eroded during the years of terror, the rumour mill is affectionately known as 'Radio Katwe', after a local suburb. With its masochistic love of doom and disaster, Radio Katwe was running Slim as the latest in a long series of soap opera hits. And there was no shortage of good material . . .

Slim was rife in Masaka and Rakai, the two south-western districts bordering Lake Victoria. The disease was spreading like wildfire, to Kampala and beyond. So many people were catching it – surely you'd heard about John, from the Ministry of Works? Slim had come across from Tanzania – the witches and sorcerers there had conjured it up as a punishment for Ugandan traders who had cheated them in the past. Not true – it had been brought by *saba saba*, the heavy field artillery from the civil war of 1979, which had released bad germs into the atmosphere. Wrong again, and sacrilege too . . . Slim had been sent down by God. It was retribution for the evil ways Ugandans had embraced as their country descended into chaos.

But even the enlightened minority, those who knew that Slim was virus-derived, that it was a local form of AIDS, the condition that was ravaging the homosexual, haemophiliac and intravenous drug-user populations of North America and Europe, even these informants insisted that down by the lake, people were dying like flies, that whole villages had already been wiped out. And thus the reporting team of Wright, Rukeba and Hooper was on its way – albeit a little uneasily – to investigate. Katonga bridge, which was effectively the entry point to Masaka and Rakai districts, seemed once again very much like a front line.

The photo, by the way, is not a bad one. In the foreground is Mike Rukeba's upper half, as he stares into middle distance. Behind him, still sharply focussed in the wide-angle lens, are the storm and the swamp. Months later, I told Rukeba that I had a copy of the photo for him. He waited several weeks, and then called round for it just as I was rushing to meet a deadline. As ever, his sense of bad timing was unerring.

Rather testily, I skimmed through my photographs to find the print for him and then returned quickly to my desk, hoping he would leave. But I was not to get off so easily, for he stood his ground, examining the picture minutely. Finally, he spoke. 'I think you will make me some more copies,' he said. I forget how I replied – that he would have to wait until the next time I went home to England, or perhaps that he could have copies made himself, direct from the print. There was another pause. 'It's a pity you cut off my legs,' he declared sniffily.

I got up, and began escorting him, gently but firmly, towards the door. 'You could take some more shots, with the legs in this time,' he added, in an attempt at conciliation. As I shooed him into the corridor, I told him it was most unlikely I would be taking any more shots of him, legless or otherwise. Belatedly, he noticed my anger. He was still spluttering a mixture of thanks and apologies as I closed the door behind him.

As the first cold droplets of rain began to fall on Katonga, I put away the camera, and the three of us jumped back inside the hired car. As we drove off, the skies opened, as if an enormous bucket overhead had just been tipped at an angle.

The taxi drove slowly onwards down the Masaka road, bouncing into submerged potholes, the windscreen wipers providing one second of clear vision in every three. Before long, the body warmth inside the car had misted up the windows, so that the driver was forced to lower his an inch, and then pass the single winding handle across so that Wright, in the front passenger seat, could do the same. In the back seat, Rukeba and I sat huddled as the chilling rain gusted on to our faces. The downpour made such a deafening roar on the roof that talking became difficult. It was a typical day out on the road in Africa: uncomfortable, yet at the same time exhilarating.

So, as the taxi guessed its way forwards through the sheets of tropical rain, as our shirts got wetter and the din grew louder, I nevertheless had a feeling of departure, of an adventure begun. I even grinned across at Rukeba for a moment and, perhaps a little nervously, he grinned back.

'I see Eddie is very happy on safari,' he shouted.

Presently, we could just make out the main street of Lukaya, the first trading centre in Masaka district. Standing under cover in the doorways and on the verandas of the small bars and restaurants were girls and young women in brightly coloured dresses. One of them spotted the two *wazungu*, or white men, peering out from the taxi, and she waved and shouted to us.

Lukaya is one of the truck-stops along the major supply route from Kenya which serves Uganda, north-western Tanzania, Rwanda, Burundi and the vast expanse of Zaire. Here, many of the long-haul lorry crews stop off for the night for food, drink and entertainment. In the months to come, many of the Western observers of the East and

Central African AIDS epidemic were to christen Lukaya and towns like it 'Trucktown' – though there was also another, blunter version. As it happened, since we had set off from Kampala on empty stomachs, I would have happily agreed to a truck-stop for some breakfast, but the rain was still tipping down, the road was disappearing beneath large, brown puddles, and we were already behind schedule. We drove on.

The taxi trundled through the regional centre of Masaka, past a bank and a hotel which appeared to have been flattened in an earthquake, though the earthquake had actually consisted of a shell or two from *saba saba*, and a number of rocket-propelled grenades fired at close range. Masaka was not the only town in this part of Uganda to have suffered the wrath of the TPDF, as the soldiers took revenge for Amin's wasting of the Kagera region of northern Tanzania in the latter months of 1978.

As we turned left down the road to the Tanzanian border, the rain began to ease off, and I pulled out my cassette recorder and some headphones. A month before, back in England, I had taped a remarkable BBC radio documentary about AIDS in East Africa made for the *File On Four* series. Although the reporter, Helen Boaden, had only spent a fortnight or so in Africa, she had managed to unearth a lot more information on the situation than had I, who was based permanently in Kampala. I began to listen through the tape once more, jotting down notes. The report was certainly well compiled, though sections of it seemed to be not just alarming, but alarmist also. Surely some of this was exaggeration?

Dr Rick Goodgame, an American working at Mulago, the central government hospital in Kampala, stated that there were no high-risk groups for the disease except 'being Ugandan'. Unlike Europe and America, where active male homosexuals and intravenous drug-users were thought of as the most vulnerable groups, the main route of transmission in Uganda was apparently through heterosexual contact. Goodgame claimed that 10 per cent of sexually mature Ugandan adults were already infected with the AIDS virus. Nelson Sewankambo, a Ugandan doctor from the same hospital, said that this figure could go as high as 30 per cent which, commented Boaden, would represent 4.2 million Ugandans.

An Irish doctor, Bernadette O'Brien, spoke of patients reacting with hysteria to the results of their blood tests, of overcrowding of wards due to the number of AIDS cases, of nurses being terrified to handle patients. She added that patients went around different hospitals looking for a cure, but were not averse to trying witchcraft remedies like dog's liver soup as well. Another young Ugandan doctor spoke of desperate patients committing suicide by electrocuting or hanging themselves. Boaden added that there were stories of whole villages being abandoned due to Slim. Benny Kanyanjeyo, a permanent secretary at the Ministry of Information (and formerly the private secretary to President Museveni), criticised the Ministry of Health for the slowness of its response. 'Are they shy?' he demanded. The picture presented was one of very high levels of infection, increasing numbers of people with full-blown AIDS, and of a quite inadequate government response.

Forty minutes past Masaka, at the end of the tarmac road towards the border, we reached Kyotera, the commercial if not the administrative centre of Rakai district. We discovered that the local arm of government, District Administrator Bob Kagoro, was himself in Kyotera, instead of sitting at his official desk in Rakai town, another hour away down a murram back road. He was occupying a VIP suite at the Milano West View Inn, one of the two new hotels in town. Wright and I decided that, in the circumstances, it would be diplomatic to request a chat.

When Museveni took over power six months before, he had replaced the old colonial title of District Commissioner with District Administrator. And whereas other officials were democratically elected by the local populace to the resistance committees which operated from sub-parish level upwards, the DAs were appointed from the top, by the President himself, and were very much his own men. Most of them were young, had fought with the NRA in the bush, and had already served in the so-called 'NRM Interim Administration' which had held sway in the south-west and west of Uganda for the final months of 1985.

Bob Kagoro, a handsome man apparently in his early thirties, was no exception. He welcomed us courteously to his suite, and immediately impressed us as a man of sincerity and quiet dignity. He weighed our questions carefully, and answered with an assurance that seemed to testify to his years of experience in the bush.

So it was that Kagoro gave us our first briefing about Slim disease, about AIDS in Uganda. He told us of the usual symptoms associated with Slim – the diarrhoea, loss of weight and appetite, vomiting, sores in the mouth and skin disease ('the skin turns dark and lacks life ... it looks funny'). He told us that Slim sufferers normally reported first to a local hospital, but when they experienced no physical improvement there, they tended to return home and resort to more traditional methods like herbal remedies and visits to the local witch-doctor. Finally they would give up hope, and simply resign themselves to death.

At about this point in the interview, I began to feel rather unwell.

I still don't know if this was due to the lack of breakfast, or to heightened sensitivity as a result of being in 'the AIDS zone' and discussing the subject in detail for the first time. Perhaps it was even because it had started to dawn on me that I myself had been taking some rather absurd risks. Whatever, I had to get out of the room. Leaving Wright and Rukeba to continue their questions, I took off for the toilet where I sat for the next five minutes with chin in hand, pinching my leg and trying to compose myself. Eventually I returned to the suite, but I felt queasy for the rest of the interview.

'The prostitutes have generally gone out of business,' Kagoro was saying as I re-entered. 'There is a serious restraint on dealings with them. Some have retreated back to the rural areas.' He went on to claim, as many other men were to do in the months that followed, that more men than women were dying of Slim. 'Are women merely carriers, or are they more resistant to the disease?' he asked rhetorically.

The DA also claimed that most sufferers were young men who, as traders or smugglers, had paid frequent visits to Tanzania. One of the worst-hit areas, he said, was Kasasa sub-county. Another was Kyebe, where Tanzanian soldiers had established a camp in the months that followed their ousting of Idi Amin in 1979.

We asked what was being done to warn local people of the dangers of Slim, and he told us that staff from the District Medical Office had been addressing the populace on the subject.

'Now we have gone a long way in putting calm in the district. We explain that modern medicine knows what is going on, that it is not witchcraft, that the means of transmission are mainly sexual, so people should restrict from their previous reckless habits in sexual relations. That things like mosquitoes, or merely sleeping in the same bed as a Slim victim, are not the means of transmitting the disease. That they should avoid sex when they can, and then stick to just one partner, and avoid syringes that are unsterilised,' he explained.

It was clear, however, that because of transport costs, not many such meetings had been held outside the main towns.

'Basically no money has been earmarked for this health education campaign,' he admitted, 'so we have to fit it into our mass mobilisation programme.'

The DA also highlighted what was to become something of a theme in the months to come. 'A number of Ugandan and foreign specialists have called into this district and taken blood samples. But that is the end of it. They do not come back to us with results. Personally I see us as being used as a source for experiments in the developed world.' Bob Kagoro is no fool, I remember thinking as we got up to take our leave.

I never saw him again, this man who provided me with my first real information about AIDS in Uganda. Within a year, Bob Kagoro was dead. There was never any official confirmation of the cause, but despite his apparently being 'swollen like a balloon' at the end, most local people insisted that Kagoro was yet another victim of Slim disease.

2 · RAKAI

The intrepid team of reporters decided to go next door, to the Colombo Guest House, for some much-needed lunch. Kyotera's two neighbouring hotels, the Milano and the Colombo, are single-storey structures of pale brickwork, which give the impression of being too smart for their rather seedy location. And they have an interesting history. Apparently two local businessmen who had been friends from youth, and who had amassed great wealth from their trading activities in the early 1980s, decided to travel together on a pilgrimage to Rome. Local legend has it that they were so inspired by the trip that upon their return they erected these two unlikely hostelries, though whether to the greater glory of God or Mammon is debatable. The Milano developed a reputation as a drinking parlour, the Colombo as a restaurant; and they quickly became popular venues, particularly for those engaged in the lucrative smuggling traffic between Uganda and Tanzania. The presence of so many rich men attracted large numbers of young women, who in turn attracted further male interest from as far afield as Masaka and Kampala. For two years, up until the new government's crack-down on smuggling in early 1986, the hotels had enjoyed phenomenal success: the alcohol had flowed, the girls had smiled, and the rooms had been full of happy punters.

But by the time we sat down for lunch that day, the downturn in the local black economy had well and truly taken hold. We were, in fact, the only customers. Nevertheless, our orders of omelettes, chips and coffee took an inordinately long time to arrive. As we waited, stomachs grumbling, we decided on our next move: to call in at a small hospital we had seen earlier as we entered Kyotera.

The Ahmadiyya Moslem Mission Hospital turned out to be a functional building of brick and corrugated iron which had opened just six weeks before, at the start of June; it was run by a Pakistani husband-and-wife team, Doctors Bajwa and Asifa Abbas. The

Ahmadiyya movement – an evangelical sect driven into exile by President Zia – had apparently chosen Kyotera simply because there was no other hospital in Rakai district. Dr Bajwa Abbas, who looked cool and smart with his moustache and starched white *galabea*, started to add that a further reason was the local prevalence of Slim, but then cut short his sentence. Whatever, it was clear that Kyotera's other doctors and health assistants were gratefully seizing the opportunity by referring all their suspected Slim cases straight to the hospital. Fifteen had been treated during the previous month alone, many of them already in an advanced state of sickness. One was a child who had had AIDS from birth.

Dr Abbas was, quite sensibly, cautious about speaking to us. He stressed repeatedly that we should not do anything that would alienate the government from the mission. He did, however, agree to tell us what he knew about Slim.

'When the immunological system is first affected, it's the digestive system which is vulnerable,' he explained. 'The water sources are not good here, so the patient often gets diarrhoea. The next system to go is the respiratory system. We treat the symptoms like diarrhoea, body rashes, weight loss, anaemia, fever, sores in the mouth – and they respond at first. But when treatment is finished, the disease recurs. Slowly, slowly, they go downhill. We don't know what the death rates are, because many are staying in the village areas to die. And the population in general is hysterical about this disease; people have developed a phobia. If a man gets diarrhoea one day, he rushes to his doctor. There was even a case of someone in this town who got a skin rash, and then just took insecticide and killed himself. We suspect heterosexual contact as the main cause, but we also know of three cases where sisters or brothers in the same family became infected. All died. Meanwhile, the price of condoms has gone very high – up to five thousand shillings each. The businessmen are cashing in.' (In those days, at the height of Uganda's inflation, 5,000 shillings was the equivalent of about 2 pounds of locally-purchased meat.)

'We have seen cases from all over the district, and cases from Bukoba, fifty miles to the south in Tanzania. We think it's in all the towns around Lake Victoria. Maybe it's because of the humid environment, maybe because there's more movement around the lake and the border.'

Dr Abbas stopped for a moment, and I seized the opportunity to ask what efforts were being made to inform the public about the risks. He told us there was a poster about 'the nature of the disease and how it is transmitted' on display at the Town Clerk's office in Rakai. Then I asked what he told patients when he knew they were suffering from AIDS.

'We don't tell the patient he has the disease: we reassure him, and give the treatment. If we tell him he has Slim, he will die in two days instead of one month,' he replied.

Heading back to Kampala, we picked up a hitch-hiker who was eager to talk about the epidemic. He himself knew of two cases of Slim, one a woman who now had skin 'like a frog's'. He told us that Slim was not caused by 'free sex', but by sharing needles for injections, or the straws that were commonly used for drinking *malwa*, the local beer. The prostitutes in Kyotera, he added, were telling people that Slim disease was not AIDS, but a special type of poisoning caused by certain Tanzanian tribes who were expert in witchcraft. When we questioned him further, he told us that a local priest had said at the funeral of a 'Slim victim' that the disease was like one of the plagues of ancient Egypt, striking down the immoral. Like Bob Kagoro, the hitch-hiker believed that men were more susceptible to the disease than women. It was interesting that the only person we had met thus far who did not concur was Dr Bajwa Abbas, the man in the best position to know, who spoke of there being a majority of female sufferers.

We drove back to Kampala with the landscape softening in the late afternoon sun. We made only one brief stop, at Kalisizo Health Centre in the northern part of Rakai district. There we spoke to a state enrolled nurse called Leo Rwabuche. In the space of five minutes, he provided the most disturbing account of the epidemic we had heard all day.

One person had died of Slim at the health centre earlier that day: Leo estimated that over the whole district between thirty and fifty died every month.

'Things have reduced a bit, since the epidemic in Kanabulemu sub-county: so many people died there in March. But the medical profession doesn't allow the doctors to tell patients that they have the disease, in case they lose heart. Instead, we only reassure. Sometimes the wives die a few months after their husbands. The prostitutes? They are moving away, and saying that they come from somewhere else – not Kyotera, not Rakai.'

Two years before, Rakai district had been renowned as the place to have a good time. Nowadays, it seemed, it was known as the place where you got Slim disease.

The next four weeks were hectic: there were so many good topics for articles and broadcasts. I investigated the so-called 'Monkey Boy of

Naguru' – who turned out to be mentally retarded, rather than raised by apes. He sat on his haunches, ground his teeth, and ate bananas when they were offered; but he also tried to eat grass, carpet, clothing, or whatever else came to hand. A few days later, visaless, I sneaked across the border into southern Sudan, from where I was able to report that the guerillas of the Sudan People's Liberation Army had managed for the first time to isolate Juba, regional capital of the south.

Later I spent some time interviewing families as they returned to the Luwero Triangle, where the struggle between the UNLA and the NRA guerillas had been most intense. It is said that as many as 200,000 people may have been unlawfully killed or starved to death in the course of the three years of fighting. Eventually, I was asked by UNICEF to script and direct a publicity film about that agency's efforts to rehabilitate boreholes and other water sources in Luwero. I spent three days planning the project with the proposed video cameraman, a visiting French photographer called Roland Neveu, before he was suddenly, and without explanation, replaced by a crew from Uganda TV. The following day I too was replaced, apparently because the TV crew objected to working with me on the grounds that I had had 'political problems' back in 1983. This was the first time under the Museveni regime that anyone had made a direct reference to my imprisonment – and although the TV crew later strenuously denied any involvement, I always suspected that they used my Luzira history as a convenient excuse for cornering the action.

To compensate for the film débâcle, Roland Neveu was setting off with Joseph, a lanky man from Karamoja in north-eastern Uganda who had become his driver and general factotum, on what was intended to be a freewheeling four-day safari through western Uganda. I asked if I could join them, and he readily agreed. Roland is a sturdy, weather-beaten man, of good humour and an easy-going nature, and although this was his first time in East Africa, he had experience of other Third World countries that belied his thirty-six years, as well as a number of scoops and famous front covers already under his belt. It promised to be a good trip. He had visited Kyotera two days previously and arranged a 'photo opportunity' with AIDS patients at the Ahmadiyya hospital, so we set off in Joseph's car with that as our first objective. I, having already filed an AIDS piece after my July visit to Rakai, was not especially eager to undertake further research into the subject. Little did I realise that Slim would become the focus of the entire trip.

As it happened, the 'photo-call' fell through: Dr Abbas had clearly had second thoughts about it, and he told us that all his AIDS cases had left for their homes the previous day. So we sat in the car outside the hospital, discussing where to go next. We knew it was no longer an auspicious time to be following up on Slim, for during the previous month, an article written by Blaine Harden for the *International Herald Tribune* had come to the attention of the Kampala authorities. Entitled 'Uganda Concedes it is Ravaged by Plague of AIDS', it had quoted the American doctor, Rick Goodgame, as saying that 'there is profound promiscuity in Uganda, and a virus which takes advantage of it. The average Ugandan has sex with great frequency, and with a great number of different partners.' The article as a whole, and Goodgame's statement in particular, were widely regarded as libellous by Ugandans in official circles, and almost overnight, AIDS had become a most delicate topic. No longer were reporters being welcomed by hospital staff, or local health officials.

'It is clear,' said Roland suddenly, 'that what we need to do is just go out and find some people with AIDS. What about these villages everyone is talking about, where half the people are already sick?' I began looking through my notebooks for names. I came up with three of them: Kasasa, Kyebe and Kanabulemu. When we asked about these at the local petrol station, it soon became clear that the latter two were actually one and the same place, situated on the lake, half a day's drive away. Kasasa, by contrast, turned out to be just down the road.

'There are very many insects inside his body,' said John Mukasa. John, a successful businessman from Kimukunda sub-parish in Kasasa, was speaking of his twenty-year-old son, whom local villagers had told us was sick with a strange disease. Further prompting elicited the information that the insects were actually viruses – 'very dangerous viruses'.

'Those viruses usually make him weak when he eats his food, so the food does not work well inside his body. He started getting sick in November last year, after he joined the NRA. When he was at Katonga, he started weakness and fever. After about two weeks, he reported back here to me. We started with our local treatment, and he became a bit all right.' Three years in Uganda had taught me that 'a bit all right' covered a range of conditions from having a very mild headache to being at death's door, so I questioned him some more.

'He became well for two or three days after getting medicine from the doctors. But then he went back to his weakness. One doctor told me that when they were fighting in the bush, it might be that he was injected with some injections that were not boiled well. And I believe that he might have been given blood by a certain person, and that blood was not examined well. And some food was not cooked well, and the way they were sleeping ... there were some insects in the bush there ...'

Mr Mukasa was becoming vaguer as he grew more distraught. Finally I decided to ask straight out if he thought his son had Slim.

'Yes, a doctor at Bwaise, near Kampala, told me that according to the signs he saw in my son, that it was AIDS, that fever which is down here in this area, that we sometimes call Slim.'

I wanted to know what he was doing now to try to help his son. Mr Mukasa replied with a long list of medical visits to Kalisizo, Masaka and Kampala, and then added that his son had spent the last fortnight with a woman healer near Masaka who used local medicines. When I pressed him further, he replied that 'she keeps her medicine confidential. When I went there last weekend, he was improving – even on his body, even on his face. He could eat some food, get a cup of tea; he could try to walk.'

The businessman went on to give me all sorts of details about the traditional healer in Masaka, how she asked for very little money for locating the medicine, and preferred payment 'after the body is OK'. But, as I discovered after packing up the recorder, Mr Mukasa had begun to wander from the truth. His son was no longer in Masaka. He was actually in the small tin-roofed house across the road, watching us from behind a curtain. We heard later that he was dying and that his father, understandably, had wanted to protect him from the microphones and cameras.

We were told that five people, all in their twenties, had already died of Slim in Mr Mukasa's village. Since the village appeared to consist of only about ten houses, we were a little sceptical. But some 2 miles down the narrow murram road, in a banana plantation on a downslope overlooking a splendid vista of rolling countryside, we came upon a cluster of six imposing graves, all cast in cement. We were introduced to Christopher Kagoro, who said that two of the graves belonged to his grandfather and grandmother, who had died in 1985. The other four, he said, were those of his brothers, who had all died in May, just three months before. I asked him how they had met their deaths, though I already suspected what his answer would be.

'They died of Slim,' he replied.

Christopher Kagoro spoke remarkably good English for a farmer living in a fairly remote village in rural Uganda, but our conversation was halting, and it occurred to me that we might well be entering into some misunderstandings. I called across for assistance from John Katamba, a young secondary school teacher whose help we had enlisted an hour or so earlier when we had stopped to ask directions in the village of Sanje.

John proved over the next few days to be an excellent translator, especially since he spoke well in both English and French. I continued the interview, with John translating for Christopher.

'How do you know that your brothers died of AIDS?'

'First of all it was fever and then diarrhoea and vomiting. It was a cycle that kept on coming like that. My brothers were ill for a long time and couldn't get cured. When people knew that they began saying it was AIDS.'

'Have other people in the village died in the same way?'

'So far ten people have died, and there are still some cases in the village.'

'What is the population here?'

'About three hundred people. They are very, very frightened, because they know that if anyone gets the disease they can't be cured.'

'And why do you think your brothers all died together, in the same month?'

'My brothers were very mobile. They used to move a lot because they had money and wanted to enjoy themselves. They were sexually very active.'

'Did they share a single girlfriend?'

'This disease is spread very easily. One can easily contract it from any woman.'

I have thought about this amazing interview on many occasions since. In hindsight, I realise its enormous significance, and know that I should have checked and double-checked more exhaustively. Although I got the names of the four brothers on tape, I should certainly have tried to establish the dates on which each of them died, their ages, the individual symptoms from which each suffered. Were they true brothers, or rather brothers in the African sense, a term which can, on occasion, embrace cousins and nephews and even other more distant male members of the extended family? Did they all really die of Slim? If so, what was the common factor in their deaths? Were they perhaps sharing a girlfriend, or a hypodermic needle? All I can say, looking back, is that I am satisfied that the story had a strong basis in truth, and was not merely invented for our benefit, to 'please' the European visitors. There were just too many bystanders and witnesses, including John, himself a local man, for it to have been a hoax. I believe that four young men from the same family died in quick succession, very possibly all as a result of AIDS. There are numerous other instances on record of siblings, and other non-sexual partners within a family, succumbing, in a short space of time, to a disease which might well have been brought on by AIDS – a phenomenon which would certainly bear further scientific examination. I only regret that I passed over my best opportunity to investigate the matter on a journalistic basis.

By this stage, however, we had still not encountered a single person who actually had Slim disease. And when we eventually did, it was almost by accident. It was late afternoon, and we were on our way to drop John back in Sanje, when the village grapevine led us to the house of Joseph Kasolo. Joseph, an emaciated man in his mid-thirties, had been 'very sick' for about four months with fever and diarrhoea. His hands shook uncontrollably; he had a persistent cough. He told us in a quiet, dignified voice that he had been to the local hospital, where he had been told that he had typhoid.

'That's what I believe. I don't have any evidence to show that I'm suffering from anything else. I don't think I have Slim,' he explained. (Earlier however, in his local language, he had told John that he suspected that he did have AIDS.)

'And the drugs you were given – did they help?' I asked.

'The diarrhoea has stopped for a while, but the fever continues, especially in the evening.'

'Have you lost weight?'

'I was certainly fatter than I am now.'

Joseph Kasolo was typical of many of the apparent Slim patients we encountered. There was no absolute medical proof that he had AIDS, rather than typhoid or some other disease. He had not been given a blood test which could prove whether or not he had the causative virus. The only real evidence was that offered by common sense, by our own laymen's eyes. Here was a man who was steadily losing both weight and strength, who was failing to respond to remedies either local or Western, and who, as it turned out, would probably have fulfilled the WHO clinical case definition for adult AIDS in Africa published at the end of 1985. As we departed, Roland held out his hand to Joseph Kasolo, and took his leave with a formal handshake; after a moment's pause, I did the same. It had taken that moment for the conscious mind to overcome subconscious phobias; I found later, however, that it is a bridge that only needs crossing the once.

Eventually, after dropping various resistance committee chairmen and local elders back at their rightful villages, the four of us – Roland, Joseph, myself and John Katamba, whom we had invited to join us – travelled back up the road to Masaka, to spend the night in a comfortable hotel. Despite our emotional and physical exhaustion, there was an air of tension and expectation in the car. We decided that in the morning we would drive down to Kyebe sub-county, on the western edge of Lake Victoria, and adjacent to the Tanzanian border. Everyone was telling us that in Kyebe the Slim situation was even worse.

3 · THE ROAD TO KYEBE

It looked more like a cart-track than a road, and not surprisingly Joseph, together with his prized Fiat 125, grew exasperated long before the rest of us. We started bottoming out just after the lorry graveyard, a couple of miles past Kibali junction where the Kyebe road splits from the main route south to Mutukula and the Tanzanian border. The old colonial milestone had indicated 22 miles to Kasensero on the lake, which sounded manageable, but suddenly the lorry ruts grew to 15 and then 18 inches in depth, and Joseph became ever more heated and protective of his machine. It was one of the worst roads that I had encountered in Africa.

For the next several miles, it became a long, straight causeway through the surrounding marsh. The scenery was bizarre, almost other-worldly; there was a sense of crossing over into an isolated and forgotten land. This feeling was compounded by the frequent intermissions in our journey; after a while when the car stalled, or got stuck in another rut, we three passengers would make our exits in silence, to push from behind, to gather stones and grass to place under the wheels, or simply to walk ahead to a point where the road was clear again. Even Joseph stopped bemoaning the presumed damage to his car, and grew quiet. All of us were tired with the numerous delays. But also, I think, we had fallen victim to the strange and eery beauty of the place.

The swamp stretched away in all directions to wooded hills in the distance, the steady sweep interrupted only by the occasional bushy thicket or clump of palm trees. Dragonflies whirred past, hurrying between their several ports of call – but there were few of the irritating insects that like to sting, or settle in clouds around one's head. The morning was deliciously fresh; the air crisp and sharp. Speech sounded harsh and unwelcome – a drunken shout in a cathedral.

We must have been in the swamp for a couple of hours, for the sun was approaching its zenith and the day growing hotter, when the first herd of cattle suddenly materialised around us. There had been no sound of lowing, no visual sighting of their approach, but suddenly there were fifty or so long-horned cows cropping the tussocks contentedly, just a few yards away. These were Ankole cattle, justly famed for their sturdiness, which they advertised with fine horns curving up graciously, for 3 feet or more, from massive foreheads. These horns are the object of veneration by the local pastoralist tribes: they are celebrated in the folklore of the Banyankole, the people after whom the cattle are named, and they are mimicked in the arm-waving, foot-stamping *guhamiriza* dances of the Batutsi, who brought their herds with them when they fled the civil war in Rwanda in the early 1960s.

All around the cows, sometimes riding on their backs and shoulders, sometimes hopping to and fro on the ground, were pure white cattle egrets, flicking and probing with their long pointed beaks. Two young Batutsi boys, no more than eight years of age, were guarding the herd, though it was some time before John pointed out to me where they stood, in the shade of a palm tree just 30 yards away, resting one-legged, supported by their sticks, and watching our party with the frankest of interest. As we smiled and waved at each other the egrets, disturbed, rose as one to settle in the branches of a tree, and the boys shouted out something which John answered by pointing down the road. A short conversation ensued, during which the boys wandered closer, beautiful with their slender frames and high, sloping foreheads. Then, suddenly, it was over, they had turned to follow the herd, and with a final backward glance, and a stone thrown casually but accurately to summon an errant cow, they had disappeared into the grass and the bushes.

We only met one other vehicle on the way to Kyebe. From a distance, it resembled an Arab dhow, leaning and tacking to an inshore breeze, for the canvas on top was high, rising to a pinnacle, and the whole structure inclined gracefully, sometimes perilously, first to one side, then to the other. It was only on closer inspection, after we had billowed towards each other in absurd slow motion, that we could identify the vessel as a battered Land-rover pick-up piled high with goods – concealed by a tarpaulin – and people. I asked Joseph to stop, and got out to take some photographs of the approaching vehicle, but soon I could make out the passengers' faces in the zoom, and could see that they were stony: nobody smiled or waved as is customary when vehicles meet on lonely roads in these parts. As the pick-up drew level we called out some greetings, and I shouted 'How far to Kyebe?' but only a couple of voices responded, and these were lost as the driver revved hard to keep the wheels spinning and bucking over the ruts. Only when they were safely past us did the twenty or so passengers on board begin to wave – and then in unison. We could almost feel their collective sigh of relief.

'So, Eddie, what do you think of your first band of smugglers?' laughed Joseph, who had almost noticeably relaxed since the two vehicles had passed each other. A couple of minutes earlier he had been trying to persuade Roland and myself to put away our cameras and get back into the car. John was chuckling too, in his usual diffident way.

'Yes, I think that's rather a rare event. They would normally prefer to travel at night,' he reasoned. 'But that is all the better for you two: now you have some good photographs.'

'What would the cargo be?' I asked.

'All the things which are cheaper to buy in Tanzania than they are in Uganda,' said John. 'I can't tell you which right now, though I'm sure there was some paraffin and some car-tyres. They're the most popular these days. I'm sure we'll find out some more when we get to Kyebe.'

After a while we crossed a bridge over a small river which marked the end of the marsh, and then began a gradual climb as the road wound upwards between banks of tall yellow grasses. The ruts were fewer now, but still vicious when met with a full load; after one particularly crunching encounter, Joseph stopped the car and said he was turning back. Collective persuasion had to be used, though before long Joseph was mollified as the sight of a primary school, and the increased frequency of roadside houses, showed that we must be nearing Kyebe trading centre.

By now it was nearly five o'clock, and as the sun began to drop down in the sky, the shadows grew longer and the light less intense. In Africa, it is always the first and last hours of the day which are the most striking, especially to visitors from temperate zones. It is then that the full mellowness and beauty of the continent can be appreciated; then that irritations and follies from the heat of the day can be set aside, or at least viewed in context. It is a good time for arrivals.

We rode the last few hundred yards through plantations of *matooke*, the green banana which is the staple diet of the whole of southern Uganda, and especially of the Baganda people who inhabit the country's heartland. The size of the *matooke* trees indicated that this was rich land, and scattered among them were small, neat houses with walls of red-brown earth, and roofs of corrugated iron. Each house had its own neatly-swept compound, often bordered by clusters of coffee bushes, the berries young and green.

The small children waved, as they nearly always do in Africa; some of them screamed in excitement, or fear, when they saw our white faces.

Presumably not many *wazungu* had visited Kyebe in recent years. But for all this naked curiosity, there seemed to be something a little reserved, a little restrained, about the welcome we received from the few adults that we saw. Several observed the approach of our car, but only turned to lift arms in greeting after we had passed. Meanwhile, we too were watching more closely than normal. I caught myself wondering how many of these people had Slim. Surely the woman over there: that's more than just high cheekbones, I thought. Then I realised that we were staring outwards like a coachload of tourists on safari: perhaps all of us had been thinking along the same lines.

We stopped when we got to the trading centre, the short street that clearly comprised the hub of the village. The four of us got out to stretch, and to search out refreshment. We had already agreed to be cautious in asking questions: the last thing we wanted was to be turned around by an over-zealous local chief, or resistance committee chairman, who might feel that publicity would saddle him with blame for the epidemic.

Roland found a store where beer and sodas were on sale, so we took some bottles and sat down on the wooden bench outside. I called John and Joseph, but they were busy talking with someone. Presently John came across and said quietly, 'The reason it's so quiet is that most people are attending a funeral. It seems that he was someone quite important, and that he died yesterday. It also seems that he died of Slim. Can you put the beers down? That man over there, on the bicycle, is going to lead us there.'

There seemed to be several hundred people present, perhaps even a thousand, although local estimates ran to twice that. The mourners sat quietly among the *matooke* trees; they had positioned themselves in groups of ten or twenty people, all facing the grave, which was a raised mound of earth covered with small rocks and marked with a wooden cross at one end. We were quite late, for the ceremony had already finished. Presently, someone introduced us to Joseph Ssebyoto-Lutaya, the Resistance Committee chairman of Kyebe. As RC3 chairman, to use the NRM shorthand, Joseph was the elected political leader of the 24,000 inhabitants of the whole of Kyebe sub-county, from the bridge at the edge of the swamp to Kasensero, on the shores of Lake Victoria. He was tall, and rather serious in manner: dignified without being pretentious. He was standing by the widow where she sat mourning her husband in the traditional Kiganda *basuuti* – a gown of cotton or satin, with puff-shoulders and a sash around the waist.

The deceased, we discovered, was one Charles Ssemujo, a sixty-one-year-old farmer and fishmonger who had been sick for four years. I asked Joseph the cause of death.

'We hope it is AIDS,' he said, using the local idiom which, as we soon discovered, seemed to equate hope and belief.

'Which you call locally . . ?'

'Slim. Nicknamed Slim.'

'And what were the symptoms he was suffering from?'

'The symptoms were at first stomach-ache, vomiting and diarrhoea. Then the skin started bringing some rashes, some big and small pimples, and losing colour. And the hair started changing – to brownish, maybe. That sort of thing.'

'Perhaps you could ask the widow how she thinks her husband got sick?'

Joseph looked at the widow, Izabid, and turned back to me. 'Anyway the widow says she doesn't know how.'

'What would you say, yourself?'

'In this area, we hope it might be dirtiness, sexual intercourses: only that, we hope.'

'But this area seems to be suffering especially badly. Why is that, do you think?'

'First, I think we have many foreigners – some from Tanzania, and others from Rwanda and Burundi. And at the same time, we have many lake shores where most of the people are dirty. Sometimes the water is bad, and sometimes people hardly have pit latrines.'

At this point, someone pointed out to Joseph that the local health assistant, Jimmy Ssemambo, was present, and with the sensitivity to protocol which is customary in Uganda, the chairman promptly referred me to 'this better authority'. In fact, Jimmy had only received the most rudimentary of training, but, as the best-qualified person in the sub-county, he was quite properly deferred to on all matters medical. He was also, as we discovered, a young man of wisdom and sound judgment. Very often, in out-of-the-way parts of Africa, I have encountered local officials of an astonishingly high calibre. I have yet to find out if they are selected by shrewd superiors, or if the office itself 'maketh the man'. But even when constrained by limited educational opportunities, real talent and empathy have a habit of shining through, as both the RC3 chairman and the health assistant ably demonstrated.

I asked Jimmy just how many he thought had died of Slim in Kyebe sub-county.

'Around three hundred people,' he replied, his broad smile barely diminished.

'When was the first time that you came across Slim?'

'During 1982, when I was just posted here, I visited a place called Lukunyu on the lake; there I happened to come across a case, which I at first suspected to be TB . . . it was a woman.'

'And when did you think that the disease might not be TB, but something else?'

'After two years, that was in 1984, when a large number of people died in a place called Gwanda, another parish here.'

Of course, even by 1986, Jimmy still had no absolute proof that the local epidemic was actually one of AIDS. Some few blood samples had been taken from the area, but nobody had ever thought to report back with the results. But Jimmy must have suspected for some time, as the stories of a mysterious epidemic elsewhere in the world featured increasingly on BBC World Service and the Voice of America, and then the first medical corroborations that Uganda did indeed have an AIDS problem began drifting down from Kampala. And now, finally, he had received some official guidance from his superiors.

'Last month, the ministry passed out a resolution concerning the control of AIDS. We were given certain points which we noted with great interest, and we informed the public. They were mainly about promiscuous sexual behaviour, and unsterilised needles.'

'And how has the public responded?'

'It has been very difficult to convince them because traditionally, people who misbehave expect that a certain unknown disease can affect them.' This was the second time that day that someone had discreetly mentioned the possibility that Slim might have other than physical causes. I wanted to know more.

'What disease is that?' I enquired.

'What disease?' Jimmy paused: he was visibly uncomfortable. Finally, he wriggled free. 'Maybe we can ask someone else around here,' he suggested, his smile now decidedly too broad for comfort. He turned to the audience which had been drawn to the microphone like moths to a lamp, but it broke up into defensive laughter. I looked around as well, but no one would meet my gaze. Belatedly, I realised that this was neither the time nor the place to discuss local mystical beliefs and superstitions.

Instead, I turned back to Joseph Ssebyoto-Lutaya, who was still standing beside me. I wanted to ask as many questions as possible with the voices of the funeral congregation in the background lending 'actuality' to the proceedings. The setting also provided a certain formality, rendering the interviews 'official' or 'on the record' almost by default. Such are the everyday preoccupations of the radio journalist.

'What is the population of this sub-county?' I asked him.

'The population is something over twenty thousand people.' Joseph spoke slowly, even haltingly, but he appeared to give each question due consideration before answering.

'How many people here are dying every month from AIDS?'

'Approximately twenty to thirty. But at present it is becoming worse and worse. It is becoming monotonous – I don't know where we can go.'

'And how many have died in Kyebe this week?'

'About twelve in this sub-county. This is the second funeral today. There are more to be held tomorrow.'

'What will happen if this continues?'

'If this continues, the death rate will become higher than the birth rate, which means that this area might become a desert within two years.' This was over-dramatic, to be sure, but was also a memorable observation. Joseph appeared to be one of those people whose speech comes already provided with quotation marks.

'And how many people are sick now, in this particular area?'

'Let me talk about percentages. It is about fifty per cent who are being satisfied that they are sick. Some are not yet proved, but we think they are also affected. So when we just add these two percentages, we can make it eighty per cent.' Even allowing that Joseph was exploiting this opportunity to advertise the Kyebe epidemic, his public utterance of such views was in itself a telling insight into the state of panic obtaining in the community.

'So do you not fear for yourself?' I asked.

'Not as yet.' The reply was very quick; once again, there was supportive laughter from those around.

'But you're saying eighty per cent. That means that of this group of five men standing here,' I indicated which with a sweep of the hand, 'four might already have the disease?' This time, the laughter was a little more restrained.

'Yes. Yes. And I can say this. Nobody in this sub-county is not intimidated. Nobody says that he is safe, or she is safe. Everybody is now in fear. But that fear is left to God. Everybody waits his or her day.'

I temporarily ran out of questions. But then, looking around, I realised what I really wanted to ask. It is relatively easy for journalists to overstep the boundaries of good taste and be excused on the grounds that they are merely seeking out the truth, and this was probably one such occasion. Dispensing with any further attempt at discretion, I asked, 'What about the widow? How is she feeling?' This time, the chairman turned to Izabid, and questioned her in Luganda.

'She says she is all right. She has been nursing her husband for four years, but for the last two years they have not been meeting sexually. She only fears that perhaps she has contracted the disease.' What greater candour could one hope for in an interviewee? But once again, it was time to change course.

'How much assistance have you been getting from the government?'

'We have just got some advice from the health departments, but at present we haven't got any drugs for this deadly disease. And we haven't got particular doctors sent by the government to this area, to make an exercise.'

'What, then, would be your message to the government?'

Joseph visibly straightened, to his most official-looking stance. 'The most needy appeal I am sending to the government on behalf of the people of this sub-county is that the utmost need of the people of this area is to have remedial steps to this deadly disease, before we get off from the map of Uganda.' Despite the hyperbole, the fear was straight from the heart.

Later, after the sun had set, Roland, Joseph, John and myself repaired to the wooden bench in the main street, together with Joseph Ssebyoto-Lutaya, Jimmy Ssemambo, and half a dozen other local dignitaries. Some beers were bought, and conversation grew more relaxed. I had asked John to find out what he could about local sorcery and magic – themes which had cropped up more than once during the afternoon. After a while, I drew him away from the others for a quick debriefing.

'People are quite sure that some cases can be caused by wizardry and sorcery,' said John, softly. 'Some Ugandan traders go to Tanzania, get things on credit, come and sell, but they don't take back the money. So the Tanzanians end up by using sorcery.'

'What types of sorcery?'

'They are supposed to have *mayembe*, that can be sent to someone to kill him. I have heard stories, but I have never seen them. I've been told that these stories are true – that these *mayembe* can do a lot of nasty things to people. And my classmates at school used to say that the people of Kanabulemu, which is now Kyebe, are dangerous people, because they have sorcery. No one will talk about it openly, but they are believed to have the powers.'

'So the people here practise sorcery, but also feel vulnerable to it? Don't you think that sort of mental attitude could contribute to the death-toll?'

'Certainly some seem to be convinced that there is a kind of spell, because once you get Slim, you can't be cured. So they have that sort of psychological feeling that something supernatural has befallen them. And certainly we've already heard of a whole house of seven people who have died.'

John and I returned to the main group, and I tried firing a few more questions about sorcery. But reticence once again took over. I could only get Joseph, the RC3 chairman, to confirm that 'the people here are very clever, very strong.' Then I asked him about trade in the area, both licit and illicit. Joseph explained that, though farming and fishing provided the staples of the area, the other traditional occupation was smuggling. A local teacher, Joseph Ssemogerere, confirmed this – so much money was made, he said, that the local children were more interested in *magendo*, or black-market dealings, than in coming to school. The Kyebe route had traditionally been popular with smugglers because there was no customs post until Kyotera, and that was easily bypassed.

Goods which were in short supply, or expensive, in one country, slipped across the border to the other. At that time the articles most in demand in Tanzania were clothes, bananas, cassava and maize flour, and the crude liquor known as *waragi*, for it was apparently more dangerous to operate a still in Tanzania. Coffee had, until recently, been the number one item for illegal export, but recent price rises in Uganda had changed all that. Coming in the other direction from Tanzania to Uganda, meanwhile, were Tanzanian-made cigarettes, tyres, salt, sugar, soap, towels, blankets, batteries, saucepans and sisal ropes. Everyone spoke of the smuggling trade's demise in the face of the NRM government's anti-*magendo* campaign, but we got the feeling that the corpse was still twitching.

Then we began asking about the ethnic composition of the region. Joseph confirmed that most of the population were Baganda, but said that there was also a fair proportion of Bahaya, from north-western Tanzania, as well as Batutsi from Rwanda and Bahutu from Burundi – refugees from those two countries' civil wars of the 1960s and '70s, when the minority Batutsi were ousted by the Bahutu in Rwanda, but held on to power after a similarly bloody upheaval in Burundi. Altogether half a million people, or about a twentieth of the population of the two small states, are said to have been killed.

Joseph said that both Batutsi and Bahaya women were prized as great beauties, and that this had led to an unusually high degree of intermarriage with the Baganda, who are otherwise often aloof, and secretive about their traditions. The inference, left unsaid, was that this cross-breeding had somehow led to the introduction of the new killer disease. Suddenly it occurred to me that whether it was soldiers, traders, smugglers, sorcerers or wives, it was always foreigners, those from across the borders, who were held responsible for visiting the calamity of AIDS on the community, whether that community was Kyebe sub-county, or Rakai district, or even the whole of Uganda. In other countries, I suspected, it was just the same. It was always somebody else's fault. Exactly the same thing, I later discovered, had happened in the fifteenth century, when syphilis ('the French disease', 'the Spanish disease', 'the Italian illness') had first hit Europe.

It was now getting late, and we clearly had to cut short our regional geography lesson in order to search out accommodation for the night. Joseph, however, announced that everything was in hand, ordered us into our vehicle, climbed in himself, and bade us drive on to the mission at Nazareth, 2 miles away. But it was clear that five people would be too much for the car, so I got out, and elected to walk there with Jimmy. The day had been so intense that I relished the opportunity to clear my head. However, it was a dark, moonless night, and I began to trip over with monotonous regularity – notably on the final ascent of what appeared to me to be a sheer rock-face, but which Jimmy assured me was actually 'a very great short cut'. He was amazed at my lack of night vision. I told him how I was used to living in cities, where there were more neon lights, and fewer carrots.

By the time we arrived at Nazareth, Joseph had already launched into his speech of celebration and introduction which cunningly obliged the incumbent, Father Eugenio K. Lukwata, to provide us four 'newspaper personalities' with both supper and a bed for the night. To his eternal credit, Father Eugenio managed to come up with both, even though it was by now nine o'clock and his young housemaids had already turned in. While we waited for the food, the girls whispered and giggled in the next-door kitchen, and the pressure lamp hissed a summons to every moth and mosquito in the vicinity. The mosquitoes, I recall, were immense and vicious, prone to feeding not just on exposed hands or ankles, but through shirts and trousers too. We, tired to the point of aching, slapped away moodily at the points of attack, and wished we could simply go straight to bed. Finally, someone asked the father, as he passed through the dining-room with a bundle of blankets, whether he would object to our breaking open a bottle of whisky. He, ever the good host, readily agreed – and Jimmy and Joseph went off at speed in search of glasses, prompting fresh waves of giggles from the kitchen.

Eventually, the entire congregation of visitors which had assembled in the small room, some perched awkwardly on the arms of the chairs, but each with a glass or mug in the hand, rose as one to toast the success of the journalistic enterprise. Soon Joseph was enthusiastically floating the possibility of Slim being transmitted by mosquitoes; we were, I recall, too tired to dismiss the theory with the contempt it deserved. Instead, we raised our glasses again and then, thankfully, repaired to the supper table. After a splendid meal, we were given paraffin lamps and towels, and one by one were led to the bathroom where a most welcome bucket of warm water awaited. We bathed, retired to our rooms, turned down the wicks and fell asleep.

4 · THE DANGER ZONE

Come the morning, arrangements were made with surprising ease. Father Eugenio agreed to drive us down to Gwanda and Kasensero in the mission pick-up, which was a sturdy beast, newly arrived from Rome just a year before. We were fortunate, for the pick-up – a Peugeot 504 – was one of only three official vehicles in Kyebe sub-county, although the ruts on the road from Kyotera testified to the large number of less official 'commercial' vehicles which passed through the area. The father also promised to drop us back on the main road the following day, which allowed Joseph to set off immediately in the Fiat, without passengers weighing him down, and check the car into a garage at Kyotera. But suddenly, despite his grumblings of the day before, he seemed sorry to be leaving us.

'You know,' he said, 'I never thought it would be hard to choose between searching for Slim disease and sitting in a bar while someone paid to have my car fixed!' But in reality it was no contest – Joseph loved his Fiat like a son.

'Take care,' we shouted as he drove off, though we were imagining his adventures in the bar as much as those in the car.

As it happened, we had our own adventures of the road to enjoy. All eight of us (Father Eugenio, Roland, myself, John, Chairman Joseph, Jimmy Ssemambo, and a couple of resistance committee members who suddenly recalled that they had urgent business to attend in Kasensero) piled into and on to the pick-up, which rolled down to the mission gates and turned eastwards towards the lake. When I think back to the ride that followed, I still get a shock of surprise.

First the road traversed the hill on which Nazareth was perched, which involved a steep ascent and descent over enormous slabs of bare rock. The road itself simply disappeared. No sooner had it rematerialised than it hurtled off into a band of lush rainforest. It turned a corner and disclosed, albeit pushed to one side and half-hidden by dripping foliage, a burnt-out tank and a rusty tractor, relics of the last desperate attempts by Amin's soldiers, seven years before, to stave off the TPDF/UNLA invasion from Tanzania. At this point, the road seemingly merged with a stream, so that the only means of progress was to surge forwards 100 yards at a time, from one dry patch of ground to the next.

Once out of the forest, the road became a causeway over a swamp, which would have been straightforward, were it not for the fact that two sizeable sections had been blown up by the same retreating troops, and had duly reverted to their pristine state. Someone had dropped rubble into the marsh, in an attempt to provide some sort of traction for vehicles, and the accepted driving technique at this point was to gun the throttle, release the clutch and barrel off over the stones, hoping that one reached the opposite shore before the dank brown waters entered the vitals of the engine. We got through safely, but our wake was so strong that it swamped a dug-out canoe used for ferrying pedestrians. After this, there only remained a brief hill to negotiate, which involved the seven passengers getting out and pushing. Thus was the first leg of our journey completed – a matter of some 5 miles, which had taken just over an hour. When we alighted at Gwanda, Roland and I looked at each other, and started laughing. I think we both felt pleasantly seasoned for the day.

It was a normal-looking structure of mud and sticks (the 'wattle-and-daub' of school history lessons) with a corrugated-iron roof. There was no sign outside. There was nothing really to distinguish it from the rest of the houses around, save for the double wooden doors that served as an entrance. In fact, this was Perpetua Nangendo's clinic, the only one of its type in Gwanda, the village where two years before Jimmy Ssemambo had first noticed an alarming increase in the number of deaths. Joseph had chosen this as our first port of call for the day.

Perpetua Nangendo, a large, kindly-looking woman, was not surprisingly a little taken aback by the unexpected arrival of so many 'dignitaries'. I began to ask her some questions, which she answered in a voice that was barely more than a whisper. Perhaps due to her nervousness, she spoke with a slight lisp.

'Perpetua, do you get people with Slim coming to your clinic?'

A long pause. 'Yes.'

'And how many came last month?'

'About ten.'

'How do you know that they've got Slim?'

'I know because of the symptoms. But usually they don't know the cause.'

'What age are the people who get Slim?'

'Mostly eighteen up to thirty-five.'

'Do all the people who have Slim in the parish come here?'

'I get less than half of them. The biggest number go to native doctors, or witches, because they don't believe that the disease is caused by physical means.'

'Why is that?'

'It is because this disease has attacked mainly the boys. Some of them think they've robbed someone, and that's why they've been bewitched.'

'In the last year, how many have died of Slim in Gwanda parish?'

'It is more than sixty.'

'And in the last week?'

Perpetua thought for a moment. 'About six,' she said, finally. Joseph added that Gwanda's population was about 9,000.

At this point, I noticed four or five hypodermic needles lying in a kidney-shaped bowl on the table in front of us. My attempt at a trick question, however, fell flat.

'How often do you reuse your needles?'

Perpetua showed no trace of indignation. 'I use the needles once. I have about thirty needles, so I have to use one needle for each patient a day, and then boil it the next day. I don't have to repeat the same needle. And when I see that a patient is a Slim patient, I have a separate needle for them, so I've got to use that needle for those patients only.'

Further attempts to elicit whether or not Perpetua actually meant that she had just one needle for use on all her Slim patients proved fruitless. Whereas her use of English seemed to indicate that this was the case, her degree of common sense suggested otherwise. And I knew from bitter experience that when someone is answering questions in a language other than their native tongue, it is all too easy for grammatical misunderstandings to spawn false incriminations. Finally, I decided to abandon the enquiry as counter-productive.

'Have you received any advice from the ministry about how to treat your AIDS patients?'

'Not really. But I did gather some information from the health people from Mulago when they came around in 1984.'

'What were they doing here?'

'They took some blood for testing, and later, most of the patients died. Apparently the results showed that they had AIDS.' So Perpetua, at least, had got some feedback.

'I see. And what advice did they give you?'

'They taught me how to isolate them. The patient should be in a separate room, and use her own cup, and her own basin and soap. And the person who is attending the AIDS patient should leave her clothes in the room where the patient sleeps – not take them out to the public. And the children around shouldn't use those things.' The advice sounded like good common sense, and yet I suspected that such precautions did not, in fact, have very much bearing on the way in which the virus was spread.

'What is the state of health of the general population here?'

'So many are now feeling sick. They have started to show up the symptoms of AIDS. Usually, they come with persistent sores in the mouth – candidiasis – which has lasted about a month. Then they start diarrhoea and vomiting. Sometimes there is fever. Some may complain of long-standing chest pains and coughing.'

'How many in the parish now have these symptoms?'

'About fifty are sick. We have two cases of mothers and children. One mother – Nassaka – is very sick. She used to be a barmaid in a local bar.'

'Where lots of young men would go to drink and have a good time, I presume?'

'Exactly,' replied Perpetua, with a faint smile of complicity.

The caravan – for such it now felt – set off on foot to search out the house of Florence Nassaka, which was supposedly less than a mile distant. Soon, we turned off on to a footpath which wound its way between the *matooke* trees and coffee bushes, brushed aside the hanging creepers and vines, and vaulted over fallen tree-trunks. The forest became darker, the trees taller, and I completely lost my sense of direction. At the front of the line Joseph, who was full of the importance of the mission, was clearly setting a crisp pace.

If there was a single encounter which was to sum up the whole of our trip to Kyebe, and which was to render Slim the preoccupation it became for me, it was our meeting with Florence Nassaka and her two-month-old son, Ssengabi. As soon as we emerged from the trees we saw them sitting outside their house in the sunshine. And yet it was a chilling tableau they presented, with Ssengabi, loosely wrapped in a cotton sheet, lying in Florence's lap, her long fingers cradling his head from behind. She herself had apparently, until recently, been a healthy, vivacious woman, almost 6 feet in height. Now, however, she looked exhausted and shrunken, the skin drawn taut round her skull, and her eyes betraying a deep languor. But it was Ssengabi who seized the attention. He was pitifully tiny, like a famine victim. The bones of his arms and legs showed through clearly, and the skin hung in loose folds from his buttocks and thighs. He appeared to weigh little more than 5 or 6 pounds. Nobody could doubt that both mother and son were dying.

For a reporter or photographer, the recording of sickness and death always presents a dilemma. Should one treat such subjects as somehow sacred, and therefore unsuitable for public consumption, or should one simply attempt to depict them as one would any other topic, with professional detachment and candour? Some months later the Ugandan government, eager to protect AIDS patients from the glare of media attention, adopted a policy that prohibited the photographing of people with AIDS. On balance, however, I feel that we were right, that day in Kyebe, to use film and tape to record the brutal realities of Slim; for Florence had agreed, and in the end permission was surely hers to grant or withhold.

Nevertheless, I also know that I participated in something of a media rape. For the next fifteen minutes, barely containing our excitement, Roland and I photographed the mother and child from every angle, with every lens. Cameras clicked and whirred, pausing only for the changing of films. There was the occasional muttered curse when one blocked the other from his desired shot. And when all that was finished, I took over with microphone and tape recorder.

Joseph Ssebyoto-Lutaya helped once again with the translations.

'What is Florence's age?'

'She is twenty-two years old.' Florence's voice, when she answered Joseph's enquiry, was thin and breathy like a soft note on the clarinet. Even speaking, it seemed, tired her.

'And what does she do for a living?'

'She has been a barmaid, selling local beer.' The two local favourites are *tonto*, brewed from bananas, and *malwa*, made from grain. The brewing is done in huge, hollowed-out tree-trunks which are often buried in the ground, and then covered with leaves, grass and earth while fermentation takes place. When the beer is ready, it is normally drunk through straws, from large communal pots.

'And for how long has Florence been suffering from Slim?' There was no point in false decorum here – it had been accepted by all, Florence and her family included, that she had the disease.

'For a nine-month period, she says.'

'When was the baby born?'

'Two months ago. He has still not been baptised.'

'Was the child sick when he was born?'

'He at first seemed healthy, and was big and looked nice, but after that he started becoming thinner and thinner.'

'Has Florence been able to give him breast milk?'

'He has never been fed by breast milk.'

'So how is he fed?'

'With cow milk only, by the grandmother and the sisters.'

'How does the mother think that she caught Slim in the first place?'

'She says she doesn't know how she got affected. She just saw the symptoms. At first she thought it was just the pregnancy, but after she gave birth she continued suffering, so that proved that she had Slim.'

'How is she suffering now?' At this point, Ssengabi started crying in a small, hopeless whimper which continued, in exactly the same tone, until we departed.

'She is not feeling all right, because ever since she gave birth she has never taken any food – just these fresh fruit drinks, only that. She can't take food; if she wants to take it, she feels the food smells badly.'

Some minutes later, we took our leave of Florence and her family. Roland and I gave some money, something which I, at least, was not in the habit of doing. On one level it was a simple gesture of assistance to people whom we had met, and who were in a hopeless situation. On another, of course, it was payment for the taking of photographs, for the interview, payment to help ease our consciences. And it was certainly something we could afford. As Roland said later, with typical Gallic pragmatism:

'Wow, this is really a big story.'

We walked through the forest for another five minutes, and arrived at the funeral of Mirina Nakalawa. Mirina, a twenty-three-year-old peasant farmer, was laid out on a bed in the front room of the family house; her body was wrapped in a shroud of bark-cloth, or *olubugo*, in the Kiganda tradition. Beside her, the women of the household knelt and wept; occasionally one of them would move her head from side to side, and emit a soft keening sound.

Roland took a remarkable photo from the foot of the death-bed, showing Mirina's face wrapped in bark-cloth, and that of a young mourner leaning her head resignedly against the bed-frame. There is natural light from a small window above, through which the faces of other young children can be made out. Two months later, this photograph was printed across a quarter-page of *The Times* of London, with the caption: 'Too young to know, too sick to move: Ugandan children, stricken with AIDS, await their end inside a mud hut, far from doctors who could not give them much help anyway.' Sometimes, one wonders how the picture departments of large newspapers and magazines actually arrive at their captions. For the inaccuracies are crucial. Whoever wrote that remarkable sentence was apparently not aware that those featured in the picture were either quite healthy (as in the case of the mourners) or else dead (as in the case of Mirina). Neither, apparently, was the caption-writer appraised of the fact that one of the few age groups to be virtually free from the risk of AIDS is that of young children between the ages of infancy and puberty.

Outside, meanwhile, the men were doing their own brand of mourning. A group had collected in the shade of a large tree, and though it was still before noon, they were quietly getting drunk. One man, however, was standing apart from the rest, next to the open grave. A wooden cross lay on the ground near by, waiting to be erected. Joseph introduced the man as Mirina's former boyfriend, Charles Sserwanga, a twenty-nine-year-old teacher.

'She has been sick for almost one and a half years,' Charles said, his voice almost breaking. 'Sometimes she could recover for some months, and then it would continue. First it was diarrhoea, and then inside her stomach there was something that could pull her.'

'Did she lose a lot of weight?'

'Yes, and the hair went a bit scary. We did not have any hope of her by the time she died.'

'Was she suffering from Slim?'

'It is hoped to be so, because the symptoms of that disease have been experienced in her.'

'Were you having sexual relations with her by the time she died?'

'In fact, by the time she started becoming sick, I stopped.'

'And are you experiencing any sickness?'

'In fact I myself am feeling normal, very all right.'

'Will you now be looking for another girlfriend?'

'I hope to do so.'

'Will that be here, or somewhere else?'

'In fact, I will have to go to another area.'

'And how many people from around here have died of Slim this week?'

'This week, this is the twelfth. We started burying people from last Sunday – until now, we are burying, we are burying, no resting, no resting.' Even in his answers to my questions, Charles had taken on the comforting rhythms of mourning.

'And we are also worried,' he added finally. 'Because any person who gets invaded, we are not sure of his survival.'

Beside the plot where Mirina was to be buried a few hours later was another grave, that of her brother, who had died in November 1985. He had been suffering from diarrhoea, and had developed pus-filled sores on his body. He had not, apparently, received absolution, or a proper church burial. Neither, it seemed, would Mirina.

'There will not in fact be any ceremony because the priest ... we fail to have him come here,' commented Charles.

It occurred to me that, instead of conducting the funeral ceremony, the priest was acting as chauffeur to Roland and myself. But why was Father Eugenio even now sitting in the pick-up, instead of coming with us and meeting the mourners? I began to recall the stress that Florence had laid on Ssengabi's unbaptised state. It seemed that the father was none too keen to have dealings with the victims of Slim.

Another short walk, another victim. Beatrice Namuddu, twenty-four years of age, was the most severely affected of all the sick people we had seen. We were invited into the small room where she lay on a bed of straw, like an animal. She had been laid there because of the severe diarrhoea from which she was suffering: in the small, airless room, the smell was almost overpowering. We took photographs. Her mother came in and pulled up her blouse, so we could see the skin of her stomach and breasts, covered with dark blotches, and hanging like a curtain draped loosely between her hips. She had no more weight to lose; her whole body was trembling. Her neck was swollen, presumably from oral candidiasis, or thrush, in the wind-pipe – her breath came out in short gasps. A large part of her right cheek had been eaten away by an ulcer; yellow fluid was oozing down over her jaw-line and on to her shoulder.

Beatrice was still alive, all right. She followed me with her eyes as I moved around the room. I felt embarrassed – I uttered soothing words, even though I knew she could not understand my English. Those eyes! They were the only features that revealed Beatrice for what she was – a woman in her mid-twenties. The rest of her face and her body looked thirty, forty, years older. The eyes showed ... what? Not fear – there was no fear there. But there was pain, and there was sadness.

I went outside, into the shade behind the house, and breathed deeply. Joseph walked over. He told me that the previous week, Beatrice had lost her baby. The baby had been a girl, just three weeks of age.

'Is it common for people with Slim to have these deep ulcers?' I asked, as much to make conversation as anything else.

'Anyway, in some cases it is becoming common. We have witnessed some sick people who have even lost their private parts before they die.'

We went back to the pick-up, only to be invited into the nearby house of a Moslem elder, who had had his daughters prepare cinnamon tea and fresh fruit juices for our arrival. He was courteous and kind, asking Father Eugenio and Joseph about what we were doing in Kyebe, and why we had come all this way. He was pleased with the answers. Kyebe, he said, needed help – and our visit would let the world know what was happening here. I started to explain that stories and pictures in the Western press did not necessarily translate into medical assistance or relief aid – but then realised that I was reneging on my responsibilities as a guest, for my straightforward reply was not what anybody wanted to hear. Sometimes in a desperate situation it is better to be offered hope, even if it is empty hope.

Father Eugenio drove us another mile down the road, to a small trading centre of three or four shops. This was Kinyiga, effectively the centre of Gwanda parish. Outside the shops were a dozen or so young men, many of whom, to my now half-expectant eyes, appeared emaciated and sick. I asked Jimmy whether I was imagining things and, like a good cub reporter, he went across to investigate.

'They think that you are doctors or experts,' he informed me on his return, 'coming to give them drugs for this Slim. But this has been wrong information, because I have been with you here, and you are not experts, you are journalists. You have been trying to report on the occurrence of AIDS.'

We turned to walk on, but I kept the tape recorder running. Half a minute later, I asked Jimmy about the house we were passing, which was closed and shuttered.

'The owner of the house died last year. He was one of the prominent traders in the area. He died of the same disease, after suffering for quite a long time. The period was about four years.'

'Have many others died in this particular area?'

'We are in the danger zone. From where we stopped in the car to where we are going is the danger zone. A large number of people have died. And we are about to reach a house where just about all of them died of the same disease.'

5 · THE FIRST VICTIM

We walked on for another few minutes, up a fairly steep path. By now it was very hot, and my mental and physical resources were wearing thin. I wanted to sit down for half an hour in the shade to gather my thoughts. Despite the refreshments we had just taken, I developed a strong desire for a glass of fresh water. I wanted to wash my hands and face; in fact, I wanted to take a bath. Then we rounded a corner, and there was the house.

Someone had pushed in several of the walls, and removed the roofing material, whatever it had been. I asked Jimmy why this had been done.

'It is because the members of the former house were all killed by AIDS, including Matiya, the house's owner.'

'Who were the members of the household?'

'The brothers and the sisters, the mother and the father.'

'How many in all?'

'Seven, and all seven have died.'

'And have the other villagers pushed down the walls deliberately, to try to get rid of the disease?'

'I don't know,' said Jimmy. 'Now we have come to a place where there is no one left to explain.'

But this wasn't quite the case. Joseph had been asking around, and had located the sole survivor from the household. He was called Emanuel Lubega, and he was thirteen years old.

'Can Emanuel tell me what happened in this house?' I enquired.

Joseph, once again, provided the translation. 'He says the story started with his brother, Deo Mukasa, who was working as a fisherman down by the lake. Some years ago, he started suffering from diarrhoea and stomach-ache, and was taken to some hospitals. It seemed he was a bit OK. But later the diarrhoea and vomiting increased at a terrible speed, and he died. That was the first man to die here.'

'What happened after that?'

'Then another one affected and died, then another one and another one, up to the seventh. The mother, the father, the four sons and one daughter. All died within three years – from June 1983 up to this year, 1986.'

'That is the entire family apart from this one brother?'

'Yes – this is the last born, and he is the one remaining here. He is just staying here, next door.'

'Does he feel fit himself?'

'He doesn't feel anything at present, he says.'

'Was there anything the family was using, for instance a hypodermic syringe, which might have spread this disease?'

'He is saying that most of them were fishermen, staying at the lake shores, so he's suggesting they might have got that disease from the lake, down there at Kasensero.'

'I believe that Kasensero is one place where there is a lot of sexual activity? Does Emanuel think his brothers might have been indulging in some of that?'

A long time elapsed while the question was being translated. There was some discussion. Finally, Joseph answered: 'He says he can't guess. They were befriending many girls, but some of the girls are still around, they haven't yet died.'

We took some photographs of the seven stone-covered mounds in the *matooke* plantation behind. It was not easy – the stones were camouflaged by shadows, and no single shot could include more than two or three of the graves. I abandoned the camera, and asked Joseph to help me talk to some of the children who had gathered to see what was going on.

'Are any of these children suffering symptoms of the disease?' I asked.

'As far as I can see, they are not,' said Joseph. 'Because as we have experienced, this disease starts from seventeen, eighteen onwards. But these are below that age.'

'What does this one know about Slim?' I asked, pointing to a young boy of about ten years.

'He says he just hears people talking about Slim. They say, "Slim came, and has killed so many people." '

'And what about this boy?' I asked, indicating a thirteen-year-old.

'He has experienced people with Slim. They have diarrhoea, and another symptom is losing weight.'

'Has anyone from his own family died?' This enquiry resulted in a lot of gentle probing by Joseph. Finally, he told me, 'The baby of his brother died from Slim – as soon as he was born. First the baby, and then the mother also.'

'Does he get any advice from his own mother and father?'

'They say never to drink from a cup with somebody who has Slim.'

I was about to point out that sharing a cup with an infected person was not really a danger, but then some of the younger kids started laughing about something. Unaccountably, I started feeling like a primary school teacher.

'Do they think that Slim's a joke?' I demanded of Joseph, sternly.

'No, Eddie,' said Joseph gently. 'They don't take it as a joke. They have witnessed many occasions when people have died of Slim. They are also in fear.'

If the 5 miles from Nazareth to Gwanda were a major safari, then the final 5 miles from Gwanda to Kasensero certainly constituted an extra day in the bush. First we had to descend from Misozi Hill to the marshy flats bordering the lake. This involved the passengers – who now numbered fifteen or more – taking a footpath straight down through the trees, while someone guided Father Eugenio down the official motor route, which was an ugly gash cut into the rock and gravel of the hillside. It was more than half an hour before the pick-up reappeared at the bottom of the hill, which was not altogether surprising, since the gradient appeared to be about one in three, and some of the stones *en route* were as big as footballs. It was noticeable that the good father was starting to make noises about his engine not unlike Joseph's of the previous day.

Almost an hour later, in slow motion, we juddered into Kasensero. There was a seedy-looking main street of small wooden shacks, mostly shops, which stretched away to the shore of Lake Victoria. Behind were a few back-alleys which quickly petered out into the surrounding thorn bushes. Down by the lake's edge were two dozen or so high-prowed fishing boats, hoisted on to the sand after bringing in the morning catch; around them grazed a herd of long-horned Ankole cattle, bending their heavy heads to the water, or idly cropping the low, sappy shrubs that grew on the alluvial beach. A few crows tugged away at the heaps of fishy debris that lay around. It all made for a nice picturesque scene.

Roland and I went off to explore. We found a small bamboo hut, little more than 6 feet square, where the local nurse, Josephine, was plying her trade. She had a handful of drugs for treating dysentery and malaria, and a few suspect-looking needles. She said that she thought forty people had died of Slim in Kasensero in the seven months since the start of the year.

'Can you give any help to those people with Slim?' I asked.

'We try,' Josephine giggled, and scuttled off into the street.

Then Joseph had the splendid idea of calling a village meeting. It took place in the shade of Kasensero's one large tree, and was attended by three or four dozen men and women, not all of whom seemed overjoyed at being summoned away from their normal pursuits. Those who had them brought chairs; the rest squatted on rush mats on the ground. Joseph addressed the people for some time in Luganda, and then he explained to us that he was going to ask them for 'right information' about the numbers of those who had died, and those who were currently sick. Eventually, he halted the dialogue with his audience to announce:

'They have estimated that 102 have been victimised by Slim so far.'

'From this village here?' I asked.

'This is not even a village. Just from this small trading centre.'

'And who was the first person to go down with Slim?'

'The first victim was one called Regina, who died in 1983.' In fact, a number of other reliable sources recall the year of Regina's death as 1982, proof that questioning a large group is not always the best way to arrive at the truth. I also discovered later that Regina had allegedly been trading between Kasensero and the small port of Lukunyu, in Nyangoma parish, another 5 miles further down the lake. Nyangoma lies to the south of the broad River Kagera – said by some to represent the true source of the Nile – but north of the first parallel which marks the Uganda/Tanzania border. It thus represents something of a geographical anomaly: 12 square miles of swamp and lake shore linked by a muddy track to northern Tanzania, yet technically part of Uganda. There is no customs or border post, and visits by the Ugandan authorities are not facilitated by the natural barrier of the river. Lukunyu is thus an ideal centre for the local smuggling traffic, and it may be assumed that Regina herself was not innocent of involvement. According to the local gossip it may also be safely assumed that Regina was not a virtuous woman.

The meeting went on, and I was invited to ask some questions. 'How big was the population of Kasensero in 1983, when Regina died?'

'They say it was about five hundred people.'

'And now?'

'They say there are now about one hundred and seventy-six people remaining here.'

'So are they taking any action to protect themselves from Slim?'

'At present they have not taken any remedial steps. They are hoping for advice from you, for example, and other doctors.'

'But we are not doctors.'

'Though you are not doctors, they are waiting for your advice, if you can provide.'

I looked around. Roland was busily changing a film. God! How journalists hate it when the tables are turned! I knew that I was not qualified to speak. And yet – here were people who had answered my questions, and who were now asking for advice because they believed, probably rightly, that I was better informed than they. Eventually, I gave a short lecture that identified sexual contact and shared needles as the main methods of transmission, and recommended the obvious preventative measures. Roland suddenly looked up from his camera, and added a few encouraging words – 'Some of the best chemists and best doctors in the world are really working very hard on this disease, to try to find some treatment.'

Then I got to ask my final question.

'Are people here still going out to night-clubs, and having normal sexual activity?' The debate about this one prompted gales of shouting and laughter. Eventually, Joseph assumed a disapproving expression, and explained:

'Anyway, they say that in this particular place, Kasensero, they are still going on with intercourses, sex and so on' (Joseph now started smiling despite himself) '. . . and they are still enjoying life!'

It was dusk by the time we got back to Nazareth. I was feeling worried by the figures from Kasensero, and so I asked Joseph to go over them with me. Firstly the reduction in population from 500 to 176 in three years – that was over 300 people, not all of whom, it seemed, had died. So where had the rest got to? Joseph suggested that many had probably been frightened by the rumours of Slim, and of powerful witchcraft; others might simply have left when the smuggling trade collapsed.

And this other figure of 102 people from Kasensero having died of Slim in the past three years, what real proof was there of that? If correct, this meant that one-fifth of Kasensero's population had died of AIDS in three years – a quite astonishing death rate of over 7 per cent per annum. Where were the figures, I demanded of Joseph – surely somewhere there was a register of deaths? The only one of which Joseph knew was a book kept in Gwanda, which he said he would try to get hold of in the morning.

Looking back, I see that the unsatisfactory nature of our discussion that evening stemmed largely from my own emotional and physical exhaustion, from a sort of post-climactic fatigue. Also, my journalistic instincts were demanding that I brought back some proof of what was happening, some dinosaur's egg from the lost world. And yet there was no absolute proof available that it was AIDS that was responsible for the suffering and death that we had witnessed. Perpetua Nangendo had said that in 1984, a handful of sick people from the area had had their blood tested, and that the AIDS virus had been detected in many of the samples. Since then, nothing. Even a register of deaths with 'Slim' inscribed against some of the names could not have been construed as hard evidence. In the end, the only evidence would be that which we had witnessed with our own eyes and ears – that of a community where people were dying in great numbers, and which was clearly in the grip of a terrible and burgeoning epidemic. In the end, that was more important than whether or not a fifth of Kasensero's population had succumbed.

Anyway, I reasoned, the most plausible explanation for the hundred fatalities was that those itinerants who, like Deo Mukasa, had been coming to Kasensero to fish or to do business, had also contributed to the figure. The hundred deaths might therefore have occurred within a group that was several times larger than the official population of 500. Joseph rather grudgingly accepted that this might be the case, and my sense of logic felt somewhat appeased. What Joseph did not realise was that my disputing of figures was actually a reflection of my horror at the situation in Kyebe. I was worried that statistics like those from Kasensero would simply not be believed.

Meanwhile, Joseph himself was concerned about the potential implications of Kasensero's gung-ho reply to my final question about sexual behaviour. As the local political leader, he was understandably eager to ensure that Kyebe reaped the maximum benefit from our visit, so in the end I got out the tape recorder, and asked him once again whether the arrival of Slim had prompted any changes in behaviour.

'As far as sexual intercourse is concerned,' he replied, 'very few have decided to practise it. Many have decided to stay with one girl or one boy; others have decided just to drink and stay without girlfriends and boyfriends. Wives have decided to stay with husbands, and husbands with wives.'

I didn't really believe him.

The following day was Sunday, and Father Eugenio had to say mass in the parish church before he drove us back to Kyotera. Roland was busy photographing the congregation for some context shots; I stood outside for a while, and played with the mission's pet goat, which had rather taken to butting me gently in the shins. Presently I shooed him away so that I could enter the church to record some hymns, but unfortunately Billy was under the impression that I was still playing. He followed me in, cantered down the aisle, ploughed through the queue for Holy Communion, and finally bestowed some droppings on the red carpet at the foot of the altar. It took several sturdy ushers to effect his removal. I am unsure what the congregation made of all this, particularly those with mystical yearnings.

Later in the service, Joseph came to the front to address the gathering and to explain to them what Roland and I had been doing in their midst. It was a nice touch, and he finished his speech in English, with the words: 'So, gentlemen, as pressmen, as news reporters, try to report whatever you have seen to the world community, especially to the international bodies such as World Health Organisation, UNICEF and so forth. I think through this, the rest of the people might survive. Thank you very much for the great work you have done, and we wish you a good journey back.' Everyone applauded, for Joseph was great at hearts and minds, and for a few moments we felt like conquering heroes. The sad truth, however, was that our visit would actually have very little direct effect on the community, save for spawning a small service industry catering for the needs of visiting journalists. Whether our reports, and those that followed, had any longer-term effects on the international response to Uganda's AIDS problem, we have no way of knowing. It is pleasant, though undeniably arrogant, to imagine that this might be the case.

I had twenty minutes of cassette tape left, so before our departure I did a few final interviews. First I spoke with Anatole Lutaaya, a young seminarian who had come to visit Father Lukwata. Anatole filled in some gaps in the witchcraft story; he said that Ugandan traders at Lukunyu had taken money from a Tanzanian people called the Bakerebwe, promising to buy them goods at Kyotera, but then had failed either to bring them their goods or to repay them. Later, when some of the traders fell sick, they ascribed it to their having cheated the Bakerebwe, who had long been renowned as powerful witches. The Ugandans then went to their own local witch-doctors, taking traditional offerings like white hens, goats and cows; these were cut open in the normal way, but their magicians told them that such spells no longer had any effect against those of the Bakerebwe. In short, the traders continued falling sick and dying. Later, some went back to Lukunyu to try to find the

Bakerebwe and repay them, but by then it was too late. The epidemic had taken hold, with more and more people coming to believe that the Bakerebwe's spells were responsible.

Jimmy Ssemambo then arrived with some figures for which I had been pressing him since the previous day. He confirmed that the first local AIDS death had occurred in 1982, and that since then, 325 people had died of Slim in Kyebe sub-county, the great majority of them in the last two years. Jimmy also confirmed that there had been either twelve or thirteen Slim deaths in Kyebe during the previous week, which constituted a massive increase in the death-rate at the very time of our visit. There seemed little doubt, however, that the figure was correct.

Jimmy also had some other interesting points to make. He added some new AIDS symptoms to those we had already encountered, including repeated headaches, and mental disorders. And he made it clear that his health centre had very little in the way of drugs, apart from the basic medicines and rehydration salts contained in the UNICEF health kits which he received every six months or so. These kits also contained large numbers of needles, but Jimmy did not share these with the outlying clinics because he wanted to encourage people to come to the health centre for properly supervised injections. Asked what he needed most, Jimmy replied that it was 'a machine to look into the structure of the blood, to sense the presence of the virus', but then, more practically, decided that it was sterilisation equipment for needles.

Like the other doctors we had met, Jimmy told us that he would not inform a patient that he or she had Slim. This was because 'sincerely speaking, when you inform someone that they have acquired a disease that is incurable, it is going to discourage them. Some may even go to the extent of committing suicide.' Three young men had apparently already done just this, one of them by drinking insecticide (possibly the same man that we had heard about in Kyotera). Jimmy felt that the most important work he had to do in Kyebe was to educate the population, which he did by means of public meetings, and personal visits to the families and contacts of known Slim cases. How much assistance, I asked, was he getting from his ministry?

'In fact it is very little. We are only provided with uniforms, but when we report every month that we need assistance like transport, we are not given. This is a problem which makes my services to people very limited. At present, I am just alone, moving from village to village, health educating about AIDS.'

I saved the last few minutes of tape for John Katamba, the secondary school teacher who had provided so much thoughtful assistance since we had first met him at Sanje, three days earlier. Why was this part of

Uganda apparently so hard-hit by AIDS? John didn't mince his words.

'Here in this region, there is a very high rate of sexual activity. It is very common in the villages – young men are very fond of going about with women. It is possible for two men, like brothers, to run after the same woman. It is not rare, or shocking at all. So it is not a surprise that many have contracted this dangerous disease.'

John identified two ways in which Slim might have come to Kyebe. 'People who have been trading in the border areas are connected with this disease. After amassing wealth, they begin enjoying themselves in bars, with women and all that. But most people still think that this disease must have arrived with the war of 1979. Many soldiers came from Tanzania, Burundi, and even Zambia, and of course this disease has spread in these Central African countries. It appears that the disease might have taken root when the soldiers arrived and increased the rate of sexual promiscuity.'

Father Eugenio proved himself a fine driver, by covering the route back to Kyotera in under four hours, and this with a full load of passengers. And throughout the journey, a Tanzanian who had travelled up through Kasensero regaled me with stories about an epidemic of similar proportions in north-western Tanzania, around Bukoba. He said that in his country, they believed that the disease came from Uganda, as indicated by its local nickname, 'Juliana', which is also the name of a type of cloth that is popular with Baganda women. My informant was on his way to Kampala, and promised to visit me in my hotel so I could take some notes. Sadly, he never turned up.

In Sanje we bade farewell to John Katamba, who had become a good friend. And then in Kyotera we met up again with a beaming Joseph, his car fully operational once more. Roland and I thanked Father Eugenio, whose generous help had saved us from disaster, and then we set off for Kampala, where we needed to be that night. After some initial conversation, all three of us lapsed into our own private thoughts. Mine, for almost the first time in four days, turned to my girlfriend Sue. I began to wonder if I had not been making a very big mistake.

6 · SUE

Sitting quietly in the back of the car, as the violent hues of sunset dissolved into blues and greys and then to the nothingness that lay beyond the headlight beams, I began for the first time to relate the events of the previous few days to my own situation. It was with a small lurch of panic that I realised just how stupid and irresponsible I had been since returning to Uganda after Museveni's takeover. And I had no excuses. I had been aware for some time that having unprotected sex, especially in Africa, involved a considerable risk of contracting AIDS. In fact, during the latter half of 1985, I had had two blood tests for HTLV-3, as the causative virus for AIDS was then widely known. When the second of these, taken just after Christmas, also came out negative, the Hospital for Tropical Diseases in London wrote a letter to my parents with the result. The next time I phoned home from Kampala, my father relayed the good news. 'The consultant has added a note at the bottom,' he told me. 'It reads, "We are hearing of very high incidences of the AIDS virus in East and Central Africa. Celibacy is strongly advised." '

But that was January 1986, and Uganda was still celebrating the NRM takeover. The killings and gratuitous violence around Kampala had stopped for the first time in several years, and people were going out to parties and discos and enjoying themselves once again. In these circumstances, listening to a voice across the ionosphere preaching chastity was rather like being advised to give up smoking on the day that war breaks out. I assured my father that I'd be careful, and then three hours later picked up another girl in the hotel bar.

And so I continued through February and March, spending one night with an old girlfriend, the next with a secretary I had chatted up in an office, the one after that with a good-time girl picked up from the terrace of the Speke Hotel. For several weeks I thought nothing of spending a twelve-hour day following the NRA to the front, returning to write and file my copy, and then retiring to bed with someone who had been a stranger an hour before. The following morning I would be up again at six. It was not just myself who felt this way – the whole of Kampala, it seemed, was enjoying a communal churning of the loins. The arrival of Museveni's army of liberators – mostly fit young men and women who had spent months, even years, in the bush – must have had a lot to do with it.

Then, in late March 1986, I flew down to the Kenyan capital Nairobi, *en route* for Sudan, which was about to hold its first democratic elections for nearly twenty years. The feeling of release which arrival in Nairobi always imparts had put me in a particularly good mood that evening, and the mood improved further when I entered the bar next to my hotel, and bumped unexpectedly into Fiona, a former relief worker based in Sudan with whom I had enjoyed a romantic interlude the previous year. She was with a Kenyan friend, but we arranged a date for the following evening.

By then it was about ten o'clock, and the night still felt young; I decided to take a taxi up to 'Buffalo Bill's Wild West Bar and Eating House'. Buffalo Bill's, or BB's for short, is an establishment famous for its succulent and attractively-priced T-bone steaks, and for its *malayas*, or hookers, who are said by many of the male patrons to display similar characteristics. There is a choice of seating: one can perch outside in the open air, on a leather saddle; venture inside, to join a party in a covered wagon, or kick one's heels in the county gaol; or alternatively one can just join the happy throng fighting to get a drink at the horseshoe-shaped bar. With the promise of seeing Fiona the following evening, a pick-up was not on my mind, but I did feel like seeing a few friendly faces, and enjoying some beers and games of pinball.

Two women in their early twenties were already playing the machine when I arrived. They let me join them on the table, and we talked a bit, but not much, in between plays. Their names were Sue and Maria, and they were cousins. I identified them both as Batutsi, which they confirmed, and they told me that their parents, like so many others in the tribe, had been forced to flee Rwanda for Uganda in the early 1960s. They had that beauty which is peculiar to the Tutsi, being slender and elegant, with high foreheads and cheek-bones, and something almost oriental about the eyes. They were also pleasant company, although neither spoke English very well. After a while I bought them each a drink. And when I ran out of change for the machine, they paid for my games; they had 30 shillings or more spread out territorially on the glass top.

And so it continued to the end of the evening. We played pinball, we talked and we drank, but I never entirely forgot the date with Fiona the following night. I really didn't want to complicate my life by going home with somebody else.

'It is a very nice game,' Maria was saying. 'You are too good.'

'What about yourself?' I enthused. 'I just love your double flip.' I mimed the move in question, a strike by both flippers in quick succession, which retrieves the ball when it appears to be heading out of play, by flicking it from the tip of one flipper across to the meat of the other, and then back up the table. 'And you keep getting us free games. Where did you learn to play so well?'

'Oh yes,' said Maria, grinning a little shyly now. 'You are right.'

Maria and I were drinking beers whereas Sue, after accepting one bottle of beer, had reverted to sodas. She now explained my question to her cousin.

'I just know,' explained Maria, eventually.

'You see,' I carried on, 'I have been a pinball fan ever since I was very small.' I held my palm out, horizontally, 3 feet above the floor, and began enunciating very clearly, separating the words. 'And the beauty of the game is that it is very simple. You press the button – like this – and the flipper moves. You keep cool . . .' with a jerk of the neck, I took up a solid stance with legs apart and arms outstretched, and then shot my cuffs a couple of times, a pinball wizard for all to see, '. . . and you watch the silver ball. Except sometimes you have to give Lady Luck a helping hand, and then you have to *push and shove just a little bit.*' At this point, I grabbed hold of the table, moved back until my eyes were almost level with the glass, and then, with much swivelling of the bottom, and exaggerated slapping of the machine with the palms, I mimed a particularly spectacular escape shot. Then I turned around, flicking imaginary sweat from the brow, to take my applause. Maria was laughing noisily; Sue, by contrast, was looking at me quite directly, with a slight smile. Then she turned to say something to Maria, who rummaged in her handbag, and finally produced a 10-shilling note.

'I think you are drinking White Cap, isn't it?' And before I could answer, Sue had disappeared into the mêlée around the bar.

It wasn't just that she was so beautiful, for that fact, and her small face, were largely concealed by the braided and becowried hair style that she had at the time, which was not one of my favourites. It wasn't just that she spoke the better English of the two. It was something else – probably something in the eyes – a quality of straightforwardness and intelligence which I missed in her cousin. It was also, I concede, not entirely unrelated to the impact on a tired constitution of several beers and some attentive female company. But it struck me quite suddenly that I wanted to take Sue back to my hotel. This realisation was not accompanied by a surge of lust, but it did feel important – and sufficiently so for me to be nervous about the outcome. But it was past midnight, the bar was closing up, and I reverted to self-protective adolescent habit by laying down some false trails.

'Now which of you two girls am I going to take home with me?' I demanded. A few hurried words passed between the two of them, and then Maria started tutting and wagging her finger at me. Sue, by contrast, held back and watched. Eventually the three of us walked off together to the car park, to find a taxi. I felt excited; I really wasn't sure how things were going to end up. But then I got in the back with Maria, and told Sue to direct the driver back to their home.

Home turned out to be Dorothy's Place, a collection of single-room apartments built on a nearby plot of waste land, near several of Nairobi's major tourist hotels. The redoubtable Dorothy was still living there. She was a former prostitute, by then in her mid-forties, who had just recently, in an infamous and spectacular row, thrown out the *balokoli*, or born-again Christians, who had held sway over her heart – and purse-strings – for the previous ten years. The tenants had derived great amusement from watching Dorothy burn her religious tracts and pictures of saints, but only later did they appreciate the benefits to be derived from a saved Dorothy, when the unsaved version suddenly announced a sizeable rise in the rents. The *malayas* who occupied most of the apartments responded by sharing four to a room instead of three.

By the time the taxi had stopped, I knew what I was going to do. I leant across to Maria, on the other side of the back seat, and gave her a kiss on the cheek. 'Goodnight,' I said. 'We'll see you in the morning.' Maria duly got out, and said a few words through the window to Sue in a language I didn't recognise.

As we set off again, Sue turned around from the front seat, and gave my hand a squeeze. 'You,' she said, in the African way that betokens affection combined with a light slap on the wrist. 'You give Maria a big surprise.'

There were three long flights of stairs up to my hotel room, and we raced each other. I got there first, but I was so out of breath that it took an eternity to get the key into the lock. As soon as we entered the room, I flopped on to the bed. The alcohol had taken its toll, and I could feel the mental and physical tiredness accumulated from several weeks of working without a break. Suddenly, cool sheets seemed preferable to warm arms.

So this, I thought, is the man who was so excited just half an hour ago. Feeling rather less than gallant, I struggled to open my eyes. Sue was just slipping out of her T-shirt. Then she stood there naked, with hands on hips, smiling down at me. I can still remember being shocked by that first sight of her body, illuminated only by the neon lights outside – I had not realised before how slight and graceful she was, how proud the tilt of her breasts.

'You want to take off your clothes?' she asked. 'Or you want me to do it?'

The main thing I recall from that first night with Sue was how unhurried we were, how she made me forget my exhaustion. In the morning, however, we slept late, and I awoke to find her long fingers resting on my chest. After a lazy breakfast, we got into a taxi and drove back to Dorothy's Place. She invited me inside to greet Maria, and I was introduced to Anna and Catherine, with whom they shared the flat. I explained to Sue that I already had a date for that night, but we agreed to meet again the following day. I spent the afternoon busy in the town centre, but caught myself reflected in windows a couple of times as I rushed between offices – and realised I was grinning. I had the feeling of being pleasantly stretched, like after a sauna, or a good game of squash. And that evening, I was not in the least upset when Fiona failed to turn up. I waited honourably until half-past nine, and then rushed up to Buffalo Bill's, where I found Sue. She was obviously pleased to see me, which made me feel even better about the way the evening had turned out. Later on, she introduced me to several of her friends, men and women, and teased me if I was too friendly.

'I see you like that one too much. Let me bring her back here for you.'

'What for?' I asked, suspecting jealousy. The answer came back quick as a flash.

'To play the machine with you, of course.' Considering her lack of English, Sue was remarkably good at *double entendre*.

I postponed my flight to Sudan by four days, so that I could spend the rest of the week with Sue. She was wonderful company – self-assured and stylish, with a great sense of fun, much of it at her own expense. She had what one friend described as 'a heart-shaped face', as well as the thing which attracted me most of all, a demonstrably good heart. There were some problems, to be sure, not least that of communication. Although I didn't yet know it, she had never been to a proper school, and had started speaking English only when she met her first *muzungu* boyfriend, just two years before. But she was natural and spontaneous, and this made her quite outstanding at communicating in other ways. We used to walk back home singing; I would hit on a melody, and some nonsense words, and Sue would chime in with a descant that hovered disturbingly between harmony and discord. We launched into one such session while an English friend of mine was driving us back from The Carnivore, a popular outdoor restaurant and disco. 'My God,' he said, turning round from the wheel in amazement. 'You two sound like you're in love.' Several of my friends were similarly beguiled.

I finally left on the Monday morning of the following week. True to character, I cut things very fine; by the time I had settled my hotel bill, and bought my ticket for the airport bus, I had just 30 shillings in loose change left, and this I gave to Sue. It was enough for her to buy a couple of pounds of meat, or to get a taxi back home if she so desired. She didn't, however, complain, but saw me off with a kiss and a wave. I promised to write her from Khartoum.

It wasn't until I got on to the plane that I began to view the previous six days with Sue in any degree of perspective. First of all, I began to feel guilty about the way in which I had left her. I realised, for perhaps the first time, that I wanted to see her again when I got back from Sudan. Now how did I expect her to survive in the mean time? She had insisted that she didn't 'do business' – or sleep with men for money. And indeed, she had never asked me for cash, although one time when we cooked dinner at her home, she had bought considerably more food than was necessary, enough in fact to feed the four girls for half a week. She had no job, no visible means of support, and because of her lack of literacy and numeracy, she lacked the skills to work in an office, or even to be a waitress. Neither, she told me, had she any intention of doing work which she considered menial, like washing clothes or baby-sitting.

So just how did she survive? The only money she had formally earned in her life, as far as I could make out, were the thousand Kenyan shillings she had been paid for appearing on the front cover of *Drum*, East Africa's indigenous version of *Titbits*. She had been dressed as a schoolgirl, sucking a lollipop, a pose requiring her to demonstrate coyness, which she did with alacrity, but which in no way brought out her youthful beauty. Although I enjoyed the slightly amused pride with which she responded to having been a 'cover girl', I always hated the photograph for its clumsy stylisation. I was surprised, also, that it had not prompted a more adverse reaction in a country which officially condemns the sugar daddies whose habit it is to seduce schoolgirls and abandon them when they get pregnant.

Sue had told me that she survived by a number of devices. If she had a boyfriend, he would buy her clothes and generally look after her; at other times a boyfriend of Maria's might step in to pay the rent, or buy food from the market. Then there were her girlfriends, some of whom clearly were doing business as *malayas*, though Sue never said as much. Some 'working girls' could generate an income of as much as 30 dollars a night, and were correspondingly generous to their friends, although inevitably there were arguments on occasions. Besides these possibilities, there was her uncle, with whom she had stayed for two years when she first arrived in Nairobi, and who could still be relied upon to cough up a few bob when she visited. And there were a number of African men-friends ('friends', she stressed '. . . not people I go to bed with') who were in business of different varieties – mostly smuggling items between Uganda and Kenya – and who would help out when they were in the money. But I was still sceptical.

One night in bed, incredulous at the impermanence of her lifestyle, I had asked Sue straight out what she would do if she was hungry, and had no money. Wouldn't she just pick up a man, as many of her friends did?

'I am not a prostitute,' she told me, very clearly. 'I cannot go with a man for money. How can I respect myself after I do that? And I always find money somehow. Do you think my friends can let me starve?' Yet many of the women who went to Buffalo Bill's would probably have given a similar answer, even though four out of five had already accepted the principle of getting money for sex, as a prerequisite of living the fast-track life. As for the men, like myself, who frequented such places, we went there fully aware of the set-up, went there because we enjoyed the slightly sleazy atmosphere, enjoyed the easiness and fickleness of the company, someone to talk to, someone to argue with, someone to fool about with, and someone – often – to go home with.

Yet not every woman who went to Buffalo Bill's was a *malaya*. And I found that I was inclined to believe Sue where I would have doubted most others in her situation. Firstly, because she was free. When she wished to, she gave of herself without looking for payment or presents – this was demonstrated in the way she made love, but it was also apparent in other ways. She did not allow herself to be exploited. Secondly, because she had the luck of the innocent, the protection of that most faithful of all gods. People really did like her; she was someone whom everybody wanted to help. And thirdly, because she seemed to end up with nice people (and I included myself, of course, in that number). Her previous boyfriend, Peter, who was a German on a year's contract work in Kenya, had recognised her talent for design, and so had taught her how to develop black and white photographs, enrolled her on a dressmaking course, and had given her an automatic sewing machine. When his parents visited, the four of them drove down to Lake Magadi, and swam naked in the soda-impregnated waters. When, at the end of his stay, his German fiancée flew out to join him for a holiday, Peter insisted that the three of them go out together for a meal. 'To my future wife, Ingrid . . .' he had toasted, 'and to my girlfriend, Sue.' Everyone, it seemed – the parents, the fiancée included – had adored her. Pictures of them all together – laughing, hugging, waving and smiling – filled the pages of Sue's photo album.

And in the final analysis, what right had I even to ask her the question? I, who had compensated for ten years' worth of public-school inhibitions with a late spring sowing of wild oats when I returned to East Africa in 1980. It was then that I spent my first night with an African woman, a prostitute who got me drunk, trailed her fingers up my thigh, took me back to her room, and later asked me to leave when her boyfriend (or perhaps another customer?) arrived at two o'clock in the morning. And that one night was enough to breach the wall of the dam. Suddenly, repressions were discarded like underwear. I was the newest convert, the most devout of all.

During my previous visits to Africa, I had already developed a great fondness for its people, especially those who had not assumed the pomp and circumstances of high office. I liked their friendliness and ability to enjoy life, their lack of affectation and their dignified coping with hardship. Now I had discovered the further joys of being with African women. I found out that generally they were uninhibited, unsaddled with Western hang-ups, and extremely sexy. Later, I also found that most were kind, and warm, and fun to be with. Over and above all this was the fact that many – for what reasons, I did not care to enquire – were readily available. Armed with these new discoveries, I felt myself quite the lady-killer, and, over the next three years I had a succession of lovers and girlfriends. Many were one-night stands. Several were women who later became friends, who took me home to see their sisters, brothers or cousins, and – often – their babies. With two I had more permanent relationships, lasting several months. But I was educated, and entertained, and amazed, by nearly every one, from the minister's secretary to the prostitute, from the college student to the mother of five.

Often, after making love, we would stay up for an hour or two talking; sometimes we didn't bother with the sex at all. Sometimes, in the morning, I would give some money (for the bus, the baby, the hair-do, whatever); sometimes I would not. If the lack of payment was resented, the woman concerned normally had too much pride, or dignity, to mention the fact – but would refuse further invitations to my house or bed. More often it was not and I was treated, to my great pleasure, as a 'brother', as part of a family, as someone who gave of themselves in ways other than just the financial. Anyway, since that first drunken evening in 1980 I had been free-living, I had been promiscuous, I had been irresponsible, and I had loved every minute of it. I was deemed to be a 'life-ist', which in Uganda is one of the great accolades.

At this point in my ruminations the in-flight snack, or something which passed for it, arrived. I began chewing the dry roll containing what appeared to be a slice of elderly goat's cheese, when the possibility occurred to me that I might simply have been a cheat, expecting sex at bargain-basement prices. And I thought, because of my romantic aspirations and claims perhaps, I was far more to be condemned than the most racist of expatriates, the one who would call black women kaffirs, niggers, whores and worse – behind their backs, to their faces, it hardly mattered – and who would regularly, once a week, get a skinful of Tusker or White Cap, and take one home for sex. Who would wake the following morning, toss a handful of notes on to the bed, and tell her to get out. Who would later tell his mates how she was 'a damned good fuck'. But who, whatever his unpleasantness, would have struck and honoured a straightforward business deal: you screw; I pay.

I could not deny that it was the economic imperative that rendered many African women 'available' to white men; that it was the bulge in the pocket which was often the *muzungu*'s most attractive feature. Given a free choice, I was sure that most African women would far sooner spend a night with a young, attractive man of their own race, age, habit and language, than with one who was often ten, twenty, thirty years older, who might be abusive and stupid, who understood little and cared even less about their culture and background. So, with all that in mind – could I still make out that I was a special case?

I inclined the seat further backwards, took another sip of orange squash (no beer, for this was Sudan Airways, national carrier for a country which had banned alcohol three years before), and sat there thinking for some time. Presently, the last dregs came gurgling up through the straw. Yes, perhaps I could, I thought to myself. I knew that, as always with self-assurance, there was some rationalisation lurking here too. But whatever . . .

The first item in my defence was that I had never felt tempted to discriminate against blacks, for in the end racial prejudice and imagined superiority stem only from fear of the unknown. In fact, in Uganda I had more black friends than white, which had caused me many a problem among the expatriate community, among whom such things were noted. And despite my laziness about learning any of the local languages (I could get by doing the shopping or asking the way in Kiswahili or Arabic, but that was it), I was treated by many

Africans as something of an honorary member of the tribe. Although I was often impatient, and failed to observe the proprieties, and was not above taking advantage of my skin colour, I had also learnt something of the African way of doing things – of sharing and being open . . . being happy to give of myself, and my time.

And secondly, I had always lived the sort of hand-to-mouth exis-tence with which many Africans are familiar: even the beautiful house on Mutungo Hill overlooking the lake, where I had stayed from 1981 to 1983, was mine rent-free in exchange for transforming an empty shell, looted clean even of bathroom and electrical fittings, back into an attractive residence. By African standards, I was certainly far from poor, but I was also, demonstrably, not 'a rich *muzungu*'. If any woman failed to pick this up straight away, then a ride along the rutted track up Mutungo Hill on the back of my Honda 90 tended to put her in the picture pretty quickly.

I could remember only one occasion when I myself felt that I had cheated, or exploited: when I discovered that I didn't like the woman I was with, but had gone ahead anyway, humping blindly in the dark. And in the morning I had gone to make tea, and then returned to the bedroom to find her turning away from me, trying to close a bulging handbag. I told her to go to the kitchen and cook some eggs, while I opened her bag to find a T-shirt, a bottle of cologne, and some money which had been lying on the window-sill. It was the only time I knew of that a visitor stole from me. And surely it had provided some sort of litmus test? I had treated her like a whore, and she had duly behaved like one.

So, I thought, what am I doing enquiring of Sue about her past? What moral code am I seeking to impose? If I can make a special case for myself, convince myself that I'm more caring than exploitative, can I not also accept that Sue's an original, rather than just another good-time girl from Buffalo Bill's?

As the chime sounded, and the No Smoking lights came on again, I made the decision. Yes, I believed her. And in the end, my reasons for doing so were not that important. For in the end it was an act of faith, just like that which she would need to make if she, in turn, was to trust me.

It was a long month in Sudan, at almost the hottest time of the year. And long before the election results were announced, and the new parliament convened, I realised just how much I was missing Sue. This time it wasn't ships in the night, and thanks for a nice week, I thought. I had been planning to fly back to London from Khartoum, and thence to Kampala, but now I felt that after two years of non-stop work, I deserved a proper holiday. I decided that three weeks down on the Kenyan coast with Sue should do the trick, and I sent a message to let her know I was coming.

I flew back down to Nairobi in early May, and we spent most of that first weekend in bed together. When I asked her if she had found another boyfriend, there was a pause and then she told me that she had: a Frenchman called Jean-Michel. 'But I don't like him as much as you, Eddie.' I felt jealous, but I knew that I had no right. We had signed no contracts.

On the Monday morning, Sue went back to Dorothy's Place, to leave me alone while I wrote one last feature piece about Sudan; she took a bag of dirty clothes, which she promised to wash for me, and said she would be back at the hotel by eight that evening. We were planning to head off to Mombasa the following day. I finished the piece at nine o'clock, but there was still no sign of Sue. After waiting another half-hour or so, I got into a taxi, and checked at Dorothy's Place and then Buffalo Bill's. It took me a few minutes to find her, where she sat in an alcove with a small sturdy man in jeans. I happened to peer down over the back of their seat from another higher level just as she was putting her arms round his neck, and kissing him on the cheek. I felt a thump of pain inside. I sat down for a few minutes, to calm myself, and then leant over the rail to say, 'I think you'd better come up here and talk. Right now.' Her face fell when she saw me there.

She tried at first to bluster it out, but I was too angry. I swore at her, told her she was a fool to start two-timing me with her French friend.

'But I am telling you about him already,' she complained.

'It's not that. I don't mind you getting another boyfriend while I'm away. But I do mind you bouncing me for him. I do mind waiting for you at the hotel while you have your arms round him at Buffalo Bill's.' God, I was getting out of breath. And it was obvious that the faster I talked, the angrier I became, the less Sue could understand.

'Eddie, I am coming to you.'

'What do you mean, "I am coming to you"?' I mimicked her voice. I was making no allowance for her lack of grammar – in English, she had everything happening in the present tense. But she tried again.

'I come down here to get a taxi. Then I see Jean-Michel and he want to buy me a drink. I want to tell him about us, that we are going away to the coast.' But by now I was clenching my teeth with fury.

'You think I believe that? Well, you don't have to tell him anything now, because we're not going. We're not going anywhere together. You can just go back to your little Frenchman and leave me alone. Go on, get out of here.'

As I stormed out, I bumped into a Norwegian friend, and stayed on to drink a few fierce beers with him. Later, I saw Sue sitting with some girlfriends, but looking sad, not talking to them. There was no sign of Jean-Michel, but my heart was still hard. I got into a taxi, and drove up to her place to fetch my clothes. Anna let me in, and I began shoving damp shirts and trousers into plastic bags. Some of the wetter items were still hanging on a line to dry, and in the end, at Anna's prompting, I left these behind to be picked up the following day. My escape clause: a couple of damp pairs of jeans.

The next afternoon, when I returned for the laundry, it did not take us very long to get through the recriminations and to make up, and eventually we set off as intended on the overnight train for the coast. And the following day we headed northwards to Lamu, which ever since my first visit there in 1976 has been one of my favourite places in Africa. It is a tropical island that serves as a place of pilgrimage for East African Moslems, where donkeys and dhows are the only means of transport, and where tall coral houses, mostly dating from the seventeenth century, are separated by cool, winding alleyways sometimes only a yard or so in width. Happily, Sue loved the place as well, though she was rather shocked at first by its 'backwardness': its open drains, the maribou storks on the rubbish tip, and the fact that there was only a single bar, at Petley's Inn. Somebody had lent me their house at the end of Lamu's 7-mile crescent moon of a beach, and it was a magical place: a sprawling building of blackened beams and coral walls, split into a succession of unlikely levels which were festooned with cushions, and open to the sea-breezes from both directions. While the cook regaled us with astonishing meals of lobster and paw-paw, sailfish and avocado, the houseboy ironed our clothes and made sure that the fridge never emptied itself of beer. We were royalty.

And yet. And yet. We had a couple more arguments, quite serious ones. After one of them, I found Sue standing in the shower, crying softly, with the remains of her *butiti*, the string of tiny beads that she wore around her waist, lying scattered around her on the wet stone floor. After the second row, Sue packed her bags, and begged me to let her go back to her friends in Nairobi. Reconciliations followed, but only after the expenditure of large amounts of emotional energy. And even afterwards, we still niggled each other about petty things, as if we had scores to settle.

But for all that, the fortnight on Lamu, and the week which we spent sailing round some of the neighbouring islands by dhow, made me feel much younger, much happier with the world. We eventually arrived back in Nairobi on a Sunday, the day before I was due to fly to London. It was pouring with rain, and suddenly I began feeling feverish, so that by the afternoon I had to go to bed; Sue, meanwhile, was clearly overjoyed to be back with her friends. In my over-sensitive state, I felt ignored, cast aside, and I took my revenge by demanding that cousin Maria join me between the sheets, to keep me warm. This had the desired effect, because Sue, in turn, got jealous. Soon she had replaced Maria under the covers.

I woke at five the next morning, and though I was weak, the fever had definitely broken. I packed my bags, and went to the room of Kapere, a Ugandan driver who was a friend of Sue's, to ask him to help by driving me to the airport. As ever, Kapere was willing. The one snag was that I had spent all my cash on the holiday. There was a fairly substantial credit transfer waiting for me in one of Nairobi's banks, but if I was to catch the Sudan Airways flight that morning – the next one was three days later – then I had to head straight for the airport. Once again, I would be leaving Sue without any money, and Jean-Michel had apparently already returned to France. I promised I'd be back in six weeks, and left it at that. Her farewell kiss at the airport was, I thought afterwards, a little perfunctory.

Absence makes the heart . . ., as we all know, and by the time I returned to Nairobi, in July, the organ in question was pounding at the prospect of seeing Sue once again. I got a taxi straight to Dorothy's Place, only to be told by Anna that Sue had set off the week before for Kampala, with her friend Barbara.

'It is only for a visit. She is due back here tomorrow,' she told me optimistically.

I was surprised at Sue setting off without me, for we had planned to travel up to Uganda together when I returned from England. Next I got angry, and then nervous. What if we crossed in the night, with her returning to Nairobi as I was flying to Kampala?

As it was, I managed to get on a flight to Kampala the following morning, and arrived there just in time to catch Sue and Barbara as they were packing their bags to leave. Barbara headed off anyway to the taxi-park, but Sue was a little strange; part of her seemed to be wishing that she was going back to Nairobi with her friend. And that reluctance on her part, that mental absenteeism, continued over the next few weeks. We told each other about our affairs, mine a night spent with an old friend in London, hers a fling with a Tanzanian whom she had met a few days before in Kampala.

'But you must have met some other nice boys,' I prodded her.

'No, Eddie, that is the only one. If there is someone else, I can tell you. I don't have to be afraid.'

But there was something wrong, it was clear. We began having arguments every few days, and they dragged on for longer and longer each time. Matters came to a head one night, when Harriet, a woman I had known back in February, before I had even met Sue, followed me to my room and knocked on the door. Sue refused to believe that Harriet's visit had not been prearranged; she promptly packed her bags and set off back to the house where she'd been staying with Barbara's sister. Four days later, four days of misery on my part, she came back and we made up. The following week, it was my turn to finish the affair, after one of our arguments resulted in my missing a deadline for an important story. We had our customary reconciliation, but I realised that for the first time I was allowing personal affairs to affect my work.

When I left for the safari with Roland and Joseph, matters between Sue and me were still very unsettled. But the events in Rakai so engrossed me that I hardly had time to think about her for the next four days. Now, in the darkness, as we sped back towards Kampala, I began to wonder what I would find. It was suddenly clear to me that I didn't entirely trust Sue any more. Of course, I had been seeing a lot of women myself back in February and March, and had never tried to keep this from Sue. But what if Sue was still seeing other men when I was out of the country, or off on safari? With AIDS as prevalent in Uganda as I now realised it was, the degree of trust between us had become a matter of vital importance. By the time that Joseph dropped me at the Speke Hotel, I had decided – Sue and I would have to have a serious talk.

I waited until we were in bed that night, lying in each other's arms. I told her about the sights I had seen, and the terrible reality of Slim disease. 'We've got to be true to each other, you know. Otherwise, you're going to get it, and give it to me, or I'm going to get it and give it to you. Can you imagine that? Killing somebody you love, just because you spent a night with somebody else.'

'Don't worry, Eddie More,' she breathed into my ear. (This had been her pet name for me, ever since our first night together. For a long time, I had been pleased to believe that it referred to my sexual appetite. I was therefore rather disappointed to discover that it was actually a reference to Roger Moore who, as Special Agent 007, was her favourite film star.) 'I don't want to mess around, Eddie,' she went on. 'I promise.'

Only later did it strike me that, for the first time, I had used the world 'love' to describe our relationship. Though, as it transpired, it was perhaps not an opportune moment.

7 · A SCOTTISH DOCTOR

The telephone bell woke me, worse than any alarm clock; I opened bleary eyes and scrambled for my watch, to find that it was ten to eight. Next I realised it was Sunday morning; the only people who would phone at this hour were from the BBC news team at Bush House. Something dramatic must have happened during the night. I shook myself awake, cleared my throat and picked up the phone.

'Good morning. Ed Hooper speaking.'

'Hello Ed. It's Mike.' I called up the Mike file in my head, and came up with nothing much in the way of a lead. Best to play for time.

'Oh yes, Mike. What can I do for you?'

'I'm downstairs with my sister.'

Slowly it dawned on me that I hadn't, after all, slept through a coup. Then I realised that the Mike in question was Mike Rukeba. I keyed all this into the memory bank, and came up with a very dim, very distant recollection of having invited him to drop by at the Speke one day for coffee. Had a sister been included in the invitation? Back in pre-Sue days had there been, perhaps, a local beauty to whom he had been offering to introduce me, someone who 'wanted to meet a nice European'?

'Your sister, Mike?'

'Yes, we came by to say hello.'

'But Mike, it's ten to eight. And it's Sunday morning. And I've had a hard week.'

'Yes, I know. I'm sorry. But you can see us just for a short while, now we've come all this way.'

It struck me once again that I really didn't like this man.

'OK, Mike. Give me five minutes to take a shower, and I'll be down.'

I gave the still-slumbering Sue a kiss on the forehead, and began searching for a towel. The albatross was back.

We sat around on the big low easy chairs in the lobby and were served, rather grumpily, with a pot of coffee. It had crossed my mind to invite Mike and his sister to join me for breakfast, but then I decided that his early morning alarm call hardly merited it. Anyway, I had more than an inkling that they had just left a 'transnight' – one of Kampala's famous all-night parties or discos – and Mike had reckoned that I was their best chance of a free feed on the way home.

'So Eddie, I have been calling on you over the last few days, but you were always out. Have you been on a hot story?'

'No Mike, not really what you'd call a hot story.' I begrudged telling him about Kyebe, I realised, even though we had been together in Kyotera a month before. Not for the first time, I got the feeling that Mike was in the habit of interviewing other journalists for his material. But then I realised that I was being unfair. Whatever his limitations, at least he was always trying. He was forever persuading other reporters to take him on up-country trips, or to read through and comment upon draft articles he had written. And he liked me, apparently he thought of me as a friend. He wanted to show me off to his sister, for God's sake, or vice versa. Dammit, I thought, I'll tell him about the safari, and then I can get back to bed.

I gave an abbreviated account of our journey to Kyebe, not being too specific about details like place-names, or the numbers of deaths.

'I think, Eddie, you are very lucky that I took you down to Rakai district that last time.'

Oh God. He was really tempting me to show him up in front of the sister/girlfriend. 'Yes, Mike, I'm very grateful; that's why I'm filling you in on all the details now.'

He smiled and turned back to her. 'Eddie and I were detained together in Luzira, in 1983,' he confided.

I thought back to our first meeting in the prison yard, when he had walked across and introduced himself, claiming that he was a stringer for VOA, the Voice of America, and that we had once met in the office of an Australian reporter. I didn't recognise him, but I listened anyway to his story of being starved and beaten in the infamous military barracks at Makindye; he showed me the lump on his head, and his protruding ribs. Uniquely for Luzira, he complained about his plight, telling me that he now had 'psychological problems', that he couldn't sleep at nights. Naturally enough, I felt sorry for him, and when he asked me if I could smuggle out a message about his plight to the VOA correspondent in Nairobi, I did so, even though I nearly got caught in the process. I ended up being pushed around a bit by the guards, and interrogated by the prison governor for half an hour; I risked my own safety on his behalf. But when I saw him again in Nairobi at the end of 1985, he was too busy trying to borrow money from me even to remember to thank me for what I'd done. And it was that failure, that thoughtlessness, that unblinking eye for the main chance, which first awoke me to the fact that Mike Rukeba was bad news. I sat up straight, and cut short the prison memories.

'I'm sorry,' I said to the two of them. 'But I've really got to go. And look, Mike ... please don't call on me again on a Sunday morning. It's when I like to catch up on my beauty sleep.' But when I got back upstairs, I found that I was too angry to catch up on any more of it that morning.

Mulago Hospital is a sprawling complex of buildings extending across the lower slopes of one of Kampala's seven hills. Built in 1962, the year of Uganda's independence, it is commonly spoken of as Britain's parting gift to her former colony, although Whitehall actually contributed only a quarter of the cost. The evidence of British involvement, however, is there for all to see, for from the outside it resembles nothing so much as a run-down estate on the fringes of Birmingham or Glasgow. But it is all too easy, as a foreign observer, to be churlish: Mulago, as the central government hospital, represents the best health care there is for the vast majority of Uganda's 16 million-odd citizens.

And yet despite my being familiar with phenomena like bed-sharing and drug-shortages which make many Third World hospitals such dangerous and hopeless places, my early morning stroll around Mulago's main block was confronting me with sights and smells that I found even more unsettling than usual. Patients, some apparently quite ill, were crouching or milling around in corridors. Visitors and relatives were carrying jerricans to upstairs wards which the prevailing water pressure could not reach. Meanwhile, paradoxically, many of the open landings had been flooded by a rainstorm during the night, and cleaners were using their long brooms to propel the sheets of water away down the stairwells; one had to take care to avoid being drenched from above. Overriding everything was that familiar, fetid smell, a jarring cocktail of urine and sickness.

As always, however, there are silver linings. Many of those to be found working in such establishments, both nationals and expatriates, are among the most dedicated and down-to-earth individuals one is likely ever to meet. I had an appointment with one such individual – the man generally acknowledged to be the leading authority on AIDS in Uganda – for half-past seven that very morning. Perhaps, I thought,

as I glanced at my watch outside his door, it was the early hour that
was causing all this squeamishness.

'Enter,' he called, in answer to my knock. 'Ah, it's you. I wondered
if you were going to make it.'

The accent was soft, from somewhere in the Scottish lowlands. The
other thing that struck me straight away about Dr Wilson Carswell was
the air of spruceness. He had a full head of well-groomed wavy hair,
a trim beard around mouth and chin, a Rael-Brook shirt and woollen
tie, and he hinted at being the sort who would go in for sports jackets
and tweedy plus-fours. He was of slender build, and looked fit and
much younger than his fifty years. On the wall were framed prints
of the British royal family, and of Margaret Thatcher. The room was
slightly cluttered: a working doctor's office. We had agreed the ground
rules for the interview the previous day: I was not to use my recorder,
and his comments were to be strictly unattributable – a restriction he
has since waived.

The first case of AIDS in Uganda, he told me, had occurred in Rakai
district in 1982, according to anecdotal and aural evidence from that
time. But it was October 1984 before a case was medically confirmed,
when an aggressive form of the normally benign skin cancer known as
Kaposi's sarcoma, or KS, was linked to AIDS. In January 1985, the
Disease Surveillance Committee of the Ministry of Health paid a visit
to Kasensero to investigate the epidemic of 'Slim disease', but concluded
that this enteropathic condition was caused by poor sanitation, and a lack
of pit latrines down by the lake shore. However, later that month blood
samples taken from Kasensero were tested at Porton Down in the UK,
and it was confirmed that Slim was also a manifestation of AIDS.

I asked him how many deaths AIDS was causing in Uganda.

'Well, we were admitting about one new AIDS patient a day at Mulago
by the end of 1985. A short time ago, Dr Roy Mugerwa, from Ward 4A
upstairs, estimated that between March and July this year, a total of
two hundred and fifty-five new AIDS cases had been seen, and that's
getting on for two a day. So the number is increasing ... and most of
those patients will die fairly quickly. But the hospital death-tolls only
record a fraction of the true number. You'll have to go and check the
parish records at the Registrar General's office. But then again,' and
here he paused, all innocence, 'not all the parish chiefs report in.'

In fact, we both knew that the parish records would not provide what
I was looking for: too much damage had been done to Uganda's pride
and spirit over the past fifteen years, and most parishes were no longer
bothering to collect such information, let alone dispatch it to Kampala
on a regular basis.

And, as the doctor went on to explain, even the Mulago cases had not all been confirmed by laboratory testing – though they did conform to the clinical case-definition of adult AIDS in Africa established by the World Health Organisation in late 1985. By this definition, a patient could be said to have AIDS if he or she presented with at least two out of three major symptoms (loss of more than 10 per cent of normal body weight; chronic diarrhoea or prolonged fever lasting for more than one month) and at least one of six minor ones (persistent cough for more than a month; generalised rash; recurrent herpes zoster, or shingles; chronic and progressive herpes simplex on mouth or genitals; oral candidiasis, or thrush; and generalised lymphadenopathy, or swelling of the lymph nodes). In addition to these, the presence of aggressive KS or fungal meningitis were considered sufficient indicators by themselves. Dr Carswell added that there was a slightly different set of criteria for assessing AIDS in children, which, in Uganda at least, appeared to provide a rather less accurate diagnosis than the adult version.

The best indicator of all, however, was provided by checking the blood serum for the presence of antibodies to the virus that causes AIDS, which was now called HIV (human immunodeficiency virus) in preference to its previous French and American names of LAV and HTLV-3. The presence of HIV antibodies was usually assessed by a test known as the competitive ELISA (enzyme-linked immunosorbent assay), and then confirmed by another test called the Western blot. There had been two serological studies carried out in Kampala since the NRM takeover, Carswell related, his voice still matter-of-fact.

'We did one study on apparently healthy blood donors, mainly young males. Three hundred and seventy blood samples were tested at Porton Down, and it turned out that forty were positive.' I continued my furious scribbling of notes, not looking up. 'That was about eleven per cent seropositivity. In another test done between February and April this year, among antenatal women at a booking clinic in Nsambya Hospital, blood from one thousand and eleven apparently healthy women was checked in the UK. They were quite representative, I should think: they included both rich and poor subjects. Anyway, one hundred and thirty-six of them turned out to be positive – that's over thirteen per cent or getting on for one in seven.'

By contrast, he told me, the latest study of blood donors undertaken in the UK itself had identified just seven seropositives out of a total of 140,000 persons tested, or one in 20,000. At this point I stopped writing, and sat up. But Dr Carswell was in full flow.

'These studies have encouraged us to bring some ELISA machines over here. They began arriving in May this year. Nsambya's got one

that was given by the British Residents' Association; Mulago was given
one by the British High Commission. The European Community is to
donate one to Rubaga and one to Kitovu Hospital in Masaka. But we
need to test other areas of the country too. All the blood used in
transfusions needs screening.'

'Yes, but about these seropositivity figures. You're saying that between
eleven per cent and thirteen per cent of apparently healthy persons in
Kampala have got HIV in their bloodstreams? That's between one in
nine and one in seven of the population – at least of the adult population.
Are all of these people going to get AIDS?'

'Opinions vary. The DHSS in Britain speaks of one in ten seropositives, or perhaps we should be saying HIV-positives, eventually
getting full-blown AIDS. And there's an article I have here from the
'Guardian', from the end of July, that anticipates up to thirty per cent.
There again the Americans are very gloomy about it. I think they
would suggest figures of over thirty per cent. But the figures from
the homosexual population in California may be quite different from
the heterosexual population in Africa. So, one's got to do one's own
studies.' Then Dr Carswell paused, and rummaged among the papers
on his desk.

'Here it is, I've found it. Last month we had a visit from Dr Jonathan
Kaplan from the Centers for Disease Control in Atlanta, Georgia. At the
end of the visit, he wrote a report for the Ugandan health authorities,
which among other things said, and I quote (here Carswell assumed
something approaching a deep southern drawl): "Many seropositive
persons, perhaps the majority, perhaps all, can be expected to develop
clinical AIDS within the next few years." '

'And how many with clinical AIDS end up dying from it?' I asked,
cutting short the doctor's transatlantic vowels.

'Well over ninety per cent for the States and Europe. There aren't
any figures yet for Africa. But the really important thing is the rate
of doubling of seropositive persons. Among homosexuals in California,
between 1978 and 1986, the number doubled roughly every two years.'

'And in Uganda? Are you saying that it's even faster?'

Carswell was about to reply, with figures, or an estimate, but he
held back. Finally, choosing his words very carefully, he said: 'If that
happens here, if there are similar rates of increase in seropositivity to
those of other high-risk groups in other parts of the world . . .'

I looked up. 'Yes, Doctor?'

'. . . then many more people will become infected in the next five
years.' He was making damn sure he was not saddled with a quotable
quote.

Later, we talked about the possible origins of the disease. Dr Carswell told me that there was no evidence to suggest that AIDS had originated in Uganda; that it seemed to have arrived in the country quite recently. The first recorded case was only four years before, he said, and a disease as unusual as AIDS would surely have been recognised earlier, had it existed, by the many experienced doctors scattered around the country in hospitals and mission stations. Earlier that year, the blood of several geriatrics in Kampala and Jinja had been tested, and no seropositivity detected. This suggested that the virus had not been present during that period, years before, when they had been sexually active (although, I thought, it was also possible that some had picked up the virus, and had died of AIDS before anyone had a chance to test them). Carswell added that HIV seemed to have come to Uganda from either the west or the south-west, perhaps from Zaire, Tanzania, or Rwanda. He made particular mention of the arrival of the Tanzanian army in 1979, and of the vigorous cross-border trading in that region.

'But if there is a greater prevalence of the virus in this part of the world, is there not also a good chance of some natural resistance building up in the general population? Even the basis for a future cure, perhaps?'

'Ah yes,' said Dr Carswell. 'As the great Pliny died AD 79 was wont to say, "Ex Africa semper aliquod novi".'

My knowledge of classical languages was being tested, and was found wanting. 'Always something new out of Africa,' he explained.

We discussed other matters: the male/female ratio ('roughly one to one'); instances of AIDS patients with paraplegia, whose nervous systems were apparently affected ('I think we're seeing the first couple of cases now'); and the local policy of not informing confirmed cases. ('Most doctors here have been brought up under the British way of doing things: telling the families, but not the patient. By contrast, the American way is to sit down, and talk it out with the subject.') He also gave me the names of six or seven Ugandan doctors who were specialising in different fields of AIDS research, together with that of Dr Okware, the chairman of the Disease Surveillance Committee, known colloquially as the 'AIDS Task Force'. Finally, he lent me a copy of the most recent *Health Information Quarterly*, published by the Ministry of Health six months before. 'Don't quote me,' he advised. 'Quote this thing instead. It's all official in here.'

I went back to my hotel to read the *Health Information Quarterly* and, as I had been promised, it was all there in black and white: a section

entitled 'AIDS in Uganda', and compiled by the Clinical Committee
on AIDS, chaired by J. Wilson Carswell. Its other members were Roy
Mugerwa, Nelson Sewankambo, Fred Kigozi and Rick Goodgame,
names which were to become familiar in the weeks and months to come.

The report began by positing that 'Slim disease', as well as a new
type of the rare skin cancer known as Kaposi's sarcoma, which had
both first appeared in Uganda in around 1982, were in fact presentations of AIDS. It went on, 'Considering the fact that Slim was unknown
five years ago, and atypical KS very uncommon, it is quite astounding
that 170 cases have been well-documented in the last 15 months ...
This number must represent only a small fraction of the total number
of the cases in Uganda, where medical recording is currently very poor
and where many patients will not come to hospital for a disease they
regard as hopelessly fatal ... [In Mulago's medical wards] ... AIDS
is the second leading cause of admission, and is the leading cause of
death.'

The report went on to analyse a group of sixty-five AIDS cases,
all confirmed by blood tests, who had been admitted to Mulago in the
three-month period from October to December 1985, and who constituted 10 per cent of medical admissions for that period. Ninety-seven
per cent of the AIDS patients had presented with marked weight loss,
88 per cent with prolonged diarrhoea, 69 per cent with oral sores and
63 per cent with an itchy skin rash. Over half of them were clinically
defined as having dehydration, anaemia, or swollen lymph nodes. Thirty
per cent had genital lesions; 20 per cent some respiratory infection,
and 18 per cent aggressive KS. Neurological symptoms were present
in 17 per cent of the cases, including mental confusion, convulsions
and paralysis. In addition to the sixty-five AIDS cases, it added, there
was another poorly-defined group with AIDS-Related Complex, ARC,
which presented with persistent generalised lymphadenopathy; most
would probably progress to AIDS later on. The age range of the
patients was fifteen to sixty with a peak in the twenty-one to thirty-five
age bracket; sex, occupation, tribe and educational background were
all reflected in the general admission pattern at the hospital.

Turning to modes of transmission, the report singled out sexual
promiscuity ('the level of such promiscuity is high among Ugandans');
blood transfusions ('about 20 units of blood a day are transfused at
Mulago hospital alone. If 10 per cent are positive, then two new cases
are likely to be occurring every day at Mulago ... equal to the current
admission rate for AIDS patients'); and poorly sterilised needles, the use
of which was apparently 'commonplace'.

Having quoted seropositivity rates of 11.8 per cent for a group of apparently healthy adults in Kampala, and 16.6 per cent for a group of apparently healthy hospital in-patients and their relatives in Masaka, the report went on to hypothesise that '10 per cent of all Ugandans are possibly positive for the AIDS virus', adding: 'In Uganda, there is not a clearly defined risk group, and the whole population should be considered at high risk.'

As it was later revealed, this early estimate of Uganda's overall infection level was far too high, for it failed to take into account the fact that, by and large, dwellers in rural areas – who comprise roughly 90 per cent of Uganda's population – were far less at risk of exposure to HIV than those in the towns. However, this was no longer the case in Rakai and Masaka districts, where a rural epidemic of AIDS was already clearly in progress. In addition, the 10 per cent estimate should, by rights, have applied to the adult population rather than to the general population. But, even if the authors were perhaps a little rash in these estimates, they were entirely accurate in their overall analysis, for all Ugandans were indeed at high risk of infection.

One of the most interesting sections of the report, entitled 'Sexual Behaviour', was compiled from data supplied by the psychologist, Fred Kigozi, who had interviewed a group of forty-eight patients – twenty-three with AIDS, and twenty-five without. He found some common factors: both groups came up with an average age of sixteen for earliest sexual activity, comprehensively denied any experience of homosexuality, oral or anal sex, and proved to be roughly equally divided between those who had, and had not, experienced a sexually transmitted disease (STD). Where the two groups differed was in the number, and type, of sexual partners. The AIDS patients had a lifetime average of eighteen partners; the control group nine. Four of the AIDS group had experienced sex with prostitutes as against just one of the controls.

I was reading this section sitting on the balcony of my room at the Speke Hotel. It was now seven o'clock and just getting dark; I could hear the familiar sound of the Speke's 'good-time girls' laughing and arguing and calling out to male passers-by from the tables below. I decided that what was needed was not a dry account of lifetime sexual partners, but some first-hand testimony. I headed off downstairs.

At the first table I approached, I undoubtedly caused some con-sternation. A couple of the girls who were regulars knew that I was resident at the hotel, and had seen me several times with Sue. They were therefore suspicious when I asked if one of them would like to come upstairs to be interviewed. Presumably they suspected subsequent reprisals from a jealous girlfriend, or else that they were being recruited as a slice of bread in a sandwich, one of those amusements for which *wazungu* are notorious, and for which they can be charged accordingly. Whatever, there ensued a lengthy and heated debate in Kiswahili, which I eventually resolved by moving on to the next table, where a trim, rather pretty Acholi girl, whom I had often seen sitting apart from the other *malayas*, immediately agreed to speak to me.

Her name was Dora, she told me, once we were installed upstairs in my room; she came from the northern capital of Gulu, and she was twenty years old. I jumped in at the deep end.

'Now, Dora, how many sexual partners do you think you might have normally in one week?'

'Three. Three times a week.'

'You would meet them in bars, or discos, or where?'

'I meet him in a disco place, so if he looks nice to me, I fall in love with him.'

'In the morning, do you normally ask him for money?'

'I don't ask him for money, because I feel ashamed to ask him. If he feels like giving me some money, he can give me. But me, I don't have to ask him.'

'Have you heard of Slim disease, or of AIDS?'

'I heard about it, but I haven't met a person who is sick of AIDS. But one time a girlfriend of mine was telling me the story about the sickness. She went to Mulago to see someone who was very sick, and she asked a certain doctor, "Please, I want to see those people who are suffering from Slim." So he took her to go and see those people. And they were looking at her with a very serious face.'

'If you're sleeping with three different men in a week, doesn't that make you afraid that you might get Slim?'

'First I ask. I first ask him, and if he's sick I say "No thank you for that," because I have to prove it.'

'Do you think you can prove it? How can you be sure he's OK?'

'I can feel it in the morning.'

'But that may be too late.'

Dora laughed nervously. 'Or after about two days there I can feel it. And then I go to see a doctor, so he can tell me whether I'm sick or not.'

'But do you know that if you get Slim, you almost certainly die?'

'Sorry?' I repeated the question.

'Oh yeah. I know that.'

'And you're not afraid of sleeping with men?'

'I'm afraid.' Dora's voice suddenly rose, and although she was still effecting casualness, there was an urgency there too. Then, more quietly, almost resignedly, she repeated her answer: 'I'm afraid, yeah.'

'When you go to bed with a man, do you ask him to put on a sheath or a Durex?'

'I want him to put on a Durex, yeah.'

'And does he?'

'Some they do, some they don't.'

'And you don't insist?'

'I don't. But I have one boyfriend who has gone out to Italy. When he comes back I won't have to mess around so much.'

Dora laughed again as I put the microphone away, but more quietly now. I thanked her, and escorted her downstairs to buy her a few drinks. I sat down with her and ordered some beer while the other girls kept a respectful distance, but I found it difficult to talk to her now. Soon, I took my leave, and went off to Barbara's place to look for Sue. I was feeling sorry for Dora, and for all the women who had three boyfriends a week, and I was hoping very much that Sue was not one of them.

8 · WARD ROUNDS

I was having lunch in the Speke's coffee shop with Nigel Beale, a British businessman who had lived in Uganda for some years. The coffee shop is an airy semi-circular annexe with an open kitchen at its hub, and six wooden refectory tables providing the spokes. The place was filling up fast and a young man, perhaps twenty years of age, and less smartly dressed than most of the other customers, came and sat at the end of our table, two seats away from me. His forehead was covered with sweat and he was looking far from well. He ordered a hamburger and chips, which he ate in desultory fashion until, as he was about to bite into a final mouthful, he was violently sick. There was no warning, and no control either: he vomited over his arm and his lap, on to his plate and over the table. He sat quite motionless looking at the mess, until a kindly but embarrassed waiter came over to lead him away to the washroom; by now he had difficulty in walking. Beale placed his paper napkin over the splashes nearest to us, and said, 'Did you see his skin? And his hair – it was falling out. He's got it, for sure – he's another of your Slim victims.'

Whether or not Beale's diagnosis was correct, Kampala indeed seemed to be full of sick people that week – and I began to see 'Slim victims' everywhere. I had already decided to collect as much medical evidence as possible, before returning to London to place what I was now convinced was an important story. My next visit was to Nsambya, a Catholic mission hospital on the southern edge of Kampala; the laboratory there had received one of the new ELISA machines some two months before. I was invited to watch as William Maawali, the chief lab technician, tested a batch of sixty-four sera, some of them controls, for the AIDS virus, HIV. The process involved spinning the blood samples in a centrifuge to separate the sera, transferring a little of each into a separate well in a specimen dish, and then adding a reagent so that the presence of viral antibodies could be detected. William covered the dish with a piece of cardboard to protect it from the light, and we waited ten minutes, until a bell rang on a big clockwork alarm. He lifted up the cardboard. About half of the samples had turned a pale shade of blue, but William explained to me that these were all right; they showed no trace of HIV. It was the others, the clear samples, which were seropositive.

The specimen dish was then inserted into the ELISA machine, which gave a computerised read-out of the results. Five of the HIV-positives were 'retests', confirming previous results, and eighteen were of suspected AIDS cases, but there were six others which came from a group of sixteen blood donors, none of whom had previously been suspected of having HIV. 37.5 per cent of these supposedly healthy people were already carrying the virus.

Of course, a group containing just sixteen persons was too small to be statistically significant, and there was no way of knowing from where the donors had been recruited, and whether they could be taken as representative of the general population. Nevertheless the experiment, seen at first hand, impressed me more forcefully than had any of the data from the *Health Information Quarterly*.

I asked William if the seropositive percentage was typical, but he was clearly uneasy about answering, lest he be accused of leaking classified information to the press. I thanked him and left. He still had his rubber gloves on, so I did not shake him by the hand, and as I walked out through the laboratory I noticed a young nurse who was also wearing gloves; she was standing by a sink, cleaning out glass test-tubes with a bottle-brush. I stopped and asked her if those were the tubes used in the blood tests for HIV, and she confirmed that they were.

'I have to be very careful that one does not break, and cut my skin,' she told me.

The following day, I returned to Nsambya to interview Sister Miriam Duggan, the medical superintendent. The sister is a quiet, self-assured Irishwoman; like most of the nursing staff at Nsambya, she dresses in the starched white habit of her order, with a matching shawl that frames the face. She was unwilling to answer any of my questions about levels of seropositivity, but she readily concurred when I enquired whether some of her staff were not at risk of contracting the virus in the course of their work.

'Yes, there is a danger of an accident victim being brought in when he is bleeding freely, and who is handled by orderlies who are not wearing gloves. If he happens to be a carrier . . .' The sister left the sentence unfinished. I noticed that throughout the interview, she avoided specifically naming the disease we were discussing. I asked her what impact AIDS had had on the transfusing of blood.

'Yes, it's terrible. We had a bad gunshot wound coming in – someone haemorrhaging – and we needed ten pints of blood, and we didn't have ten pints of screened blood of the right group. So what do we do – take the risk of giving unscreened blood, or let him die?' The sister could not recall what had actually been done, but she added, 'Building up a sufficient blood bank is essential if one in ten has the virus. Precautions are being taken, we are screening, but only those who we think might have it.'

I asked her what specific precautions were taken to prevent the virus being spread to the staff.

'They put gloves on when handling dangerous items; linens are put into bleach to soak, and are then washed, and then put into an autoclaving machine which applies heat and pressure, before they are reused. But it's a tremendous strain on hospital resources.'

It was some months before I realised just how much of a strain. For not only had Nsambya's ELISA machine been donated, but so had its fridge, centrifuge, water bath, rubber gloves, and most other AIDS-related disposables – all gifts from people who had been alerted to the crisis by Dr Carswell, notably the British community in Kampala, and friends in British hospitals. Even the supplies of laboratory detergent had been brought back by hand by Nellie Carvalho, the Ugandan sister in charge of blood testing, when she had flown to London to be trained in the use of the ELISA machine – and once again, it was Dr Carswell who had organised and arranged funding for the visit. At this early stage in the AIDS crisis in Uganda, the response of a non-government hospital like Nsambya was entirely dependent on this type of charity and personal initiative.

I returned to Mulago Hospital, to arrange interviews with some of the AIDS specialists there, and the first man I managed to contact was the American physician, Dr Rick Goodgame, whose comments had featured prominently in Helen Boaden's radio documentary of two months before. In America, he had said, it was the homosexuals, some of whom 'might even have sex with five, or ten, or twenty men in one night' who could be identified as a high-risk group for AIDS, whereas the overall countrywide prevalence of the disease was low. 'We have tried to identify high-risk groups in Uganda,' he had continued, 'and there is so much infection, and the epidemic is so widespread, that actually being a Ugandan is a high risk.' It was these dramatic words which had opened the programme.

If I had been hoping for more dramatic quotations from Dr Goodgame, I was to be disappointed. He told me that he had been instructed not to speak again with the press, and it was clear that he did not take the warning lightly. After his contributions to the BBC programme, and the *International Herald Tribune* article, I was not altogether surprised that he had been muzzled. We therefore agreed that the subject of AIDS was off-limits, though he invited me to accompany him and six or seven student doctors around Ward 4B, which had already assumed the nickname of 'The AIDS Ward'. This experience was in many ways as instructive as anything he could have said in an interview – symptoms and diagnoses were discussed with the trainees, personal histories recounted, and possible methods of treatment outlined. In the course of the ward round three new patients were, I believe, marked down for HIV testing, representing three more potential cases of AIDS.

Dr Goodgame suggested that I should really get the permission of the medical superintendent of Mulago, Dr Kigonya, before seeking to interview anyone else. This was reasonable enough, and I duly waited in the corridor outside his office for the next two hours, while he saw a long stream of doctors and other officials. Eventually I decided that I was getting the Ugandan version of the bum's rush, and when he emerged to go to another meeting, I buttonholed him.

'Yes, Mr Hooper, my secretary had told me you were outside. I've arranged for you to speak with Dr Sezi, who is one of the senior consultants dealing with AIDS at this hospital.' Dr Kigonya indicated a man standing just behind him dressed, like himself, in a smart, expensive suit. 'He will tell you whatever you want to know. He will be my voice on the subject.' And with that, he was off.

Dr Charles Sezi looked somewhat displeased about being delegated to speak with me, but he escorted me to a committee room and agreed to answer my questions if I could be brief. He was, he told me early on, not only a senior consultant but also a fellow of the Royal College of Physicians, as well as being head of the publicity section for AIDS at Mulago. I did not enquire exactly what being head of publicity entailed, assuming it meant that he dealt with enquiries from the press. Certainly he was never lost for a quote. In fact, he simply spewed them out.

The following were his considered opinions about modes of transmission: 'People are fussing so much about sexual activity. Even if the Pope in the Vatican got AIDS, even if the cardinal here got it, I would not be surprised. The thing is transmitted by needles, by unsterilised injections, and by blood products. Anyone can get it. I don't think it is sex which is playing the major role, as the world tries to put it.'

And on the accuracy of ELISA: 'We need a bit of time before we are able to say the machine is foolproof. At the moment, there is not a single physician who has tested a million cases, or for that matter half a million cases, and correlated the results with the clinical manifestations of AIDS. In Uganda we have a lot of conditions which might cause confusion – for instance even worms affect the serum in various ways.'

Yet again, on the press: 'They have overdone it. They have the belief that the country is full of AIDS, and they produce all sorts of figures which are not true. The seropositivity is stated to range between ten and twelve per cent, which appears to be a very high figure. It's not based on proper studies, it's based on biased series, and we are not even certain of the accuracy of the work done. However, it's our feeling that the international media is after something else regarding the AIDS situation in Uganda.' (When asked to elaborate, he side-tracked to the assertion that AIDS mimicked diseases like typhoid, TB, malaria and other fevers, and that doctors were mistaking these diseases for AIDS and then misinforming the press.)

Dr Sezi said that health education that highlighted the dangers of mingling blood, or sharing needles, was most important. He added that sexual intercourse around the time of menstruation should not be encouraged, but clearly felt that promiscuous sexual activity *per se* was not something to warn the public against. Among all the medical authorities to whom I spoke, in Uganda and elsewhere, Dr Sezi was the only one to hold these views. It was only later that I realised the degree to which his extraordinary comments were largely defensive reactions to allegations about Ugandan promiscuity in the foreign press.

But all my hard work in buttering up Sezi, doing a taped interview and so forth, reaped no reward in the end. I asked him if I could interview three other doctors in the hospital – Mugerwa, Sewankambo and Kigozi – and rather to my surprise, he agreed. I duly saw each doctor, and made appointments for the following day. But when I turned up, each in turn found that he would have to cancel; one even acknowledged that he had been directed to do so by higher authorities. Finally I understood what duties being head of the publicity section entailed.

I expressed my dismay at being boycotted, whereupon Dr Roy Mugerwa, the co-ordinator of AIDS programmes at Mulago, changed his mind and agreed to meet me privately at the Speke that evening. And although he was circumspect throughout the interview, he did provide some useful snippets of information about the AIDS research work which had been undertaken thus far in Uganda. 'In the first study, we discovered that this disease occurred in an equal sexual ratio between males and females, and we also demonstrated that the disease occurred mainly among women and men who are of the ages when we expect maximum sexual activity. A further, more recent study was carried out in Rakai district, where we visited families where there was a case of

AIDS, and took blood from all the household members. When we analysed the results, we found that the sexual partner of the AIDS case was the one who was positive, and the other inhabitants, those who were living in the same house, were almost invariably negative, regardless of their age.' (It was later revealed that 71 per cent of sexual partners as against 2 per cent of other household members had proved to be HIV–positive in this study.)

At the end of our talk, I asked Dr Mugerwa how he would react to a doctor who claimed that unsterilised needles and blood transfusions were the main methods of transmission of AIDS in Uganda. 'I would like to know what his evidence is for making such a statement,' he replied, cautious to the last.

There are four major hospitals in Kampala, the third of which, Rubaga, is another Catholic mission hospital like Nsambya. In design, Rubaga combines Mulago's 1960s council estate with Nsambya's colonial mission station – a combination that is nearer to the best than the worst of possible worlds. There are grassy slopes where patients can sit and take the sun, and areas set aside so that the healthy may cook and wash clothes for their sick relatives and friends.

Dr Bob Tamale is the senior house officer in Rubaga's medical department: a self-confident young man with an urgent manner, and an accent that suggested the possibility of an internship served in England. He invited me to his flat for a pot of tea; by the time it was mashing, we had already dispensed with the pleasantries and moved on to the subject of AIDS. He was quite straightforward, making no attempt to conceal the seriousness of the situation as he saw it. He claimed that since ELISA testing had started two months previously, over 25 per cent of Rubaga's blood donors had turned out to be seropositive.

I pointed out that this was double the figure which most members of the AIDS Task Force were quoting. One of Tamale's colleagues, who had joined us for the tea-break, broke in: 'Most of the ministry officials have not been to visit these AIDS-affected areas like Rakai to see for themselves what is happening. Nor do they work at the hospitals where many AIDS patients are admitted. I think it's only the Carswell group that has really brought to the notice of the government and the country at large the gravity of the situation.'

'Then why do you think that Uganda is suffering so badly? It does seem to be among the countries that are worst affected.'

Dr Tamale poured me another cup. 'That's a difficult question to answer. But what I should mention is that our morals over the past years have tremendously declined, and that sexual promiscuity has been quite high, indeed rampant. Yet we are just now becoming aware of the modes of transmission of the disease. Hence, due to the lack of health education, it has already spread like wildfire.'

'Have you noticed a change in sexual attitudes since more has become known about modes of transmission?'

'There are two schools of thought right now. Some say the disease has been here over the past five years, and since the incubation period can range from five months to five years, everyone should have got it by now. Since they haven't, they say they are going to go ahead as normal. However, the more educated class is tending to play things a bit cooler, they're using methods of contraception, and I think their morals as far as sex is concerned are a bit improved too.'

'And how many AIDS patients do you have in Rubaga at present?'

'We have ten suspected AIDS patients out of fifty in the medical ward, and the presence of these patients has caused some anxiety among the nursing staff. They are concerned that there might be other modes of spread, making them at risk when they nurse these patients.'

It was not a convenient time for me to visit the medical ward, so instead I sought out Dr Hanny Friesen, Rubaga's senior paediatrician, who was just setting off to her flat for lunch. She invited me to join her. We sat outside at a table in the shade; in the background a cock kept crowing, over and over. I noticed that she spoke with the soft-drawn-out vowels of someone born near the North Sea: from Holland perhaps, or Germany. Thus far, she told me, she had had on her ward eleven proven cases of children suffering from AIDS.

'Is the virus in these cases passed on directly from the mother?'

'In these eleven cases, the mothers are seropositive as well, but I have also three cases where the mothers are positive, but have not passed it on to their children, who are seronegative. So I can't prove where the children have got it from.'

'Do you suppose in the womb, or through breast milk?' I prompted. I was feeling hot, and finding it hard to empathise with Dr Friesen's professional caution.

'Those are the two possibilities, but I am still questioning why do I have seropositive mothers with young children who are breast-feeding who are seronegative. Why didn't they get it?'

Presumably, I suggested, because mother-child transmission of HIV occurred predominantly in the womb, but Dr Friesen was unwilling to commit herself further.

'How long do the seropositive children normally survive?'

'I think the oldest so far was one year and seven months. Several have died, and some mothers have run away with their children, so you don't know what has happened afterwards.'

'And how old is your youngest adolescent case?'

'I don't know – they go to the adult wards. I have a mother of nineteen, I think, who is positive.'

'But it does seem that there is an age gap between newborns who get HIV from their mothers, and the adolescents and young adults who get it through sexual contact. And yet, in this country, so many children receive frequent injections. Surely that weakens the case for transmission through dirty needles?'

'You don't know ... did those young adults acquire the virus through sexual contacts only, or did they acquire it several years ago from a needle, and develop the disease only later?'

'But how do you explain the lack of any cases between the ages of four and fourteen in Uganda?' I felt myself to be hot on the trail now, spurning all sidetracks and false scents.

'It might be our ignorance at not recognising it yet. I don't think you can draw very many conclusions from that.' Dr Friesen was clearly not to be drawn. And, as I pressed her more, her vowel sounds grew softer, hailing from ever further to the north. At present she was speaking from Schleswig-Holstein, but threatening to head off into the Nordic wastes. I squinted up at the midday sun, and asked whether she viewed AIDS as the most serious disease on her ward.

'I think the whole AIDS problem has to be seen in perspective. If you have a ward of eighty children, and you have forty with measles and two with AIDS, then I think the measles problem is still bigger – as far as paediatrics is concerned – than the AIDS problem.'

'But what of the future? The disease is clearly increasing at an alarming rate in Uganda. Are you not bound to get more seropositive babies?'

'Yes. Most likely we get more. And more.' Now she was one of those lonely women in an Ibsen play. I felt myself slipping into the same hopeless mood.

'Already it seems that twenty-five per cent of your blood donors are seropositive.' Suddenly, Dr Friesen was back on her toes. 'Yes, but you have also to see where those donors come from. Often they go to the market and get men to donate – they pay them for it. So – it's a certain selection of the population in Uganda. I don't think you can then conclude that twenty-five per cent of the whole population is seropositive.'

It was in the ward that I really saw Dr Friesen in her element, saw how her love and sympathy for the children translated into professional care. Bosco, seventeen months old, had a large head that was clearly out of proportion to the rest of his body, and there were several sores and raised lumps on his face and chest. A sticking plaster below his nose testified to the only way in which he could be fed. He saw us, and then turned round shakily in his mother's arms, to cry on her shoulder. She was called Aida, was nineteen years old, still beautiful, not showing any obvious symptoms. She didn't yet realise that she was seropositive, and that soon she too would almost certainly get sick; it was apparently quite common for the infants to fall ill before their mothers. When I asked if I could photograph her with John Bosco, Aida posed with naïve charm, and then asked if she could have a copy. I never went back to give her one.

'Bosco looks very emaciated. What are his symptoms?' I asked.

'When he came in, he was very much underweight; he had severe oral thrush, he had some sores on the chest, but the malnutrition was actually the most important sign. He has a long-standing history of diarrhoea and vomiting, and now he has started coughing. On the X-ray, he has signs which could be fitting tuberculosis.' Dr Friesen's voice sounded rather too breezy for the words she was saying; it didn't quite conceal her feelings.

'Can Bosco survive?'

'From the time he was admitted until now, he is going down. Slowly but surely.'

'And are his symptoms typical of children with AIDS?'

'I don't know if you can call them typical symptoms. Until now, the positive children all have more or less the same signs and symptoms as the adults . . . a chronic gastro-enteritis, severe oral thrush, losing weight, not reacting to any treatment.'

By the time I left the ward, Bosco had fallen asleep in his cot.

When I returned to Mulago to see Dr Carswell, I felt unaccountably angry with him, with myself, with the whole of Uganda. Fortunately, he recognised the symptoms. And somewhere, a barrier was crossed. I told him about Dr Sezi's arguments against sexual transmission, and he laughed.

'Yes, he does make Lord Hailsham sound like the Liberal party, doesn't he?' And then he began to talk. He told me that Dr Kaplan, the American virologist, was of the opinion that the virus was almost exclusively sexually transmitted in Uganda, on the basis of the zero seropositivity encountered among geriatrics and primary school children. I asked him for his own opinion, and it was some time before he replied.

'Unless they tell all the sexually active, and all those who are about to be sexually active, of the major risk factors in transmission, they've got no chance. It would be as if they'd decided not to tell the homosexual population in California.'

Later, he confessed to doubting whether even such warnings about the dangers of sex would do much good. 'It would be like the campaigns against smoking, drinking and eating the wrong foods. They're all modes of behaviour which are difficult to alter dramatically over a short period of time.' And he went on to tell me that the next edition of *Health Information Quarterly* would list 484 officially-diagnosed AIDS cases in Uganda, of which 200, already seropositive on ELISA, had all just been confirmed by the very costly, but correspondingly more sensitive Western blot test at Porton Down.

'You see – we're not just making this up,' he said pointedly.

'Do you think that the people back home should feel at all threatened by what's happening here?' I asked.

'It's difficult to sell it to the people in the UK,' he said. 'What is Uganda's problem today may well be their problem in the near future. Certainly, it's going to get much, much worse all over the world.'

That evening, Sue and I went out with Roland Neveu and Joseph for a farewell night on the town. Roland had taken all the photographs he wanted, and was about to fly back to France. We had agreed that I would give my own photographs only to a couple of African magazines, and Roland promised to keep me posted about where he was selling his, so that I could offer my story to the same outlets.

It was quite a long night: we started off at Susannah's, a seedy night-club decorated with potted palm trees, and situated in the sub-urb of Nakulabye, on the rough side of town. This was the place for the best live music in Kampala. In this case a twelve-piece band from Zaire was playing the lovely shuffling sounds of Lingala, starting off with the monotonous rhythms of jangling guitars, slightly out of tune, and building, twelve minutes later, to a sweeping brassy climax that had the whole place on its feet. Unfortunately, the whole place consisted of barely thirty people, several of whom got involved in a fight which started on the dance-floor and ended up in the street outside, with someone getting a fairly comprehensive kicking. We decided it was time to leave, and headed instead for the centre of town, and the Chez Joseph disco, universally known as 'Chezz', which was always packed by this time on a Friday night. Inside it was very dark, a heaving mass of bodies; the atmosphere was heavy with sweat, and a single strobe light fractured the beat. 'Hello,' shouted a girl I didn't know, as I squeezed past her on my way through to the bar.

I was the only one of our party who didn't dance that night. I sat outside in the cool night air, thinking percentages: ten, twenty, twenty-five; then looking at the groups at the other tables ... one in ten, one in five, one in four. It was a funny sort of countdown.

9 · A TOWN IN THE NORTH

For me, the town of Gulu has always been unlucky, a place of ill omens. I first passed through there in 1980, soon after my arrival in Uganda, when I was on safari through the north of the country with some friends. Unbeknown to us, the town was on a war footing: not only soldiers, but civilians too, were mobilising to avenge themselves on the neighbouring region of West Nile, home of Idi Amin, who had persecuted and murdered the Acholi inhabitants of Gulu district right up until his overthrow in 1979. Between 10 and 20,000 people are believed to have been killed in West Nile in the month that followed – nearly all of them civilians. All we witnessed, however, were the preparations, as the lanky youths of the Acholi militia marched through Gulu's streets, banging their wooden staves on the ground, and staring at us with hard, challenging eyes.

Early the following year, I was working for the World Food Programme, and had to revisit Gulu in the company of Obote's newly-appointed Minister of Supplies, who was drunk by the time we left Kampala. He kept passing us on the road, and waving at us stupidly from the back seat of his Mercedes. When we reached Gulu, it transpired that the government hotel, the Acholi Inn, had room only for the minister, so I had to spend the night in a blue-painted lodging house on the edge of town. Also staying there was the minister's driver, who returned in the Mercedes at around one o'clock in the morning, substantially drunk, and in the company of a young woman of whom he wished to have immediate carnal knowledge. So urgent was his need that he blundered into my room, dragging her behind, and had almost thrown her down on the bed before he became aware of my presence. With a grunt of disgust he left the room and returned to the car, where he serenaded his lady friend with the ministerial cassette player, at full blast.

At this juncture, I threw on some clothes and followed him, to acquaint him with my feelings about his performance. Afterwards I went back to bed, but before long a fight seemed to have broken out downstairs; there were the sounds of bodies crashing into one another, and of heavy breathing, then of a magazine being slapped into a rifle, and finally of two voices, one screaming, the other soft and persuasive. Something about the tone of the driver's voice, its complete lack of inhibition, its madness, kept me awake and in fear for the rest of the night. In the morning I initiated an enquiry and discovered, as I had suspected, that until he was restrained by the nightwatchman, he had been heading upstairs to kill me.

I felt, however, that Gulu was the sort of wild west town where casual murders could easily happen, and a young Swiss traveller whom I met later that year confirmed this when he told me of the night he spent in a hotel there. Apparently two UNLA soldiers intent on a little looting had broken into the room next door to his, and had then shot dead its occupant as he tried to run away. By the morning, however, the blood had been washed from the floors, and nobody knew anything at all about the incident.

In short, by 1986, I already had bad feelings about Gulu. So perhaps I should not have been surprised when my next contact with the town turned out to have such disastrous consequences.

It was on the Monday morning that things really started going wrong. Over breakfast I met Nigel Beale, which in itself was an unusual occurrence, since he did not normally come to life until late afternoon or evening, when it was his habit to hold court at one of the tables outside the Speke. His style on such occasions was one of boozy acerbity; he was sharp-witted and sharp-tongued, but the overall effect of the jaded sage was somewhat spoilt by the lack of any leavening humanity or concern for his victims.

But on that particular morning, Nigel was helpfulness itself. There was a big story from Gulu, he told me; I ought to get hold of Sajat. Sajat was a Pakistani mercenary, and the former chief of staff of another of the anti-Obote guerilla groups known as the Uganda Freedom Movement, or UFM, and since the Museveni takeover he had been inducted into the NRA as a commander. Sajat was a big drinking buddy of Beale's, but I had known him even longer, since Luzira in 1983. He had been the 'star prisoner' in those days, one of the very few real guerillas that the UNLA had managed to capture, and was consequently held in solitary confinement. But one day I had wandered over to the windows of his cell, and managed to say hello to him before a warder rushed across to order me away. These days, he was always hearty when I met him, a man of flashing smiles and crunching handshakes.

Sajat told me that two days before, on Saturday morning, there had been a major attack on Gulu barracks, the NRA's main stronghold in northern Uganda, by members of the former UNLA. He said that the rebels had taken over the barracks for two hours, that there had been 'quite a number of casualties', and that they had eventually retreated to the bush with six heavy field guns and several other small arms. He told me that the information came from one Commander Doto, the Director of Operations and Training for the NRA's First (and only) Mobile Division, who had travelled up to Gulu the previous day and witnessed the scene of the fighting.

Soon afterwards, I bumped into another NRA commander of my acquaintance, who confirmed that there had been an attack, although he was rather vague about the details. I spent the next three hours trying to phone Commander Doto, as well as the NRA's overall commander, Elly Tumwiine, and the numbers two and three (after Museveni) in the Ministry of Defence – Dr Bata and the Hon. Amanya-Mushega. Eventually, I got through to Commander Doto, who told me that the report was 'not reliable at all. Such a thing has not happened'. Could I travel up to Gulu myself to check? 'For that, you must seek the army commander's permission.' I carried on phoning, but all my attempts to get through to Tumwiine and the two defence ministers proved fruitless. I got hold of Sajat once more, who insisted that Doto and the others were merely trying to keep a lid on the story.

There are times in every reporter's life when he has to decide whether or not to trust his informants. Sometimes, however much one tries to check and double-check, there is still a point at which one has to back one's hunches, to make an assessment of someone's reliability and truthfulness. This was one such time. Unfortunately, I made a bad choice. I decided that the information from Sajat and the other commander was reliable, that there had indeed been an attack on Gulu, and that Commander Doto was covering up. I filed the story, beginning with the words 'NRA commanders have confirmed that . . .' quoting Doto's denial, and mentioning the unavailability for comment of the top three men at Republic House, the army headquarters. I had not yet realised that in the previous month a gulf had opened between the original NRA and those, like Sajat, who had been brought in from the UFM. If I had, I might have been rather more careful.

The storm broke on Thursday. Army commander Tumwiine was reported on Radio Uganda as having denied that any attack had taken place; he condemned the BBC news report as 'highly irresponsible'.

I felt uneasy; perhaps my informants had been wrong. The following morning, Friday, I had an appointment with the Minister of Health, Dr Ruhukana Rugunda. The doctor, a large, friendly man with a full beard and baritone voice to match, had always been particularly complimentary about the Minority Rights Group report on Uganda which I had spent much of 1984 compiling, and which had detailed the human rights abuses perpetrated by Obote's UNLA. 'You fought with us, you really fought,' he would say, clapping me on the shoulder. And whilst I did not appreciate the claim that I was 'with' anybody, I did appreciate the compliment.

I decided to level with Rugunda straight away about being the author of the BBC report, and to ask him if he knew any details about the attack. I was taken aback by the vigour of his reply.

'I can't believe it. I really can't believe that you are the one responsible for this false report.'

'But are you sure it's false? Two of your commanders have told me that an attack took place.'

'And who are they?'

'You know, Doctor, that I can't tell you that.'

'Well, I can't think who they could be, but the stories they have given are totally wrong. We have been discussing this matter in cabinet, and everyone is furious with the BBC, the army commander in particular. We couldn't think who sent this false report. And it was you – I can't believe it. You have made a serious mistake. A very serious mistake indeed.'

His vehemence had me seriously worried. I felt sands shifting beneath me.

'Well, of course, I shall do all I can to check again . . .'

But the minister cut through me. 'Yes, you had better go straight away and check your story. And when you find it is wrong, you had better correct it. This time I expect that nothing more will happen, because it is you, and we know you. But be sure that you never make a mistake like this again; I don't think that that could be tolerated.'

This struck me as going a bit far – and I had no intention of being browbeaten by the minister. 'Well, Dr Rugunda, as I said, I shall check the story again, but I must say that I have been quite unable to contact anyone senior from Republic House who can give permission for me to travel up to Gulu.'

'You don't need permission. Just get in a car and go. Find out if your story's true or not.'

After that, the interview was hopeless. Dr Rugunda told me in a deadpan voice that my tentative figure of 2 dollars per head per year for Uganda's expenditure on health care was 'not too far from the truth'. He added that the government was not receiving as much assistance as it would have liked from the international community, but accepted that 'the primary responsibility of rehabilitating the health services falls squarely on the shoulders of the people of Uganda.' But he was still stiff with anger, and refused to answer any of my questions about AIDS, because 'there has been a lot too much talk about AIDS recently, and it is not even the most pressing medical problem we have. I have nothing more to say to the press on the subject. If you wish to discuss it further, the man to speak with is the head of our AIDS programme, Dr Okware.'

The following morning, I hired a car for the trip up to Gulu. I was accompanied on the journey by Catherine Bond, a young Englishwoman who had been living in western Uganda with her family, until their house had been broken into and looted clean by the UNLA. Her parents left, but Catherine stayed on to work as a freelance journalist, and over the previous few months we had frequently teamed up to share expenses on up-country trips.

On reaching Gulu, our first stop was at the mission hospital of Lacor, 3 miles outside the town, to meet the Italian medical super-intendent, Dr Pietro Corti, who had been based there since 1960 and who was widely respected throughout Uganda. He turned out to be a sturdy-looking man in his mid-fifties, who proudly showed us a framed certificate on the wall, evidence of an international prize he had just won for his work in Uganda. We had woken him from his siesta, but he brushed aside our apologies, made some strong coffee, and then asked how he could be of help. I explained that I was doing research for an article about AIDS in Uganda, and asked him straight out if he had encountered any cases in the Gulu area. As he began to answer, I was struck by his Italian accent, which was still pronounced even after so long a time in an English-speaking land.

'We started to realise more than two years ago that we had cases of young men and women having diarrhoea, being sick, having lung disease, sometimes suspected of TB, sometimes other things – that they were not reacting to any treatment, but going downhill slowly, slowly. We felt very uneasy about these cases, and then we learnt more about AIDS in other places like Kampala, through Dr Carswell, and we started to co-operate with him in trying to find out more. It was January 1985 when we had our first confirmation of AIDS here. We started to send sera to Italy, to England, and also to Mulago, and so we came

to realise that AIDS was an important disease, both in Kampala, and in
Gulu. The impression is that, as far as numbers are concerned, we are
a bit behind Kampala, but not very far behind. I would say every six to
ten months we more or less reach the level of the Kampala people, but
this is a rough estimate of course.'

'So how many of the population around Gulu are currently seropositive?'

'We've tested mainly suspected cases of AIDS, and they were strongly
seropositive, of course; from a third to two-thirds of the sera were
positive. But when we did non-suspected cases in the hospital, picking
medical staff and paramedical staff, young nursing students and so forth,
we came to realise that we had already – and this was just one year ago
– a percentage of twelve to fifteen per cent positive. And now we are at
the level of fifteen to twenty per cent positive. We hope to get an ELISA
machine and testing kits soon, so we can make a good assessment of
the situation, and screen the bottles of blood. We now do one to two
transfusions per day; we used to do more, but now we've cut it down
to the absolute minimum.'

'So why is there another pocket of high seroprevalence in Gulu,
when it would seem that otherwise the disease is mainly concentrated
in southern Uganda?'

'I wouldn't say that, because everywhere where there are doctors
aware and interested in the disease, they find out. I know that in
Kalongo Hospital, they collected about two hundred sera in a few days
– hospital patients, suspected cases, out-patients with other diseases,
the people living around and so forth – and they had a response of
twenty per cent positive. This Kalongo is a bit far away, a bit in the
bush you might say, in Kitgum district.'

'How many confirmed cases do you have right now in Lacor?'

'We always have about six to ten clinically confirmed cases, and
another four or five suspected cases. We keep them in for quite a long
time, to try to help with the secondary infection, so some of them die
in the hospital.'

'Do you think that the two civil wars of 1979 and 1985 helped
spread the disease?'

'I don't think that the NRA had to come to Gulu to spread AIDS.
They may have brought more than what we had. The wars have been
one of the main elements in spreading AIDS in Uganda – I don't think
there is any doubt – because exactly the same thing happened to all
the other venereal diseases ... and I think now in Uganda they are
demonstrating that AIDS is almost purely a sexually transmitted disease
– besides the blood transfusions, of course. But if you calculated the

increase in sexually transmitted diseases in the last fifteen years, it's something absolutely unbelievable. I believe I found here the first case of congenital syphilis in 1964, four years after we started working here ... the early form of the disease you cannot miss. One case out of four, years before, and right now we get two or three cases a month. There is no kind of moral custom holding on among the people, and certainly the presence of the soldiers and their violence has been one of the main reasons for both physical damage and moral damage.'

I pressed Dr Corti again about the degree to which the soldiers of the former army, the UNLA, had been responsible for bringing AIDS to the north. In reply, he claimed that he had encountered only one confirmed and two suspected cases among the former soldiers; a claim which I found surprising, to put it mildly. For several years now, the UNLA – and its main tribe, the Acholi – had been infamous throughout southern Uganda for the brutalising of women; it was alleged that such practices as mass-rapes, sexual mutilations, and the forcible marriage of schoolgirls had been widespread. It seemed incredible that so few of Lacor's AIDS cases should be former UNLA soldiers. I wondered if Dr Corti feared that questions of this sort might prompt a witch-hunt against the local people, with AIDS as the excuse. So I dropped the subject, and asked him what was being done to alert the people of Gulu to the dangers of Slim.

'Well, we are starting to think of a campaign in the churches and so on, to do something about it. Otherwise, these people are going to be in a big, big problem.'

They are indeed, I thought, as we drove off and I ran back through the tape. I scribbled down a note to remind myself about Dr Corti's casual assertion that Gulu's current level of 15 to 20 per cent seropositivity was several months behind that of Kampala.

The afternoon was going on, and it was time to visit the barracks – this being, of course, the main reason for the 400-mile round trip. Already, Dr Corti and others we had met had left us in little doubt that no major attack had taken place the previous weekend, so this was a visit I little relished making. Still, it had to be done. Catherine and I walked up to the main gate and asked to speak to the garrison commander. We were left outside the guardhouse for fifteen minutes before an adjutant came to escort us to his quarters.

The Commander of the Northern Brigade, Onesmus 'Pecos' Kutesa, readily invited us into his bungalow. It was furnished with a three-piece suite and not much else. He had just got married the previous weekend, in fact on the very day of the alleged attack, he told us. He was furious about the BBC story.

'Now, do you see any evidence of a battle here? Do you see any buildings destroyed, any bullet-holes in the walls?' (We had not, but there again, neither had we been afforded the opportunity to check for ourselves. It seemed churlish to mention it, though, for the commander was still in full flow.) 'I wonder what I could do to this reporter from the BBC. I wonder if there is any legal case I could open against such a reporter. I wonder, if he walked into my camp here, if I could just lock him in my cells and leave him there?' We all laughed. I did a radio interview with him, to put the record straight. 'Bloody hell. He knew, didn't he?' I said to Catherine, as the gates closed behind us.

We had the opportunity to interview local residents, of whom there were surprisingly few in evidence. Only one of those we spoke with recalled any shooting on the previous Saturday morning, and he insisted that it had been 'meaningless, nothing big'. We did hear some talk about a rebel attack around that time on the nearby village of Pabo, but it was clear that the story I had filed had been wrong. Nevertheless, Gulu did have an unexpectedly tense feel to it. Back in March the NRA had taken over almost without a shot being fired, and the population had slowly emerged from hiding (women first, as always) to find that this new army from the south was not about to rape and murder the northern population, as the outgoing UNLA officers had predicted. But now in August, the honeymoon was over. When people could speak to us in confidence, they mentioned a deterioration in NRA discipline over the past few weeks: drunkenness at roadblocks, looting from homes at night, and the commandeering of lorries, allegedly for 'army business'. On the other hand, everyone agreed that some standards still obtained: that the NRA was not, for instance, indulging in any gratuitous killings.

And this was the story I filed for the BBC when we got back to Kampala. I spoke direct to the news editor for the day, explained that I had previously filed what appeared to be a dodgy report, and asked him if he would be able to give the latest account as much prominence as possible.

'Don't worry, Ed. We've all made mistakes at some time or other,' he reassured me.

The new, correct story went out as third item on the next World Service bulletin.

There was a sequel. Three days later the town of Gulu really was attacked, and by 3,000 armed men, most of whom were former UNLA soldiers. They held the town for several hours. I've often wondered if my two Gulu broadcasts in any way precipitated the attack, or if it was all just a coincidence of timing. As it happened,

I flew back to England that same morning, and for the next few days was busy working on the AIDS story. It was thus almost a fortnight before I learnt about the other repercussions of the Gulu affair.

10 · THE BUSH TELEGRAPH

Back in London, there were a number of disappointments awaiting. Chief among these was the fact that the AIDS story did not arouse the degree of excitement I'd anticipated. After transcribing the eight tapes I'd recorded, I touted cassettes and transcript around the various programme offices at Bush House, the headquarters of BBC World Service, and Broadcasting House, that of the BBC's domestic programming. Nobody seemed very interested. 'We've already done three pieces on AIDS this year,' said one producer. 'It's all too depressing for an early morning show,' said another. 'Can't hear what people are saying,' said a third; 'they do all have such strong African accents, don't they?' In the end, I was lucky to find one programme, *Development '86*, that was interested enough to offer me a fifteen-minute slot, split into two weekly parts, and a producer, Graham Hill, who was willing to spend well over a day in the studio, splicing tapes and recording my linking commentary. The end result was dramatic in content, but wooden in delivery: as ever, I just couldn't get the hang of reading into a microphone from a prepared script.

This wasn't, however, a problem which would trouble me for very much longer, at least not with the BBC. Almost two weeks after my return to London I discovered, quite by accident, that I had been taken off the list of News Department stringers, those who receive pro rata payments and expenses on a regular monthly basis. I phoned Ian Richardson, the deputy editor of News Intake, and he brusquely confirmed that my services were no longer required. He added that, due to a mix-up, they had been unable to inform me of the fact either by phone or by letter, but that Catherine Bond had already been appointed in my place. I could hardly argue with the decision, though the manner of its implementation was shabby, to say the least. In fact, I had tendered my resignation back in June, when I realised that the feature articles for which I'd already been commissioned would not allow me the time to follow up on every breaking news story; and at that time Richardson's boss, the News Intake editor, had urged me to carry on. I knew that my reporting was hardly in line for a Pulitzer, that I had missed stories and made other errors, but now I was being dropped for a mistake which I had both admitted to, and had made a genuine attempt to rectify.

Suddenly the BBC's avuncular chumminess had gone, to be replaced by a remarkable corporate closing of ranks as news of my demise passed along the Bush House telegraph. Other programmes to which I had been in the habit of submitting feature pieces and interviews stopped contacting me. One senior producer later told me that Ian Richardson had been phoning round the building, advising him and his colleagues not to use my material. He himself had resisted the advice, but it seemed that others had proved more malleable. This incident marked the end of my career as a news reporter, and the winding-down of my relationship with the BBC. I felt depressed about the way it had happened, but I was also left with the nagging feeling that, over and above the mess I had made of the Gulu story, someone had put the boot in. Someone, somewhere, had stitched me up.

But some months passed before I began to do the right sums. I was spending an evening with Nigel Beale, who had drunk rather more than usual, and suddenly he looked at me very directly, showing his teeth, and said, 'You see, young Hooper, whenever someone does me wrong, I always get even with them, however long it takes me. Always.'

And then I thought back to the time just after the takeover, in February or March, when Beale had been away in England, and I had spent a couple of nights in the company of his Ugandan girlfriend, Helen. The rest of the addition was not so difficult.

There were more than enough other matters to keep me busy during the rest of my home leave. I had a check-up at the Hospital for Tropical Diseases, which included another HIV test, my third in the space of a year. It also turned out negative, but I felt decidedly nervous as I waited more than a fortnight for the result to come through. In the mean time, I occupied myself with the fiddly jobs that always take so much longer than expected: stocking up on equipment, getting in touch with papers and magazines, interviewing exile groups, and doing research in libraries and cuttings files. In addition, I sold some more feature pieces about Luwero and southern Sudan. And I wrote two versions of the AIDS story, the second of which I held back in the hope of placing it as text to Roland's pictures in one of the bigger European magazines.

Roland phoned me once at home, soon after my return, to tell me that he was still busy editing his video of Kyebe, and had not yet placed his stills. After that, however, he seemingly disappeared: he failed to phone again on the date arranged, and my efforts to contact him in both Paris and New York proved fruitless. I waited a further ten days, but when there was still no word, I decided to try to sell the story accompanied by my own pictures, some of which had turned out surprisingly well. I was breaking my agreement with Roland, but then he also, it seemed, had forgotten his agreement with me. I gave some prints and duplicates to Picture Search, a small but energetic photo agency based in Surrey, and then flew to New York for a week; I felt sure that America's preoccupation with AIDS would guarantee interest in the story of a heterosexually-transmitted epidemic.

And so it turned out. I sold lengthy accounts to the *New York Times* and to the United Nations magazine *Development Forum*, both accompanied by photographs. The former, in particular, aroused a great deal of interest. And before I flew home, loaded down with Minolta lenses and Banana Republic safari gear, I was approached by a well-known New York photographer who had seen my material and who wanted me to escort him to Kyebe and Kasensero. The idea was to combine his photographs and my text, and a very large sum of money was mentioned. As it turned out, this was all pie in the sky, but it was apparent that what with the *New York Times* article, and Roland's Kyebe video which had just appeared on American network TV, the 'AIDS villages of Uganda' had suddenly become a much sought-after story.

It was a typically wet autumn evening in London. I had walked only a hundred yards down Praed Street before the downpour began in earnest, and soon I could feel trousers and shoes starting to cling and get soggy. I broke into a run, and by the time I'd located the medical school at St Mary's Hospital, and the entrance to the Wright Fleming Institute, I was sweating under my raincoat. I was almost fifteen minutes late for my appointment, but fortunately Dr Anthony Pinching, senior lecturer and honorary consultant in clinical immunology, was still busy at his desk. He turned out to be a smartly dressed, dapper man, with slicked-back hair and neat moustache; and his greeting was brisk, bespeaking eagerness to get started. It was, after all, six o'clock on a Friday with the weekend beckoning, which was the only time he had available before my flight back to Uganda two days later. In the end, he forfeited the better part of his evening in order to give me a briefing that reflected the best of the theoretical and factual knowledge about AIDS that was available at the time.

Dr Pinching explained that, as a clinical immunologist, he had been interested in immunodeficiency disease since 1981, when the first reports began coming out of America. Realising that such a malady would most likely not be confined to the far side of the Atlantic, he and his colleagues had quickly initiated the first AIDS research programme in the UK. But as the interview progressed, I came to realise that the doctor viewed AIDS as an ethical and political, as much as a medical, issue. My first question, for instance, concerning the latest theories about the origin of HIV, prompted the following response:

'I think the origin of the AIDS virus is a highly academic question. I would regard it as part of the archaeology of AIDS, and if you happen to be an archaeologist, it's interesting. If you happen to be interested in the medical problems of, for example, Africans with AIDS, then I think it's rather irrelevant, frankly. It is the pursuit of the origins which has led to so much misunderstanding about Africa and in Africa, and has led to many African countries denying the problem; I think that's been very damaging to efforts to prevent spread and to cope with the epidemic in Africa.

'I can create hypotheses, but they may never be fully testable scientifically, because the archaeological record is incomplete. The *likelihood* is that the AIDS virus HIV is derived in evolutionary terms from a related virus that is found in other primates in Africa, and perhaps other parts of the world as well, but particularly in the African green monkey. The virus probably causes a disease similar to AIDS in some primates, while in others it lives as a passenger, not causing disease. It may be the shift from one species to another that causes it to become a disease-producing virus.

'I think it is reasonable to speculate that at some time in the past the virus moved from a primate to the human species. It's quite possible, indeed probable, that this occurred in a remote rural population, possibly in Africa, possibly somewhere else in the world. From its current characteristics, it's clear that the virus is now fairly well adapted to the human species. If that remote rural population was socially, and specifically sexually, isolated from other cultures, then the virus could have existed for quite some time without anybody being aware of it. Even if it did cause disease it might not have been particularly notable, because of the death rate from other factors.

'It is reasonable to speculate that after a time the breakdown of rural culture and the move to the towns, for reasons of economy, famine or war, led to people carrying the virus to urban communities. And the different patterns of sexual behaviour prevalent in those urban communities allowed the new virus to spread, and to result in what we now see as the current epidemic in Africa and elsewhere. And I think it's important to talk of the African problem as an epidemic – that is something that is still spreading – rather than an endemic situation, which would suggest that it is static.

'Clearly, if someone contracted the virus in one of those towns, in Africa or elsewhere, and then went to other parts of the world, then again the virus would spread according to prevalent modes of human behaviour, whether it be through homosexual activity, the sharing of needles and syringes in drug abuse, or whatever. In a sense the *soil* of sexual behaviour has been in existence for quite some time, whereas the *seed* – in this case the virus – has only recently been introduced. It's a reasonable hypothesis. It's clear that the part of the fossil records that is missing, and may always be missing, is the one that everyone is searching for: the first planting of a seed. If it's a very remote rural population, probably nobody went to take blood from them, and if so, we'll never find the answer. We don't know exactly where syphilis came from, though we know it appeared somewhere around the time of Christopher Columbus. Maybe we should concentrate on other rather more important issues.'

So I asked Dr Pinching how long, on average, it took for HIV to cause disease. He explained that the virus had the capacity to attack two of the key systems of the body – the immune system and the nervous system – but added that a substantial percentage of those infected did not apparently progress to any disease, or else got a form of disease that was less severe than AIDS. He said that on the evidence of 'cohorts' of infected people who had been studied for up to four years, about 15–20 per cent seemed to get AIDS, 30–40 per cent developed minor forms of illness, and the remainder appeared to be quite well. Among those who got the disease, it seemed to take an average of between two and five years, or rather longer in neurological cases. He went on to say that co-factors such as having a history of STDs – sexually transmitted diseases – or in the case of women, having had more than one pregnancy, increased the risk of progression to AIDS.

He stressed repeatedly, however, that because of the time-frame, nobody knew whether those seropositives who currently appeared to be healthy would remain so over a longer period. And in fact, by 1989 it was apparent that many more of those with HIV would go on to get AIDS, and that the average time from infection to disease was eight years, or even longer. However, there was also evidence to suggest that certain African strains of HIV were more pathogenic, and thus led to disease more quickly.

I then asked Dr Pinching about the principal symptoms of AIDS, and the different ways in which it presented around the world. Again, he couched his answer in accessible language:

'AIDS itself makes someone susceptible to a wide range of different infections in different body systems. People are rendered susceptible to "opportunistic infections" – organisms which take advantage of a window in the body defences to cause a disease they would not otherwise cause. These infections can affect the lungs, the gut, the nervous system, the skin, the lymph glands, and many other organ systems. The pattern of infection seen in different parts of the world varies, because the infections people get depend on which organisms are common in their environment. Many of these infections are ones which we all carry around with us, and which are normally contained by the immune system; only when the immune system becomes damaged can they re-emerge to cause disease.'

He went on to outline the three main routes of transmission – sexual, blood to blood, and mother to unborn child. Regarding the first route, he cited having a high number of sexual partners as the obvious risk factor. He posited that among couples, be they heterosexual or homosexual, in which one partner started as HIV-positive and the other HIV-negative, transmission of the virus eventually occurred in more than half of the cases, though there was some tentative evidence that women infected their male partners slightly less easily than the other way round. The number of sexual exposures to the same partner was apparently not so significant; it seemed to be very nearly as risky to have one exposure as to have several. Perhaps certain people possessed innate resistance to the virus.

In Africa, he said, the peak age group for HIV infection seemed to occur at least five years later in men than in women 'which reflects the sexual anthropology of the region, that older men go for relatively younger women'. The peak for African female AIDS patients seemed to be in the mid-twenties, and for males the early thirties, he said.

Regarding blood-to-blood transmission, Dr Pinching pointed out that it was far more difficult to screen blood donated for transfusions in Africa and other developing areas, because of the limited resources available, combined with the difficulty of identifying any high-risk group. As for infected needles or syringes, whether those used by Third World health assistants or by 'First World' junkies, here too a single exposure to the virus was all that was needed. Although holding a needle in a flame effectively inactivated the virus, the cleansing of plastic syringes posed greater problems, necessitating boiling for lengthy periods or flushing out with bleach.

The last route of transmission, that of mother to child, provided no less gloomy a scenario. 'The evidence to date would indicate that rather more than half of the children born to infected women will themselves be seropositive, and of those children, at least a half will develop AIDS within the first year of life. What the risk is to the remainder has still to be established; we need to look to Africa to determine that more precisely. There's also a higher level of neurological disease among infected children.'

I enquired whether there was any cause for concern about blood-sucking insects like mosquitoes and bedbugs, in the light of recent research which had proved that HIV could exist in the gut of a mosquito, at least under laboratory conditions. Dr Pinching confirmed that there was compelling epidemiological evidence to demonstrate that such insects were not, in practice, a route of spread, probably because the amount of inoculum injected into the bloodstream of the person bitten was so small.

We then turned to the various dilemmas of responsibility that the AIDS epidemic had raised. Dr Pinching maintained a firm stance on such issues. He believed that doctors had a responsibility to inform confirmed AIDS sufferers, and confirmed HIV carriers, of their status. 'It's a matter of basic medical ethics that the patient should be told before anyone else.' He also felt that, after proper counselling and education, it was important for doctor and patient to discuss together such issues as the identification of others who might have been exposed to the virus, and the future sexual behaviour of the patient. 'I think people have to take responsibility for their own sexual actions, and if they've wittingly or unwittingly taken risks with other people's lives, then they have to take some responsibility for picking up the pieces afterwards.'

In addition, he had strong views about the obligations incumbent on official bodies. 'It is crucial that every individual in society knows about AIDS, how it is transmitted, and how it is not. That is the only way of achieving prevention, when it comes down to it, because what people do in their private lives, and in their sexual lives, is something known only to them. It is they who have to make rational decisions about AIDS, based on what they know about what they do. Only informed individuals can do that, and it is up to governments, doctors, scientists and the media to ensure that they have that information. The next generation, in particular, has to make decisions about its sexual life style on the basis that AIDS is here, and here to stay. I think that must change sexual patterns around the world.' Also internationally: 'I think the developed world has a serious responsibility to help the developing world in this matter. I'm pleased that African countries have put colonial history behind them, and welcomed help from people who have offered it in the right spirit and with the right motivation. And all of us can learn lessons from the epidemic in Africa.'

Dr Pinching stressed that a viable AIDS vaccine was yet to be discovered, and that some doctors were arguing that, because of the nature of the virus, there might never be an effective vaccine against it. But even if one were to be developed, the cost of a worldwide vaccination campaign might well prove prohibitive: the hepatitis B vaccine, for instance, was priced at over 100 dollars per head. 'But if you compare this with the cost of looking after people with AIDS, it of course vanishes into insignificance.' In the mean time, he added, the only proven way of reducing the risk of HIV transmission during sex was to employ a barrier such as the condom.

When asked about figures, the doctor told me that the United States currently had 24,000 people with AIDS and perhaps 1.5 million virus-carriers (a ratio of 62:1); that the equivalent figures for the UK were 490 and about 30,000 (61:1); and that for Africa 'I really have no idea. I think many people fear that the scale in Africa is already much larger than the scale in the United States. If the sexually active range from twenty to forty years, and if 15 per cent of urban adults are infected, then you can calculate what sort of figure you're talking about.' He mentioned Zaire, Rwanda, Burundi, Uganda, Tanzania, Zambia, Kenya, the Central African Republic, Gabon, Congo and Malawi as some of the worst-affected countries, but stressed that their rural populations had far lower levels of infection.

So what, I asked finally, would be his best and worst case scenarios for the AIDS epidemic in Africa?

'Oh dear,' he sighed. 'I don't believe myself to be a prophet, least of all a prophet of doom. I think that if we look at countries where the virus is very common, in parts of Central Africa, even a best-case scenario is pretty gloomy. I think a lot of people are going to die, in peaks of social value, for infection seems to be most common among the higher socio-economic groups. The spread to children is another desperately worrying development. I think even if we can contain the situation, and stop the spread now in Africa, there will still be great holes socially and economically. It's a sobering thought.

'Elsewhere in the world, I hope that by getting the facts across to people, by concentrating people's minds on the main issues of spread, and taking their minds away from the non-issues, we may be able to avert a major spread to the general population. At the moment, a lot of people say that they're not at risk, but then carry on with dangerous behaviour in respect of this virus. We still have a very small heterosexual epidemic in the West, and we have the capacity to prevent it occurring on any scale. A small change in sexual behaviour – which is perhaps all we can expect – will make a very big difference. But if we wait till people are dying all around us, that will be much too late.'

'And what is your worst-case scenario, Dr Pinching? Is there the potential of an AIDS Armageddon?' Of course I had to ask.

'I think it's sensationalist, but on the other hand I think that AIDS is quite the worst public health threat we've seen in centuries, perhaps ever. We're going to have to learn to live with it. I think we can live with it, but only by a major effort by the whole community throughout the world. It's probably unhelpful to look at a worst case, because I think there's no point in just scaring people. Panic is not a good motivating force; you have to create constructive concern.'

I thanked Dr Pinching for the interview, and told him that I hoped it would contribute to the process of promoting that constructive concern. And then, feeling motivated, albeit a little chilled, I walked out into the cold, unfriendly night.

11 · KAMPALA DAYS

Over the next few months the 'AIDS villages of Uganda' continued to fascinate the international media; reporters and photographers from many of the world's leading journals and broadcasting stations descended on Uganda looking for powerful or sensational copy, depending on house-style. At least some of them arrived with the apparent expectation that Kampala's streets would be lined with the Belsen-like faces of the walking wounded; disappointed there, they popped Sterotabs in their water bottles, and set out for the banana groves. But nearly all were impressed by the fact that Uganda was suffering a heterosexual AIDS epidemic: 'It's not only the gays who gotta watch out now,' was one reporter's bottom-line summary as he bought me a beer the night before flying back home.

However, all this attention was becoming something of an embarrassment to the Ugandan government, and some officials felt that their openness in allowing reporters into the country to cover the story had been counter-productive, since it merely reinforced the outside world's conception that Uganda was ridden with AIDS. And, as I was later to discover, other officials were less than happy with me, for having 'broken' the Kasensero story in the first place.

Meanwhile, I was now occupying that time-honoured position of the locally-based reporter with inside-track knowledge. As such, I tended to get taken out for lunch or drinks by visiting luminaries of the fourth estate. This was all fair enough; any hack arriving on foreign turf knows that one of his primary sources will be his local counterpart, whether a national or an expatriate resident. Often the two will team up for a while, the resident's local knowledge augmenting the newcomer's professional skills and expense account. The trick for the local man, of course, is to give good value while not giving away all of his sources or story ideas.

*

It was in October that the opposition to the National Resistance Movement government first became a tangible force. During my stay in England, the Ugandan Minister of Energy, Andrew Kayiira, who had previously been leader of the other main anti-Obote guerilla force, the UFM, had been arrested by a posse of NRA soldiers, and held in Luzira Upper Prison on a charge of treason. Also charged with treason were various former UFM soldiers, including Sajat; several Baganda politicians of a generally conservative persuasion, including two other cabinet ministers; and Anthony Ssekweyama, chief editor of the staunchly-contentious *Citizen* newspaper. Ssekweyama had himself been detained and charged with sedition several times under Obote, and his latest detention by the Museveni regime – albeit on treason charges – caused some observers to raise questions about the NRM's public dedication to free speech. The government, meanwhile, let it be known that the treason trial would shortly be heard in court, a pledge which seemed more dubious with each passing week of inactivity.

Given the NRM's sudden abandonment of its one-time UFM allies, and of a large slice of the former Conservative party and Democratic party representation in cabinet, it was hardly surprising that in the first week after my return from England, I was greeted by a long list of complainants, all eager to detail cases of NRA/NRM corruption, tribal nepotism or worse. When hearing such grievances, it was always necessary to give some thought to the possible 'slant' of the source; it was noticeable that the loudest protesters were normally either from tribes like the Langi and Acholi, which had formed the backbone of support for Obote's and Okello's regimes, or else were Baganda, the country's largest and wealthiest tribe, but one which had never been permitted to hold the reins of power for any significant length of time. Baganda privates made up the largest ethnic group in the army, but the commanders remained predominantly Bahima or Banyarwanda, a fact which the NRM's stated emphasis on nationalism and detribalisation did little to conceal. With the latest arrests, it looked as if the Baganda were being manoeuvred even further into the wings.

Also conspicuous in its distrust of the new regime was a large part of the foreign business community, especially the British. Many were people who had been resident in Uganda for a long time, who had found it expedient to remain even through the mad years of Amin, and the even more violent years of 'Obote Two'. Although some were clearly genuinely attached to the country and its people, others of this group were right-wing to the point of racism, and had stayed on only because of the entrepreneurial opportunities that abounded when there was a lack of both security and competitors.

There were several watering-holes where the expatriate community was wont to congregate. On Sundays, a large percentage would descend on one or other of the rival sailing clubs at Entebbe and Kazi, on Lake Victoria. These were essentially whites-only establishments, though a *de facto* agreement obtained whereby African wives or girlfriends could also attend, if appropriate. Then on Saturday afternoons many, especially the menfolk, would call in at The Freemason's Arms, an occasional pub operating in the masonic lodge that proudly occupied a residential plot half a mile from Kampala city centre. Masonic meetings were still apparently held there, as indeed – elsewhere in Kampala – were meetings of the League of St George, a radical right-wing organisation little known in Britain, but which seems still to be thriving in several of the former colonies.

But the bastion of the British community in Uganda was without doubt the twice-weekly club held at the British High Commission. The security situation was still felt to be too unstable for the club to remain open after dark, but on those two evenings, between five o'clock and half-past six, large quantities of alcohol were consumed and, emboldened no doubt by being on diplomatic premises, expatriates talked more freely than was usual. Again, no official exclusion policy existed, but in practice the only Africans who attended were pretty and female. I once saw a visiting UN consultant knocked senseless to the ground, after his Ugandan driver had had the temerity to walk into the club to hand over the car keys.

Beer was expensive, being purchasable only by tickets that were themselves purchased in hard currency. By contrast, talk was cheap. Although one had to treat information from this source with caution, since so often was it laced with drink and ulterior motives, the club was nevertheless an invaluable place for a journalist to pick up on the latest gossip. On the occasions when I attended, it was rare for the evening to pass without my being buttonholed by an irate contract worker or worried businessman, and filled in on the latest rumours of escalating rebel attacks, communist infiltration, or the imminent downfall of the regime.

The trouble was, almost everybody made the same claims – that their sources were the real inside sources and so forth. It was noticeable, however, that those who might have been expected to have better information than most tended to be those who kept their mouths shut better than most. What the British High Commission club really proved was that there were many rather frightened white people in Uganda who were driven, just as the Ugandans themselves were driven, to create a network of gossip and speculation, an English-language Radio Katwe, to explain away the mysteries and fears which might otherwise have proved overwhelming.

Amidst all this input, all these 'reliable sources', were the occasional quiet voices who provided first-hand evidence rather than hearsay. Among them were Ugandans without a political axe to grind (and after the years of terror this group, sadly, was a small one), relief workers who had been working in 'difficult' areas and, occasionally, overland travellers and passers-through. One such, from the latter group, was Arthur Stern.

I had first met Arthur in July, while I was waiting at Moyo, on the Ugandan/Sudanese border, for a lift into southern Sudan. From the beginning, I felt a great liking for him, for his frank openness, which at times crossed over into *naïveté*. There was also a bond between us, for he too had spent a month in Luzira, after being arrested by security in a back-alley as he was collecting a forged rubber stamp for a visa extension. The stamp, apparently, had been ordered by another traveller; when he then fell sick, Arthur, not untypically, offered to collect the stamp for him, and ended up carrying the can. During his stay in gaol Arthur got hooked on Uganda, much as I had done three years earlier, and after his release he stayed on to explore the country, accepting hospitality when it was offered, sleeping rough or in cheap hotel beds when it was not. By the time we met, he had already been tramping Uganda's roads for some three months, and in the ten minutes before his truck arrived, I recorded an interview with him about his travels. It was a good piece; Arthur spoke warmly about his experiences and the people he had met, and the interview was broadcast by the BBC a couple of weeks later.

By this time, Arthur was back in Kampala, having spent the interim travelling across northern Uganda, one of the last people to have done so before the districts of Gulu, Kitgum, Lira and Soroti became restricted zones, as they were plunged back into the chaos of civil war. He straight away called on me at the Speke Hotel to share his news. He did not have the larger picture, which only became apparent some months later: that of an unfocussed and violent rebellion by former UNLA soldiers who had begun to band themselves together into rebel groups with names like the Uganda People's Democratic Army and the Holy Spirit Battalion – and of an increasingly brutal response by the NRA. Instead, Arthur returned with a sheaf of notes about individual instances of NRA misbehaviour and abuse of power in the north; he had names, places and dates.

He detailed cases of NRA soldiers extorting money at roadblocks, of returning at night to loot villages which they had previously searched during the day, of arresting former soldiers when they came to surrender their guns and, in three instances, of murder. He also provided detailed accounts of NRA interrogation and torture techniques, notably the infamous 'three-piece-tying' or *kandooya*, whereby a suspect's elbows and ankles were bound tightly behind him, until either the nerves of his arms and legs were destroyed, or he suffocated for lack of air, or he started talking. The gist of Arthur's account was that, for the first few months after winning the war, the NRA had exhibited exemplary behaviour, going so far as to stage public beatings, and even executions, of miscreants among its own ranks; but that all this had changed with the most recent troop redeployments. Suddenly, NRA discipline had deteriorated as looting, 'eating', and the process of revenge on the old enemy had begun in earnest; the carefully-nurtured relationship of trust between conquerors and conquered had apparently collapsed almost overnight.

Arthur was deeply shocked by all this; I, having had more experience of Uganda under previous governments, was rather less so. I agreed with Arthur that it would be most disturbing if the latest developments represented a carefully-orchestrated government plan to bring the population of the north to its knees – but there was no evidence that this was the case. Rather it was remarkable that the NRA, after years of hardship and suffering in the bush, should have managed to conquer the home territory of its traditional persecutors almost without a shot being fired. In the circumstances, I felt, it was hardly surprising if some minor instances of indiscipline crept in as the honeymoon period came to an end. I decided to keep the reports on the back burner, and to listen out for further developments.

But now, two months after Arthur's journey, the whole of Kampala was abuzz with talk of civil war in the north and east, and of revolt fomenting among the coffee and banana plantations of the central region itself. Once again, the drums of the Baganda were throbbing through the night, and everyone seemed on edge. For, as all Uganda knows, when the Baganda are talking, it is best to pay attention. Otherwise it is all too easy to believe one has just heard a different message entirely.

By this time, Sue and I were hardly receiving each other's messages at all. The on–off relationship continued, but now it was more off than on. One evening, Sue went out with a girlfriend, allegedly to have dinner at the house of a Rwandese couple; she didn't return until half-past seven the following morning. When I opened the door to her, she was a little nervous and out of breath, but there was something else as well, something rather hard and devil-may-care. Never before had she simply failed to come back to the hotel, not unless we had argued and then parted amidst threats of a terminal split. I felt that she was lying to me, and that a point in our relationship had been passed.

A few weeks later it happened again. Sue spent all of one Saturday sulking, and refused to join me at a friend's house for dinner. I returned later than planned, at around midnight, and found Sue half-way down the road to the Chez Joseph disco, having wheedled a 5,000-shilling loan from the hotel receptionist to pay for the entrance fee. I escorted her down to the discothèque, but I refused either to join her inside, or to give her any money for drinks. Again, she failed to come back to the hotel; again she told me later that she had met the Rwandese friends, and had gone home with them. Intellectually, I didn't believe her any more. Emotionally, I couldn't resist it when she returned and we argued, and then slowly she melted, and told me how sorry she was for hurting me.

But the arguments continued. Sometimes, when I asked her to do something, she would shout, 'What are you asking? You don't own me. You are not my husband.' That one was rather obvious, and invited obvious rejoinders. But another time when the gloves were off and voices well-raised towards the end of a row, she shouted at me, 'I'm just wasting my time with you.' I felt that this illustrated, with disturbing clarity, the degree to which she now viewed me in terms of a future investment, a potential ticket out to the West.

There was another explanation, however, one which I rarely examined seriously. It was that Sue did genuinely care about me, but wanted more commitment. I felt, for my part, that I had made my feelings for her fairly clear, but I was forgetting that the only man in her past about whom she talked with some emotion – Peter – had finally left her to marry another woman. Neither, it seemed, was she simply looking for a meal ticket. She told me that another past boyfriend, a handsome young Swiss, had actually flown back to Africa to ask her to marry him; she had declined, feeling that he was immature, and more in love with her in bed than out. Certainly Sue knew her own mind. She was chatted up constantly, especially by *wazungu*, sometimes even when the two of us were out together and I left her alone for five minutes. She always gave the impression of being flattered, or amused, and then sent her aspiring suitors away with aplomb, and a smile.

And despite our constant arguments, we always seemed to make up again afterwards. This impressed her friends enormously. 'She always goes back to you; I think she likes you too much,' a young teacher friend of hers once told me. Other of her women friends were clearly far less impressed, feeling that I was not much of a catch. They told Sue that she should have grabbed someone much younger, richer and more handsome, and I well knew that she could have done this with ease, if she had so wished.

Our affair therefore continued to be punctuated by a series of partings and reunions. I would send her long, intense letters of accusation and concession, ever trying to achieve the happy equilibrium, the mutually-acceptable compromise. I wrote these in the largest, clearest handwriting I could manage, still not quite coming to terms with the fact that Sue did not merely have reading difficulties, but that she couldn't read at all. Goodness only knows what her friends made of my wistful epistles as they struggled through them on Sue's behalf. In retrospect, I see that the letters' main purpose, from my point of view, was cathartic as much as conciliatory.

And once again, my work was suffering. I no longer had to send regular news reports to the BBC or elsewhere, but I was failing to complete even the undemanding workload which I had set myself. *The Times* phoned to ask me for a big feature on southern Sudan for the Op Ed page – in the centre of the paper, opposite the editorial. Instead of working all night to produce something really good, I merely sent another feature piece which I had already put together for an African magazine; it was quite inappropriate, and naturally was never used.

Another evening, the BBC World Service programme *24 Hours* asked me for a two-way interview; it was arranged that they would phone back an hour later to make the actual recording. Since Sue and I were in the midst of a simmering argument, and because I needed a clear head while I made some preparatory notes, I asked her to go downstairs to the bar and wait there until I finished the interview. She refused. I lost my temper, and grabbed hold of her to march her out of the door; she wriggled free, and threw herself face down on the bed. In the scuffle that followed, I hit her – a fairly light blow to the top of the head, but a blow for all that. Then I threw her out of the room, and she sat outside the door, sobbing. I was almost incoherent through the interview that followed, unable to concentrate on what I was saying for more than a few seconds at a time. The upshot of all this was that Sue had a headache, *24 Hours* never called again, and we had reached a new low point in our relationship. In the remorse and reconciliation that followed, I still found it impossible to believe that I had hit her. 'I think I'm losing control,' I whispered into her ear later on. 'I wonder if we're going to be all right.'

Sue told me later that around this time she used to think that I was fairly crazy. And among the African community in general, I had apparently taken on something of an exaggerated persona: I could not walk the length of Kampala's main street without bumping into half a dozen people who grabbed my hand or wanted to talk, not all of whom I recognised as previous friends or acquaintances. In other ways too, my life was hectic: I seemed always to be arguing with waiters and taxi drivers, buttonholing ministers in the lift, asking provocative questions at press conferences, or following stories across the open drains of Shauri Yako market and then (pausing only to wipe the shoes) into the carpeted, pot-planted offices of the UN.

Looking back on that period now, I see that I did possess a certain bravado. And yet, on another level, that apparent fearlessness was merely a cover, a whistling in dark alleys. The more conspicuous one became, the less likely it was that one day the hand would come down on the shoulder, as it had before in 1983. And the more that one assumed that one had the right to do this or that, the more often it was that one got away with it. This noisy, sometimes confrontational approach probably served me better as a journalist in that place and at that time than the classic softly-softly technique would have done. The flip side, however, was that inevitably I made enemies.

Early that October, I made an enemy in the army. Together with a visiting journalist from Nairobi, I travelled up to Soroti in north-eastern Uganda, to investigate the escalating epidemic of cattle-rustling in the area. On arrival in the town, we went to see the local DA, Commander Rwakatale Amooti, to inform him about our presence, and of our intention of visiting some of the villages where raids had taken place. He was clearly uneasy about our leaving the confines of the town, but reluctantly acknowledged our right to do so. We spent the next day interviewing villagers who told us horror stories of massive, organised raids in which not only were cattle taken, but men were shot, women raped, and teenagers taken hostage and forced to help carry the loot. Over a thousand of the local people – the Itesot – had been killed in the raids since the NRA takeover, and much of the eastern part of Soroti district had been devastated.

It was apparent that the Karamojong, the traditional cattle-rustlers from the vast, barren region bordering Sudan and western Kenya, were largely responsible for the raids, though the picture was complicated by the fact that they had been joined by a large number of former UNLA soldiers, which had lent a political slant to the unrest. Two or three witnesses in the course of the day also mentioned, rather casually, that some of those who had arrived towards the end of the raids 'were wearing new army uniforms'. It took me some time to realise that they were suggesting that NRA soldiers had also been involved. On top of this, many of the villagers we interviewed complained that it was the NRA's decision to disband the Teso militia, the traditional local defence force, which had cleared the way for the attacks.

Early in the afternoon, as we were interviewing a farmer who had lost all his forty cattle and his household property in a raid three nights before, another man came pedalling up on a push-bike. He had just come from the main road, he told us; an army Land-rover had stopped in the local trading centre, and its occupants had angrily demanded to be told the whereabouts of the *wazungu* reporters. Sensing trouble, the villagers had sent them off in the wrong direction. When we returned to Soroti that evening, we went straight to the DA's house, to tell him we were back, and to ask if there had been any problem during the day. But Commander Amooti was out, and despite leaving a message for him, we received no reply before leaving for Kampala early the following morning.

I had been getting increasingly fed up with the poor service and rising costs of the Speke Hotel, so on my return, I decided to move to the Imperial, a great crumbling mausoleum situated just a hundred yards further down the road. And it was there, three days later, that I heard a knock on the door, and opened up to find two remarkably lanky young men who announced that they were from Military Intelligence, and would like to come in. They were in plain clothes, so I demanded to see their ID cards before inviting them to enter. There was a problem about my recent visit to Soroti, I was told; their boss had told them to examine all my cassette tapes and photographs of the trip. I replied that there was no way I was handing over anything just like that, and presently one of them asked if he could use my phone to confer with 'the big man'. Half an hour later he arrived in person, identifying himself as Commander Joseph Musoke.

Musoke made it very clear that he wished to listen to my recordings; I told him that this was quite unacceptable. Musoke stroked his chin. I asked what he intended to do about it; was he going to arrest me? There was no question of that, he reassured me, no duress; it was simply a question of whether or not, as a freelance journalist based in Uganda, I wished to be viewed as a friend by the authorities. I told him that nothing would make me more happy, but, as he must know from his time in the bush, you could not betray the people who helped you, and I was not about to identify my interviewees. We had reached an impasse.

Musoke and the two beanpoles spent another twenty minutes pointedly not putting me under duress, until it was quite clear that they had no intention of disappearing. I was getting worried because I knew that Sue was liable to arrive at any moment, and I didn't want her to be seen with me by these people. So I decided to offer a compromise. I would play them the tapes if they would allow me to edit out the names and locations of the interviewees. After a moment's reflection, Musoke agreed. So I plugged in my headphones, played through the introduction of each interview to myself, and then relayed the remainder through a set of speakers. Nothing very incriminating was said, and after half an hour, clearly bored, Musoke got up and took his leave, closely followed by the two boys in plain clothes. The whole affair had passed off fairly easily, and I was happy that I had betrayed none of my sources, but for all that, I was shaken by the almost offhand way that extra-judicial pressure had been brought to bear. It was only later that I learnt that one of the leading officials in the area was himself helping to organise the rounding up of Itesot cattle, and their transportation by truck to Kampala and western Uganda.

12 · NAIROBI DAYS

Early in November, Sue and I travelled back to Nairobi. As ever, I kept very busy for the first few days. There were films to develop, cassettes and articles to dispatch to London, friends to catch up on, items of luggage to repossess from various of their cupboards, contacts to be made, and interviews arranged. On this occasion, one of my priorities was to call in at the *Newsweek* office; the magazine was apparently interested in using one of my photographs of Florence and Ssengabi for the cover of its next edition, which would be featuring an article on the heterosexual AIDS epidemic. A *Newsweek* cover is one of the great glittering prizes for photojournalists – in terms of reputation as much as payment – and I could hardly believe that one of my first serious news pictures could achieve such prominence. The reason, of course, was topical subject matter rather than photographic expertise.

In the midst of all this excitement, it hardly occurred to me that Roland Neveu would be extremely upset at developments. Roland's own photographs, I discovered later, were still with *Newsweek*'s rival *Time*, which had rights of first refusal in return for having financed part of his trip. But as it turned out, I wasn't to get a front cover after all: during the following week, the Irangate scandal broke, and it was finally a mug shot of a worried President Reagan that adorned the outside of the next issue. A black and white version of the Florence photograph was used inside to illustrate the AIDS article.

By the time this edition was on the streets, I was already in Sudan, writing a series of features about development projects there. I spent the next four weeks working fifteen hours a day: Sudan, with its lack of alcohol and other forms of conventional Western entertainment, tends to lend itself to this sort of intensity of purpose. But upon returning to Kenya in mid-December, the only intensity of purpose I still felt was centred around Sue. And so it was to be for the next three months, as I grew more jealous, and she increasingly intractable.

For almost the first time, I grew wary of visiting her at Dorothy's Place, for I never knew what to expect. One time I would be welcomed with open arms, sat down and brought tea, made a fuss of; the next time she would be cool, clearly not pleased to see me. By the time of Sue's return, Maria, Catherine and Anna had moved to a two-room apartment, which enjoyed a constant stream of visitors. These included numerous fairly respectable-looking men, both black and white (the blacks mostly being younger and better-looking). Especially when Sue was being less than welcoming, it was hard to believe that one or two of them were not occasional boyfriends, at least during my absences.

In addition, there was Jonathan, a young orange-haired Australian actor who was travelling round the world in the company of his large, in fact larger-than-life, orange-haired mother. We had first met Jonathan in Kampala, where he had learnt to speak Luganda, the lingua franca of the capital, in a matter of weeks; and what with this, his strong personality and his unusual looks, he proved to be a big hit with the local women. Sue was among those who liked to spend time talking with him in Luganda. Later on, Jonathan travelled down to Nairobi, and by the time Sue and I reached there in November, he was already going out with her cousin Maria.

At least this is what I was told when I met him at Dorothy's Place, although I could never entirely rid myself of the suspicion that Maria had merely agreed to go along with this version of events for my benefit, and that Jonathan was really having a furtive affair with Sue. Suddenly the free and easy atmosphere of the place, which I had always loved, only added fuel to my fears. The fact that the three beds sometimes slept six, even as many as nine people, depending on the number of visitors needing accommodation, actually meant that there was less, rather than more, opportunity for clandestine trysts. But this was not always easy to remember.

The apartment was inert till noon, a dedication to slumber, but after that it slowly built up momentum. By early afternoon it was a hive of activity, with one girl making tea, another cooking *matooke* on a charcoal stove, a third attacking a great pile of ironing, and a fourth sitting on the front step varnishing her nails and chatting with passers-by. In addition, there were the visitors – women wrapped in *khangas* on their way to the showers, kids popping in to show off their new toys, smartly-dressed men in expensive cars, and young entrepreneurs in flashy nylon shirts, just down from Uganda with another haul of contraband. Occasionally, there would be a particularly important visitor – a prince from one of Uganda's defunct royal houses, or a Greek businessman, perhaps – who would command respect from the entire household. And then the whole place would pull together, the VIP would be given the best chair, each in turn would come across to say hello or give him a friendly kiss, and the girl who had been dozing all afternoon on the sofa, nursing a hangover, would be told to wrap herself up and take off to the bathroom. But other times were less hectic, with the jokes and conversations rolling along endlessly in Kiswahili or Luganda or English, as one visitor poured out glasses of whisky, and another rolled a joint.

At around this time I took Sue along to a private hospital, so that we could get ourselves tested for HIV. Afterwards there were four days of nervous waiting but then we were both, to our great relief, pronounced seronegative. That night we went out for a celebratory dinner, and I explained to Sue that, provided neither of us had had any other partners during the previous two months, we were now officially AIDS-free. For my part, I promised once again that I had been monogamous since July, having finished with my other girlfriends in London and Khartoum. Sue duly gave me her word that she had been seeing no other boyfriends behind my back. So we drank a toast to our mutual lack of viruses, and vowed to keep them out of our systems.

The test results encouraged me to become something of an unwanted crusader among Sue's friends at Dorothy's Place, trying to explain to them the risks involved in sleeping with more than one partner. On reflection, I see that the message was gauche and ill-conceived, since the clear inference was that Sue and I were safe due to our exclusive relationship, whereas their own more easy-going ways put them at risk. I was implicitly branding Sue's friends as good-time girls and prostitutes, which was bound to cause a lot of ill feeling.

On the surface, however, these discussions remained good-humoured, albeit rather prone to getting side-tracked.

'Come on, Eddie. You know that's a *muzungu* disease. It's spread by all your homosexuals in America and England. And even if we do have it in Kenya, we know who brought it here, don't we?'

I would try to explain that a lot of people – in Uganda for instance – already had the virus, and would most likely carry it silently for years, transmitting it to others, before any of them visibly fell sick. But this merely invited a reply such as, 'That's Uganda; everybody knows there's a lot of it up there. But we don't know of anyone who's died of AIDS here in Nairobi.'

Sue's friends were basically right in maintaining that Kenya's AIDS epidemic had only just begun. But like many, they failed to see the difference between the virus and the disease, and failed to grasp that the far more crucial epidemic – that of HIV – was already well underway in Kenya. I began to despair of getting the point across, and it struck me afresh that unless there was undeniable physical evidence of an epidemic, such as neighbours falling sick and friends dying, then people remained poorly tuned to the dangers. Even the local Kenyan nickname for AIDS, *misada*, meaning 'economic aid' in Kiswahili, had none of the relevance of Uganda's Slim.

But of course, it was not just that I was failing to put across the medical background; there was denial here too. For I was attempting to deliver a warning which many of the women simply could not afford to hear. The majority had already got hooked on the fast-track life – the clothes, the drinks, the constant round of clubs and discos – and, as with heroin addiction, there were not very many ways to support the habit. They could of course have woven mats or made earrings for the tourists for a couple of dollars a day, but why bother when you can make ten times that much by taking somebody home for a single night? The fact that most of the somebodies refused to use condoms was, viewed in these terms, simply an unavoidable risk. For such women, sleeping around had become a matter of economic necessity rather than choice; going back to the village was no longer even an option.

And of course in reality, beneath their blasé exteriors, many of the women were already frightened. They knew that they must have already been at risk for months, if not years. Occasionally, when one was on her own, she would confide to me that perhaps she was already infected, but would prefer not to know either way. But what if you passed the virus on to a boyfriend, I would ask; what if you got pregnant and gave birth to an already-infected baby? Anyway, she would say quietly, it was too late to worry about it now. On the contrary, I would answer, the likelihood is that so far you're OK, and the only way to be sure of staying so is to start using condoms straight away or, even better, get a regular boyfriend and then both go along for a blood test. Sadly, almost every girl had a story about the nice man who came to the end of his contract, the boy who went off with someone else, the one who got away.

Meanwhile, neither Sue's friends nor myself were entirely blind to the fact that I probably had some mixed motives for the gospel of sexual conservatism that I was now preaching. It is only now, looking back, that I can see that at around this time Sue was torn between accepting me as her permanent boyfriend, and breaking free altogether so as to search for someone else. Meanwhile, our relationship was becoming ever more volatile. It was Christmas Eve when it finally exploded.

I called at her place just as it was growing dark, to suggest that we set off for the friend's house where I was staying, and where we had both been invited to celebrate Christmas.

'I'm not going,' said Sue, avoiding my eyes. 'You can go on your own.'

'Oh come on, Sue. You've known about it for days, and besides I've already accepted for the two of us. It's going to be a great party. I've been out all day getting presents and planning things. Don't spoil it.' But my cajoling only made her more determined.

'I don't care. I want to spend Christmas here with my friends. You go on your own. You can give my presents to somebody else.' We argued some more, but soon she fell silent, and sat herself down on a bed, facing away from me. I looked at her back for a long time as I thought over the options, and finally made up my mind.

'Well, screw you then,' I said quietly, but with emphasis. Then I turned on my heel and walked out the door.

Instead of just leaving for my friend's house, I walked down the hill to Buffalo Bill's, and started drinking. Soon, I saw Maria and Catherine, who both knew of the difficulties that Sue and I had been having. I sat them down, bought a round of beers, and asked for their advice.

'I'm finished,' I told them. 'I'm not taking any more of this rubbish.'

Maybe I convinced them that it would be kinder to tell me the truth; maybe they'd decided that it would be better for everyone if I got out of Sue's life. Perhaps even there was some jealousy involved; Sue and I both needed a lesson. Whatever, the vow of silence which the girls normally maintained was for once broken.

Catherine told me that she had heard from Barbara that Sue had had another boyfriend while she was in Kampala – a Frenchman. I protested that Sue had never mentioned any other affairs in Kampala, apart from the night she had spent with the Tanzanian.

Both girls looked down at the table. Then, slowly, in her broken English, Maria told me that Sue was 'not a good girl'. She added, her brow furrowed with the effort, 'She is a very stubborn girl, Eddie. I tell her, I say always, "Eddie is good man, he is good", but she no like to hear me. Eddie, I want another drink.'

I bought another couple of beers, and then, after a few minutes, excused myself. 'Where are you going?' asked Catherine, suddenly worried. 'Eddie, you mustn't say anything to her. Don't tell her that we were talking to you.'

'I'm not going to tell her anything,' I said. 'I've got nothing to say to her. Nothing at all.'

By the time I got back to Dorothy's Place, I was breathing heavily, not just from the climb up the hill, but from tension as well. The blood was pounding in my head. I intended just to collect my shopping bags, together with the clothes which Sue had borrowed at different times, and take my leave. Let's end it with a bit of dignity, I remember thinking to myself.

As I opened the door, I could see Sue doing some ironing. She seemed perfectly happy, as if she'd quite forgotten the earlier altercation.

'I've come to collect my clothes,' I told her.

'Well, I'm busy now,' she said. So I walked up the two steps to the bedroom where Sue kept her belongings in a big red suitcase, and began looking through the neatly-ironed clothes inside. Sue was watching from downstairs.

'Can't you wait?' she enquired, but she was already unplugging the iron; she walked up the stairs and stood beside me. Suddenly, to my amazement, I came across a shirt which I'd been keeping at the bottom of my shopping bag, intending to change into it that evening. I could only think that Sue must have been searching through the bag to see what presents I'd bought her. It never occurred to me that she might have removed the shirt in order to iron out the creases.

'What are you doing with this?' I demanded. There was no reply.

'I asked you what you are doing with my shirt.' I felt numb, but still tried to speak clearly, so that Sue could understand what I was saying. The effort made the words come out staccato and lifeless. To compensate, I started shouting.

'Look, that shirt was in the other bag. If we've decided that we're not spending Christmas together, then you've got no right to be searching through my bags. Why have you got my shirt?'

Again, Sue didn't answer, but this time she looked up at me with a funny sort of smile. For no reason I can think of, I cracked.

'I asked you a question,' I screamed. Then I reached out to slap her face. She was quick enough to flick her head away to the right, but as she moved, my other hand was already coming up to strike her. This hand had closed into a fist. As soon as it landed, I realised that I'd hit her hard, without any restraint.

She spun around quickly, holding her hand to her face, and then ran down the stairs. Her flatmate Anna had heard the commotion, and came running in from outside, followed by Jonathan. Sue was shrieking, covering her face with her hands; I was acting as if everything was normal, and began walking down the stairs to return the shirt to the shopping bag. Jonathan rushed up, and held me back.

'That's enough, that's enough,' he was shouting.

'I know it's enough. I'm just putting my shirt back.'

'I said that's enough.' I kept on pushing against him, but made no headway; all the strength had left me. Sue ran outside, still crying, her hands still over her face.

Later, Jonathan went next door to see how she was, and I paced up and down the room while Anna pointed a long kitchen knife at me and told me to keep my distance. I was hardly aware of her presence; I even brushed against the knife as I passed.

'Why don't you get out now? Haven't you done enough?' she said, thrusting the knife in my direction.

'I'll go when I'm ready. I want to take my things with me.'

'You can't make her love you, don't you know that?'

'I didn't want to make her do anything. I just wanted her to tell me the truth. She didn't have to tell me she loved me if she didn't, if all the time she was seeing someone else.' My throat was so dry I could hardly get the words out.

Presently, Jonathan came in from next door. 'Her eye's pretty bad; it's swollen up like a golf ball. The people next door are getting hold of some ice. Look, Eddie, I think it's better you don't hang around here. I was just going out to a party; I think you'd better come along with me.'

So, presently, I walked out carrying my bag and the shirt, thinking, this is how it ends. This is the last time. And Anna was shouting from the doorway, still waving her knife: 'Don't come back. Don't ever come back.' And I could hear Sue's voice through the open door of the next apartment; it sounded like she was under a blanket. 'He hit me for nothing. I didn't do anything.' She was speaking in English, so it seemed she wanted me to hear. I started to head back to say something, I don't know what, but Jonathan pulled me around.

'Come on mate,' he said, speaking my own dialect. 'Time for us to go.'

When I woke the following morning, I felt less ashamed than I had expected; in fact, I began to detect something uncomfortably akin to a bully's pride. The people with whom I was staying were very supportive, telling me that Sue had probably had it coming anyway. They made sure that I kept busy on Christmas Day, took me to a discothèque, introduced me to other single women, and generally made a great effort to help. But after three days of hectic forgetfulness, I decided that I had to get away from Nairobi, and boarded the night train for the coast. Unusually, I didn't speak to any of the others in my compartment, but instead stared out of the window into the night, remembering other train journeys of the past.

I arrived in Mombasa determined to link up again with one of the girlfriends I used to have in the town; but after two hours of driving round in a taxi, and asking judicious questions, I discovered that one was now married to a pilot, and the other was living with an Asian shopkeeper. So I booked a room in my favourite cheap hotel, showered, changed, and walked out into the busy streets. It was still only mid-morning.

I walked down to the bus stop for Likoni Ferry and the south coast, where some friends of mine had a house. And there I met Emma, seventeen years old, pretty in her loose-fitting T-shirt and jeans, a constant chewer of gum. I forgot about my friends. Emma took me back to her place, a small coral hut in the shrubby bush lying on the other side of the road from Shelley beach and its tourist hotels. We spent the rest of the day together: talking and cooking with her friends, drinking palm wine, playing with the neighbour's kids, dozing on her tiny bed in the heat of the afternoon. Later we walked across to the seashore and waded out into the warm water; after a while we made love, discreetly and casually, with her sitting astride me in the shallows. As we finished, a uniformed security guard from a private beach club strolled across to check what we were doing. We smiled up at him, daring him to challenge us further.

Then, in the evening, we went back to Mombasa to eat in an open-air bar, to play pinball and get drunk. Despite the pleasantness of the day, we had run out of things to say long before we went back to my hotel. During the night I woke a number of times, and then would wake her also, and hold on to her tightly in the dark. Above these sweaty embraces, the fan swung lazily, sending down the odd puff of cool air. Come the morning, I felt indifferent and empty; I just didn't want to be with her any more. I gave her some money and waited for her to leave. Before doing so, she asked if she'd be seeing me again. She wasn't in the least surprised or hurt when I was non-committal in reply.

During the day, in between acts of intercourse, I'd even been preaching to Emma about the risks she was taking, by doing her business without taking any physical precautions. But it was fully two days later, on the morning of New Year's Eve, before I woke to the quiet but certain realisation that I had just signed my death warrant: I had spent a day fornicating, without a condom, with a young and inexperienced prostitute. I reached for a cigarette to steady my nerves, but the pack was empty, as were the other packs scattered around the room. In a bid to punish myself for what I'd done, I decided then and there to give up. Within an hour, I had caught the last bus up the coast to Lamu, arriving exhausted and angry at nine in the evening, and later I sang a lonely 'Auld Lang Syne' with two equally lonely Dutch women, on a stone bench overlooking the harbour.

I stayed on Lamu for the next four weeks, pouring my heart out to the German anthropologist with whom I used to go for daily walks, getting drunk every night in the Civil Servants' Club, having a fight in the early hours of one morning with a junkie from Stoke Newington, and spending long periods in the museum library, trying to write a historical article on the town, which never got finished. I was going crazy without nicotine. And I was reeking with misery and self-loathing.

When I got back to Nairobi I found that Sue had collected her clothes from the house where I was staying, but had also borrowed a pair of sun-glasses to cover her eye, with the request that I collect them from her later. I waited two or three days, but it was all the excuse I needed to abandon my previous resolve, and call on her once more.

We were shy to see each other again, and in the end it was she, extraordinarily, who broke the ice. She told me that, by hitting her, I'd proved that I really loved her. She came over to my chair, and we embraced, to the applause of the other women who had gathered in the room to ensure fair play. And then she told me how her eye had been swollen for three weeks, that finally she had had to go to hospital for an injection before the swelling subsided.

'It is not a very good Christmas for me,' she laughed ruefully. 'But Anna and Jane and Catherine and Maria are all very nice. They stay here to look after me.'

But even then, my madness had not gone away. Later that evening, I began shouting at her about the Frenchman in Kampala: why had she lied to me about him? At first, she tried to tell me that it had not been serious, that she had only seen him a few times, when I was away in England or Sudan. I knew this wasn't the complete story though, that she'd two-timed me for him at least once, when she'd pretended that she was going out for dinner with her Rwandese friends.

'You're still not telling me the whole truth,' I insisted.

'I think I am telling the truth about the important things,' said Sue quietly. Without thinking, I banged the metal bowl in my hand down on the table in protest, and Sue quickly excused herself to find a cigarette. She never came back, although I slept on her sofa for the rest of the night.

We danced the same old dance for the week that followed. At one point, when I called to try and make up, I was presented with a note from Sue; she had obviously asked someone else to do the writing, but it bore her signature. It said that she didn't want to see me any more, that she had waited a month for me after the fight, that I had gone away without telling her where I was going; now she wanted to find another boyfriend. The other women of the house were all there, all eager to see how I would react.

'What does she say, Eddie?' asked one of them. Foolishly, I read the letter out loud to them; it prompted some noisy debate.

'What are you going to do?' I was eventually asked.

'Nothing,' I said, summoning as much dignity as I could manage, as I got up to leave. 'It doesn't matter to me any more; she can decide whatever she wants. I've finished with her.'

'Shall we tell her that, or will you leave a note?' asked Grace, an older 'mama' who lived nearby. Grace professed to have magic powers, and two nights before, at BB's, had told me that the affair between Sue and me was 'too strong. You will end up killing her, or else killing yourself.' Later, she had offered to heal the rift between us if I came to her place the following day. However, suspecting that she was more interested in furthering her own ends than mine, I stayed away. Now she was taking revenge. But God, I thought, she doesn't miss a trick.

But of course, I hadn't finished with Sue, not yet. I went back to Dorothy's Place a few days later, found her in, and eventually, after some hours of pleading, persuaded her to come away with me on safari. I wanted to get her away from her friends for a few days, and from the peer pressure they exerted.

It was a delightful house, a so-called 'self-help *banda*' with two beds, a bathroom and a thatched roof. Behind was a small cooking place with a pile of firewood on its stone floor. The hut looked out over the Amboseli plains behind which towered Mount Kilimanjaro, the highest point in Africa, which most of the time was hidden by cloud. Every evening, we shared a meal with a Canadian family who were staying in the *banda* behind ours. He was a writer, she an anthropologist working with Canadian Indians, and they had two small, very energetic kids. Every morning they would take us along on a game run through the park; every evening, after the meal, we would walk together to the small bar which catered for the park rangers and the domestic staff working at the big tourist lodge half a mile up the road.

One day – our third in Amboseli, I believe – I was woken before dawn by the sounds of a large animal snuffling and stamping, seemingly right outside the hut. I got up, wrapped a *khanga* around me, and opened the door a fraction. Outside, silhouetted against the first delicate tints of daybreak, was a bull elephant. He was standing some 30 yards away, and his trunk was swaying to and fro in the air, trying to make out my scent. I pushed the door to and woke Sue, putting my mouth close against her ear and telling her not to make a noise. Silently, we pulled on pullovers and jeans, and crept outside on to the balcony. The bull had heard us, and had half-turned away towards the purplish line on the horizon. But he stopped, not yet willing to leave, and then pulled lazily at a tussock of grass, which he put in his mouth but didn't chew. Perhaps he was used to getting gifts of food from the tourists.

We watched him for ten minutes or so, as the horizontal band changed through purple to crimson to pink to orange. I was holding Sue tightly, for dawn on Kenya's upland plains is a bitter contrast to the heat of the day. Being so slender, she always felt the cold, and was trembling throughout her body. 'Isn't he wonderful?' I whispered into her hair. Sue didn't answer, but held me tighter, with both her arms around my waist.

Afterwards we went back to bed, and waited until the body heat built up beneath the blankets. Presently, she showed that she wanted to make love. I got out to search for a Durex, which had become an essential bedroom accessory since my adventures with Emma.

'No, I don't want you to use one,' she said.

'That's all very well, but after Mombasa I might be carrying some nasty disease. I'm not going to risk giving it to you.'

'I don't care.' This was said softly, and after some thought.

'No, I'm sorry Sue. You know I don't like using them either, but you must try to understand. If I get AIDS, then it's my fault for screwing around. But imagine how I'd feel if I gave it to you as well.'

I found a sheath, and got back into bed again, still holding it in my hand; I made no attempt to put it on. Sue was stroking me, but in an absent sort of way. It was some time before she spoke. 'It doesn't matter, don't you see? It doesn't matter if you give me AIDS, not when you love me. If you have it already, then you can give it to me as well. We can have it together.'

She turned to look at me, waited till I turned to meet her gaze. Then we kissed, and I let the oily packet drop from my hand to the floor.

The resolution of our problems made me feel eager to get back to work, so two days after our return from Amboseli, I decided to leave

for Kampala to catch up on the news, and to do some writing. I told
Sue that I would be away ten days, and would then return to Nairobi,
to 'give her escort' back to Uganda.

It felt good to be in Kampala once more; I felt full of stories
waiting to be written. The day after my arrival, I called in at the
Ministry of Information, to let the under-secretary know that I was
back, and while waiting outside his office I met Helge and Paul, a
writer and photographer from the Hamburg-based magazine, *Tempo*.
They were in Uganda to cover the AIDS story; I asked if they would
like to join me for lunch. They agreed, and before our pork chops and
chips had even arrived on the table, we were making plans to travel
together, first to Rakai district and then to Tanzania. My only problem
was that, not anticipating any immediate photographic work, I had left
my camera back in Nairobi. There was nothing for it: I would have to
fly back down and pick it up. It was four o'clock on Friday afternoon
but somehow, before the shops and offices all closed for the weekend,
I managed to get the income tax clearance that was necessary before
leaving the country, and a ticket for the morning flight.

It was still early on Saturday morning when the plane touched
down in Nairobi, and I made straight for Sue's flat. There was no
sign of her. Her friends professed ignorance, suggested that she must
have gone out shopping while they were still asleep. I hired a taxi to
my friend's house to collect the camera bag, did a couple more jobs
in town, and then returned for Sue. It was lunch-time; she was still
not back.

Her friends were clearly uneasy: they assured me that everything
was all right, but their stories were changing. Now it was said that
Sue had not slept in the apartment the previous night, but in the
room of another girl who was away for the weekend. There was no
answer when I knocked at the other girl's door, and I began to feel
quite nervous. I went back to sit on Sue's sofa, and tried, for the
next two hours, to concentrate on the Kenyan papers. I was half-way
through a crossword when she came in; it was about five o'clock. She
looked straight through me. Two paces behind her was a craggy-faced
man with short, blond hair.

The three of us stopped still for a second or two. Then I got up
and shook both their hands. Sue had got her breath back, and was
just starting on the introductions – but I was already walking out of
the door.

13 · JOHN AND PROSCOVIA

It was mid-morning in Kasensero. There was a warm rain falling – the first of the day. When the shower had finished, I walked through the back door of the café, and out into a different world. About 10 yards away was another row of tin-roofed huts, and in the sticky area between were a few upturned beer crates and a bed, resting on its side, which provided a fulcrum for the social activity of the place. A couple of young men leant on the bed, joking with the girls who emerged periodically from the huts to hang out washing or to start fires in the charcoal braziers.

The girls were also young, teenagers it seemed, and were dressed casually in blouses, cardigans and *khangas*, although one was still wearing a gold lamé dress, presumably from the night before. The boys called out to the girls as they passed. Presently one of the girls lunged forward and shoved a boy's elbow from the bed-frame; she ran off again, laughing over her shoulder, but flopped to a halt a few yards away, not expecting pursuit.

After half an hour or so, when I felt that the novelty of my presence must have worn off, I wandered across to a hut where two girls had just finished preparing lunch. They were friendly and happy, quite keen to pose for a photograph. The prettier of the two, Judith, claimed to be nineteen, but a man who came across to help with translation insisted that she was actually three years younger. She apparently came from Bukoba, the first major town across the border in Tanzania, and had been in Kasensero for one month, visiting her brother. Yes, she had a boyfriend here, just the one. The other girl, Noel, was eighteen, and told me that she came from a village a few miles away. She had been in Kasensero a week and intended to stay one week more: 'God will decide.' She didn't do any work as such; neither had she a boyfriend, she said.

At this point, the translator decided to make some enquiries of his own in Luganda, the local lingua franca. It was only later that I played a tape to a Muganda friend, and he explained to me what had happened.

'Don't you think that once in a while you meet with men?' the translator had enquired of Noel.

'I do, but not very often,' she conceded.

'She controls herself while she is here; she doesn't practise sex,' he then told me in English. I recall that he was grinning broadly at Noel at this point, and that she in turn began to giggle.

By this stage, a crowd had gathered, mostly made up of men and boys. Some of them started to barrack Noel about her answers. While she was arguing with one man, another leant forward and poured some *waragi*, the local liquor, over her plate of sweet potatoes and greens. She spotted him, and promptly swung the plate of food in his face; I was standing next to him, and also got splattered with the thick green sauce. While some of the bystanders came over to apologise to me, the intended victim of the attack, clearly feeling humiliated, punched Noel heavily in the mouth. People rushed in to separate them and I, feeling responsible, sheepishly withdrew with recorder and camera bag.

Shortly after the punch-up, one of our party managed to procure a large chunk of Nile perch for lunch. A local man offered to fry it for us, and it soon became apparent that our cook also spoke probably the best English in the village. His name was John Ziwa, and he was a fisherman in his mid-twenties; he told me that he had come to live at Victoria Harbour (the old colonial name for Kasensero) two years before, after experiencing 'personal problems' in his home town of Masaka. He liked it by the lake, he told me. 'We get fish free of charge, we sell, we get money, we enjoy.' I took to his forthright manner straight away, and asked if he would like to give me an interview after we had finished lunch. He readily agreed, promising that he would escort me to his hut so that I could talk to him and his girlfriend in private.

When I listen again now to the tape of that interview, I am surprised, even shocked, by how harsh I was, how determined to brush aside John's defences and rationalisations. My own experiences with Sue, just a few days before, may well have contributed to the grilling I gave him. Perhaps, to some degree, I was interviewing myself.

'Would you say that this place, Kasensero, is famous for Slim disease?' I began.

'Yes, it is famous for it.'

'And do you have any idea of how many have died here from Slim?'

He conferred briefly with another young man in the room. 'About one hundred and twelve people have died in the last two years, which is since I came here.'

'And are you not afraid?'

'I'm very afraid, and in fact I suspect myself to be one of them.' I switched tacks.

'Do you have a regular girlfriend?'

'I do. She stays with me all the time. She is my wife, let me say.'

'What is her name?'

'She is Proscovia Namugasa.'

'And you say that you stay with Proscovia all the time, that she never goes out with other men?' John looked down at the floor, and his voice dropped also.

'Sometimes she does. Since I see her about three times a week, I suspect her to sleep with other men.'

'Does she have a job as such?'

This time, John was much slower in answering. 'She is just a bar-girl. She gets her money that way. I love her anyway – what can I say?'

'Does she expect you to give her money?'

'Yes, a little.'

'How much do you like to give her after you've been together for a night?'

'Something like three thousand shillings.' (The official exchange rate at that time was about 1,400 shillings to the American dollar, but the black-market rate – a truer reflection of real values – was over ten times higher, at 15,000.)

'And how do you think that you catch Slim?'

'Really, that I can't tell.'

'But are there any people who have come and talked to the people of Kasensero, and explained how it is possible to catch Slim?'

'Yes, very many times, they try to do so ... But most times they are news agencies, they are not doctors.'

'They are journalists?'

'Yes. Anyway, they try to explain how it comes and how to avoid it, that is all.' It sounded as if Roland and I were not the only ones to have become active participants in the story, rather than mere observers.

'So how do you think you can get Slim?'

'Just through sex,' he answered in a ringing voice, as if pleading 'guilty' in a court of law, but holding his head high all the same. 'That's the only way we know here.'

'But John, if you know that, and that Slim has killed so many people already, then why are you sharing a woman with other men?'

John sighed briefly. But then, once again, he spoke out clearly.

'I don't have anything to do, really. I have to sleep with my girl if she comes.'

'But you told me you fear that you may already be infected.'

There was a long pause. 'I feel fine. And I'm suspecting the scientists and doctors to get some treatments, according to the journalists. The journalists say so. So . . . why should I fear much?' His voice trailed off, and I remembered Roland's brief message to the village meeting six months earlier. How ironical that perhaps his few words of hope had, through repetition, attained the status of scientific wisdom, and been used to help maintain the sexual status quo.

'What about the other people here? Are they fearing?'

'Some people have stopped having sex. Some have stopped, and some carry on. Since it began, since that disease came, no changes. People die, and some live. We have to follow the situation.'

'And how will you spend this evening, John?'

He laughed. 'Had I had any money, I would be enjoying as usual. But as I'm bankrupt, I will just go to my place and sleep.'

'OK, but if you were not bankrupt . . .?'

'Tonight, I would call my girl, and enjoy with her in the bar, drinking foreign beers and local beers. And then we would go back to our home.'

The hint about finances was fairly plain. And although I had no intention of paying him for the interview, I was happy to give him something for preparing and cooking the fish. John would doubtless be taking Proscovia to the bar that evening.

Later, Proscovia was persuaded to join us inside the hut. She was a strong, statuesque woman; although only in her early twenties, she appeared older and more mature than most of the other women in town. Through a translator, she told me that during her four years at Kasensero she had seen about 200 of its people die of Slim. She added that formerly there had been about 800 people living and working at the trading centre, that it had even been worthwhile for a mobile disco to bounce down from Masaka at the weekends, but that nowadays there were only about 150 who remained. Of these some ten or twenty were bar-girls and the rest were mainly bachelors, she said. Proscovia insisted that she was currently 'controlling herself', that she had no other partners but John. But when John popped outside for a 'short call', she spoke again, in a soft voice, to the translator. 'She says she fears, but she doesn't have anywhere to go, because this disease has circulated everywhere in the world,' he informed me quietly. It felt as if Proscovia was rather less fond of John than he of her.

I was just packing up the tape recorder when John re-entered, and asked if he could sing a Jim Reeves song 'for the listeners'. Naturally I agreed, and plugged in the mike once more. To my surprise, he plumped for the country-and-western version of a popular hymn.

'The world is not my own, I'm just passing through it,' he sang,
'My treasures are laid up somewhere beyond the blue;
The Saviour beckons me from heaven's open door,
And I can't feel at home in this world any more.'

After several verses he finished, and the room fell quiet. Nobody was quite sure whether or not the choice of song had been deliberate.

Later, at John's request, I took a photograph of the two of them outside the hut. In the background, staring at the camera, is a group of rather surly-looking young men with thumbs hooked into the pockets of formidably-flared pairs of trousers. In front is John, legs astride and looking proud, with his arm round Proscovia's shoulders; she, meanwhile, is trying to hide her face, while resisting the pull of his arm with all her might.

The visit to Kasensero took place on the second day of my safari with Helge and Paul. Early on the Tuesday morning the three of us had set off from Kampala in a hired car which came complete with Christopher, a remarkably stubborn Muganda driver, at the wheel. Christopher had his own firm ideas about where he wanted to drive, and for how long, but once we discovered that much of his advice was based on self-interest and a desire for inertia, we began to overrule him with consciences intact.

By contrast, I found travelling with Helge and Paul immensely enjoyable. Paul, the photographer, was quiet and easy-going, but Helge was a one-off, an extraordinary combination of lateral thinking and bumbling charm. He was almost six feet three inches tall, with a long hank of blond hair which kept falling into his eyes, and the ever-present uniform of a rather stylishly-cut beige safari suit, worn without shirt or singlet underneath, but with the jacket tied loosely at the waist with a belt. He had a habit of sitting quite silently for long periods with a beatific smile on his face, and then suddenly asking a pertinent and unexpected question in his sometimes ungrammatical but ever-evocative English.

When we arrived in Kyebe it was already quite late on Tuesday evening, but I managed to locate Joseph Ssebyoto-Lutaya and Jimmy

Ssemambo almost immediately. Although I had spent only two days with them the previous August, it felt like a reunion with old friends. They introduced our party to the new priest of Nazareth parish, Father Augustine Ntabana, who insisted, of course, on providing us with bed and board.

The first question I asked Joseph concerned my interviewees of six months earlier. Straight away he could recall every name and every date. Florence Nassaka had died in September, whereas her baby boy Ssengabi had managed to survive for a further four months, until January. Florence's final wish had not been granted, for Ssengabi was never baptised. Beatrice Namuddu, mercifully, had expired barely a week after Roland and I had photographed her on her bed of straw. Only one of the Slim patients I had interviewed, a fisherman from Gwanda, was still alive. And the following day I was to see him myself, hobbling painfully along the far side of the street in Kasensero. He also spotted me, but turned away. Clearly, he didn't want further questions, further confirmation of his fate. I too was glad to let him be.

Jimmy, meanwhile, told me about the recent visits by doctors and journalists. Dr Roy Mugerwa had headed a team of five doctors which had called at Kyebe a fortnight before, and taken blood from the apparently healthy occupants of half a dozen households. And one week prior to the Mugerwa visit Dr Anthony Lwegaba, who was forever referred to as the man who 'discovered' Slim, had appeared with a couple of Italian journalists in tow. In addition, there had apparently been a visit by doctors from Makerere University who, it was said, had exhumed several bodies. Radio Katwe had it that certain graves had been empty, further confirmation that there was serious magic at work in the area.

At the end of 1986, there had also been a visit by Catherine Bond and another British journalist who had recently arrived to work in Uganda, Catharine Watson. The Two Cathys, as they were already known, had ventured as far as Lukunyu, the small port to the south of Kasensero, almost on the Tanzanian border, after which Catharine Watson had filed a report for a British paper in which she claimed that condoms were 'catching on' in the area, that the government's health education posters were reaching even the most isolated clinics, and that prostitution was declining. In support of the latter claim, she quoted Dr Lwegaba as saying that 'of Lukunyu's two hundred prostitutes, only one hundred remain'.

Our own impressions, however, did not tally with Catharine's. We saw only one AIDS poster during our visit. The number of prostitutes at Lukunyu, we were told, had never been up in the hundreds. And, far from condoms catching on, we discovered that there was no real demand for them in Kyebe, and that (as Catharine also pointed out) people were even unsure how to use them. Just over a thousand condoms had been brought to the health centre since 1985, but most of them were still unused; in August, we had even seen some of them on sale in one of Kyebe's shops, at 400 shillings each, less than a tenth of the price in Kyotera. But, apart from the medicines, syringes and needles supplied by UNICEF, these condoms represented the sum total of material assistance which Kyebe had thus far received in its fight against AIDS.

It also seemed that, due to lack of resources, the only health education about AIDS actually taking place consisted of generalised warnings issued at church services and funerals, and the *ad hoc* advice dispensed by Jimmy Ssemambo to infected individuals and their families. My own impression was that the general level of awareness about AIDS in the community was still very low, and that there was a great need for a well-designed public education programme to be implemented forthwith. I suspected that this applied not just to Kyebe, but to most other communities in Uganda as well.

Almost everyone we met agreed that the number of deaths had dropped somewhat from the cataclysmic level of the previous August. Various theories were put forward to explain this, none of which appeared to hold very much water: that local people had responded promptly to the health education warnings; that they had recently begun to build up resistance to the disease; that they were now too embarrassed to report it; that the rains of the previous August had made it a particularly bad month.

Perhaps the most interesting theory was that the resistance committee members were becoming disillusioned with the NRM system (and in particular with the cadres, newly graduated from the NRM political school, who were widely viewed as 'spies from Kampala') and were consequently no longer bothering to keep proper records of deaths. When I pressed members of the RCs for their actual figures on Slim fatalities, they came up with estimates of between eighty and one hundred for the whole sub-county during the six months since my last visit. The cadres, however, were apparently saying that these figures were too high, and even Jimmy Ssemambo expressed some doubts about them when I tackled him on his own. There again, he was unwilling to make an alternative estimate, having himself been absent from the district for the past three months.

It dawned on me that all sorts of vested interests could conceivably be involved here: that whereas the cadres, for instance, might be eager to keep the death figures down so as to minimise panic among the local population, and potentially adverse reports in the international press, the RC members might well be seeking to raise them in a bid to maximise external assistance. It seemed likely that the issue of AIDS had already become politicised in Kyebe, and that all of the various figures for fatalities were therefore best treated with some caution.

I recalled, however, that there was supposed to be one official register of deaths: that for Gwanda parish, which had been alluded to several times during my two trips to Kyebe, but which had never materialised. I kept asking Joseph and Jimmy to help me get hold of it, and eventually, just as we were setting off in the car one morning, the Defence Secretary for Kyebe RC3, Decker Sekimwanyi, came running up brandishing a well-thumbed exercise book. On the cover were the words: 'Gwanda: Record of People Who Have Died in This Place Since 1986'. It recorded 134 Slim deaths out of a total of 200 fatalities in Gwanda parish during the fifteen months from November 1985 to January 1987 inclusive; 37 of these Slim deaths had apparently occurred in the final six-month period. Since the population of the parish was roughly 9,000, these figures indicated an AIDS mortality rate which had recently dropped from rather over, to just under, 1 per cent per annum. The Gwanda figures seemed consistent with the estimates I had heard of between 300 and 400 AIDS deaths in the whole of Kyebe, mostly in the past two years, given that AIDS was probably somewhat more rife in Gwanda (which includes Kasensero within its boundaries) than elsewhere in the sub-county. In addition the exercise book confirmed that the week of my previous visit in August had indeed been the worst on record, with six AIDS deaths in Gwanda alone.

The Gwanda record of deaths could, of course, have been forged by interested parties, but I found this most unlikely for three reasons. Firstly, because of the difficulties I had encountered in getting hold of it at all. Secondly, because the exercise book, dog-eared and stained, with entries made in different hands, had all the appearance of being genuine; if it was a forgery, it had been most painstakingly and cleverly done. And thirdly, because if someone had been eager to falsify the figures, they would surely have been tempted to pitch them far higher. On the other hand it was clear that those diagnosing the causes of death were laymen, without any formal medical training.

Later on it struck me that given the 50:1 ratio of virus carriers to AIDS patients that was generally viewed as an acceptable rule-of-thumb by medical authorities, then as much as half of Gwanda's population – or, to put it another way, the great majority of its sexually-active adults and newborn children – might be harbouring the virus. The overall situation for Kyebe sub-county could be almost as bad, but perhaps a year or two 'behind'. Joseph Ssebyoto-Lutaya had hypothesised to this effect fully six months earlier; perhaps his melodramatic-sounding statements had not been so outrageous after all.

I discussed these ideas with Helge and Paul, who both gave the appearance of being slightly stunned by what they had seen in Kyebe. I hypothesised that if the formula was sound, then perhaps a 1 per cent per annum death rate, and a consequent total infection rate of 50 per cent, was very nearly the highest that AIDS could achieve in a community where the main transmission modes were sexual and perinatal.

'I don't know about these figures, but I think that this place should be the worst affected place in the world,' said Helge. 'It is almost incredible that so many people are dying now, at the end of the twentieth century. I suppose it is like the plague in Europe, six hundred years ago. The doctors cannot stop the disease spreading, they cannot find a cure. And by the time that people are understanding what is happening to them, it is too late for them to do anything.' As always, he brought me back to basics.

Helge was, however, impressed by the way that the people of Kyebe accepted Slim as something unpleasant but undeniable, and by the pragmatic way in which they responded to the epidemic. A good example was Gerald Muwanga, the twenty-five-year-old businessman whom we had met the previous day, and who had apparently been showing the symptoms of full-blown AIDS for a couple of months. At the time, Gerald had just left Kyebe health centre where he had been given a few packets of oral rehydration salts and some anti-diarrhoeal tablets, these being the only palliatives that Jimmy Ssemambo had available; his brother was giving him a lift back down the hill on the luggage rack of his push-bike. Although clearly exhausted by the bumpiness of the ride, Gerald invited us to visit his home; naturally we accepted, and helped him off the bike and into the back seat of the car. Back at his house, he sat on a sofa between his parents and siblings, and answered our questions with disarming frankness, while a young sister brought us tea. Neighbours dropped by to say hello: Gerald was still very much part of the local community. It was a world away from the isolation wards of Europe and America, from the talk of compulsory testing and the confinement of carriers.

Whatever the exact death-figures, there was certainly no shortage of evidence to prove that a catastrophe was taking place in Kyebe. During our three days there, we came across several households which had been decimated, or worse. First, we returned to the house where seven out of eight people had died, and where I had previously interviewed Emanuel Lubega, the sole surviving son. This time we spoke to Emanuel's grandfather Francis Baziwane – an old man, or *mzee*, in his eighties. 'Everything is in the hands of God,' he told us, as he opened his palms to the heavens.

At a house in Katongero village, behind Nazareth mission, six out of ten people had died in the course of eighteen months; at another house 50 yards away the death rate was five persons out of eight in two years. The grandfathers of the two households, both in their sixties, ascribed the deaths variously to malaria, coughing and diarrhoea, never to Slim; the second of the men, Josephant Eliyoezijja, added quietly that 'God must have his reasons'. Meanwhile, other people round about were adamant that Slim was the culprit, describing symptoms which accorded with the diagnosis.

By and large, it was clear that Slim had reinforced the community's inherent leaning towards fatalism and religiosity. Even Joseph Ssebyoto-Lutaya was not above repeating rumours. 'Some people have the feeling that God may have decided to punish us because of the things we have done,' he told me, 'things like robbing friends, beating parents and loving indiscriminately.'

'Surely all communities are guilty of some malpractices?' I reasoned with him. 'And not all are stricken with AIDS.'

But Joseph was not convinced. 'People think God is very angry,' he repeated sadly.

Others, of course, preferred to blame the Tanzanians and their powerful witches, though others again saw witchcraft as a potential ally against the disease. We were introduced to an apparently healthy mother, Noelana Nasamala, whose emaciated seventeen-month-old daughter Antonia was suffering from coughing and diarrhoea. It transpired that Noelana's four-year-old daughter was quite healthy, but that her husband had died 'from stomach-ache' eight months earlier. On Antonia's stomach were a dozen small scars in a cluster, evidence of ritual scarification carried out by a traditional healer. I asked if there had been any improvement. Noelana laughed nervously, but did not answer. All that she would say was that she had paid 'only one thousand shillings' [7 US cents] for the 'cure'. I began to think about the number of people who, in a stricken area like Kyebe, would be approaching traditional healers for treatment, and I wondered whether the healers were in the habit of sterilising knives and razor blades between patients.

The fear of Slim gave life to other superstitions too. Many in Kyebe seemed convinced that Slim must be spread by mosquitoes and other bloodsucking insects, despite the clear evidence to the contrary. Another group alleged that a new sickness causing welts and discolouration of the skin, and affecting all ages including children, had arrived in Kyebe at about the same time as Slim. Later, I mentioned this claim to a Ugandan doctor, who deemed it most likely that the welts were in fact caused by such common creatures as spiders or millipedes, but that in the general panic caused by the epidemic, people were managing to convince themselves otherwise. A number of other people spoke of a major 'headache problem' which was affecting only those between the ages of fifteen and forty. Although intense headaches are indeed one of the symptoms of Slim, it may be that some headaches were prompted more by hypochondria, and excessive worry about the disease.

Neither was the shepherd any less confused than his flock. When we first met the young priest, Father Augustine Ntabana, he had just returned from administering extreme unction to six dying people in the village of Misozi, four of whom apparently had Slim. But Father Ntabana explained that there were several impediments which might prevent his giving unction to the dying, including 'illegal marriage' and 'living in sin'. Only if such people were to marry at the end of their lives, he said, could he prepare them properly for God. He was reluctant to specify if he had been forced, for this reason, to withhold his services from any of his dying parishioners.

The father was a brave man: he did not run away from the epidemic as had his predecessor, and he stressed the importance of enlightening the community about the ways in which Slim was spread, and counselling its victims. But he betrayed his own helplessness and frustration by constantly erupting into righteous anger. Speaking about people with Slim one evening after dinner, he said: 'The majority are just young men who have contracted the disease through illegal sexual intercourses with different partners.' There was tangible conflict here, but we could not decide if it was between professional forgiveness and private intolerance, or vice versa.

One for whom Father Ntabana would presumably have had little time was Dick Ssentamu. He had originally fallen sick with a stomach-ache and chronic diarrhoea some four years before, and the length of his illness suggested that if indeed he was an HIV carrier, then he probably had ARC, AIDS-related complex, rather than full-blown AIDS. In Kyebe, however, he was simply referred to as yet another 'Slim sufferer'.

Prior to his illness, Dick had worked out of Kasensero as a fisherman. Now he was fifty-two years old, dressed in rags and, since his wife left him, living alone in the shell of what had once been his home; the roof had gone and one of the doorways had fallen in. Dick was everything that Father Ntabana despised; he was irresponsible and proud of it. He

spent admirably little time, however, moping about his fate, and one felt
that there was no chance that he would suddenly repent of his sins in
order to enter the Kingdom of Heaven.

Dick came out of his hut to greet us when we arrived, even though
he appeared to be in some pain. We all sat down together on the grass.
Joseph, as ever, translated. Presently, I enquired as to whether Dick
had been in the habit of seeing women other than his wife.

'He says he was a man, he used to like women. He used to
exchange women down on Lake Victoria shore. He was not a joke,' he
says. Everyone laughed, and Dick himself, now the centre of attention,
pulled his lips back in a rather ghastly grin.

'He tells us he has been sick for four years now. Does he feel
that he is getting better, or worse?' I asked.

'A month ago he was dying. Now he has recovered a bit. But he
says he doesn't fear death. What he has seen is enough. He has seen
days.'

This constant harping on his past prowess was amusing, albeit a
little pathetic. I searched for some evidence of a more serious response
to his fate, for a glimmer of enlightenment, if not contrition. 'What does
Dick think about condoms? Would he use them?'

'He says that if you bring them, he'll try one.' By the time we had
finished laughing about that one, I knew that I was cast in the role of
straight man, so I played the part.

'What will his last wish be?'

This at least prompted a few moments of reflection. Then he
answered, but Joseph waited some time before providing a translation;
his gaze flicked nervously from Paul to Helge to me and back again.
Finally he told us.

'He says he would like a white woman ... so he can say that
he has tried so many things.' Dick was still sitting on the grass and
chuckling as we got in the car and drove away.

We arrived back in Kyotera after nightfall, to find that the decline in the
town's fortunes had really taken hold: we were almost the only people
taking refreshment in the Colombo that night, and next door, in the
Milano, the only unaccompanied young ladies to be seen were the bar
staff. But the NRM campaign against smuggling was probably as much
responsible as Kyotera's unenviable AIDS reputation. We had been told
that only two lorries a week were now plying the 'smugglers' route' to
Kasensero, compared to five a day a couple of years before. And even
the more legal trade through the main border crossing at Mutukula had

apparently dropped substantially, now that blind eyes were no longer in the habit of being turned.

During the course of the evening I discovered that Bob Kagoro was sick, in fact too sick to work. I expressed my regret, and asked what was wrong. 'Nobody knows, but it is not Slim,' I was told, all too quickly. And the DA was not the only one to have fallen ill. We were told that one of the local witch-doctors, who had had the temerity, a year before, to post a sign outside his hut claiming that he had found the cure for Slim, had since sickened and died from the very disease he had allegedly conquered.

Some things, however, never change. When I retired to my 'executive suite' at the Milano (very reasonably priced at 10,000 shillings, or 66 US cents, a night), I found a paraffin lamp, a folded towel and a lady's wooden Afro-comb laid out neatly on the bedside table. The comb was a further suggestion that the hotel frequently entertained women guests who were without very much in the way of luggage. I went back outside and established, in the space of a couple of minutes, that even at this late hour it was still quite easy to arrange for some female company. And how much would that cost me? It was very cheap – perhaps even only 5,000 shillings for the night. My informant offered to effect procurement. But in the best tradition of the *News of the World* investigative reporter, I made an excuse and left.

In the morning, however, there were other things to think about. Helge explained to me that he and Paul had had a long discussion, and decided that they no longer wanted to travel on to Tanzania, as originally planned. They felt that they had already got enough of a story in Kyebe, and were also concerned that we might all end up getting arrested if we stayed around this particular corner of Africa very much longer.

In the end, despite their insistence that I should take the car and go on to Tanzania with Christopher, we decided to return to Kampala together. And because Paul wanted to build up his stockpile of AIDS photos, we spent the rest of the day calling in at villages along the road back to Masaka, and then following directions to the nearest Slim household. But I quickly lost interest. I began to feel oppressed by the fact that wherever we went in Rakai and Masaka districts, even in the tiniest of villages, AIDS had been there before us.

Once back in Kampala, I decided that I wanted to return to Nairobi, to try to sort things out with Sue. Nevertheless, I had to stay on in Uganda over the weekend, partly in order to deliver the several million shillings which Helge and Paul had left me for the hire of the Mercedes, but also because I had decided to have my blood tested once more by someone whom I trusted absolutely to give me the right result, good or bad. It was now eight weeks since my encounter with Emma, long enough for antibodies to appear if they were intending to do so.

I was fairly nervous when I entered Dr Carswell's office, early on the Monday morning, but it quickly became clear that he too was in a state of anxiety. He was less circumspect than during our previous meetings, and he also seemed to be cracking a lot of jokes, and laughing at them for longer than seemed appropriate.

He listened to my account of high-risk behaviour, and agreed to take a blood sample, adding that since a batch of sera was about to be tested the following morning, I could collect my results and still catch the Tuesday afternoon flight down to Nairobi. As he was putting the tourniquet round my arm, I asked him about the latest AIDS figures from around the country. He told me that Dr Okware, who was now chairman of a thirty-man National Committee for the Prevention of AIDS, had been quoted in the latest edition of the government paper *New Vision* as saying that between three and five new cases were now being diagnosed at Mulago daily. And Dr Carswell added that, from what he heard, the mission hospitals of Nsambya, Rubaga and Mengo were also seeing about four new patients a day between them. That made eight new cases a day, or nearly 3,000 a year, for Kampala alone.

'What population do you reckon on Kampala having?' I asked.

'There's probably about half a million here, and perhaps a further half-million can be included from the hospital catchment area in the ten miles or so around the capital.'

'And how fast do you think that the epidemic is growing?'

'Look at the pattern at Mulago. In 1984 there was one case a month; in early 1985 one case a week; by late 1985 there was one case a day; and there's currently about four cases a day. I don't think that's an exaggeration; in fact privately I would say it's an underestimate. Anyway – draw that on a graph and see where it takes you.'

I did some quick calculations, and worked out that therefore, on average, the number of AIDS cases at Mulago had doubled every five months over the past three years. Carswell agreed that this was a tremendously fast rate of increase, compared with American and European models, in which the doubling of cases was generally considered to take about a year. But I also noticed that he was very carefully sourcing all his 'sensitive' information to other doctors such as Okware. It was only later that I realised that, though he had been chairman of the Clinical Committee on AIDS when I had spoken to him in August 1986, he had not been appointed to the NCPA that took over two months later. Neither had Dr Goodgame.

Then I told him about my latest journey to Kyebe, and asked if he had any further information about the incidence of disease in up-country districts.

'We can say that everywhere in Uganda is now reporting seropositives, apart possibly from northern Karamoja. Rakai is worst, Masaka is somewhat behind Rakai, and Kampala is behind Masaka.'

I pointed out that Dr Corti in Gulu was saying that Acholi district was already encountering seropositivity levels of between 15 and 20 per cent, and that it was some months behind Kampala. Dr Carswell did not deny this.

'Gulu's effectively blockaded now, and that's probably stopping the disease spreading. In just the same way, when Katonga bridge was closed to traffic last year, it probably helped slow the rate of spread to Kampala. But it also led to an increase of movement across Lake Victoria, from Masaka to the Sese Islands and Jinja, which has helped spread the virus along that route.'

Finally I asked about the current blood transfusion situation.

'All the hospitals have cut down on the consumption of blood. We now try to give it only on those occasions where the patient would die without.'

'But haven't all the blood banks been screened since the ELISA machines arrived?'

'There aren't really many blood banks, as such, except for a fridge here and there. It's the risk of power cuts, you see. Much of the blood is taken from relatives as and when it's needed, and obviously, in life-and-death situations, there isn't always the time for it to be screened. Blood screening began last May, and nowadays nearly all the stored blood in Kampala is being screened, which is about forty per cent of the national total. We've removed a few bottles, and saved a few lives. But up to May last year, if you had an accident and needed five bottles of blood from the fridge, you had about a fifty per cent chance of getting infected with HIV.'

'How many bottles have you actually removed?'

'About eight thousand bottles a year are used in Kampala. So up to eight hundred, roughly, are being removed.' But Dr Carswell did not sound altogether convinced.

The next day, Arthur Stern and his Mututsi girlfriend Christine joined me for lunch at the Imperial. By this stage, my concern about the impending HIV result had turned to high anxiety.

'I've got this really bad feeling, Arthur. I just know that I've got it this time. I should never have gone with that girl Emma down on the coast.'

'Oh come on, Ed. I'm sure you're exaggerating. You're not likely to get AIDS just by sleeping with someone once.' But even Arthur's mellow Californian outlook was not reassuring on this occasion.

'That's just the point: you very well can get it like that. And besides, it wasn't just the once. The daft thing is, I even had a pack of condoms with me. And because the first time was in the sea, I just didn't worry about it . . . . I was hardly going to stop, get out of the water, and go back to her place to fetch one, was I? And when I didn't bother the first time, there didn't seem much point in bothering after that either.'

'OK. But you've slept with a lot of African women before now, and you didn't catch the virus from any of them. So why should this one girl be different?'

'I don't know why. Probably because with the other women I never really realised the risks; this time I knew the risks perfectly well, but went ahead anyway. I just didn't care. Now, if that isn't a case of bad karma, then tell me what is.'

'Look, Ed. I think maybe it's about time we got a taxi and found out the worst,' said Arthur. He was a good guy.

Outside Dr Carswell's office I took a deep breath, then knocked and entered, but as soon as I saw his smile, I knew that my theories about cosmic justice had been disproved once more.

'It's good news, I'm glad to say,' he told me. 'You're quite OK; you're seronegative. But I do hope you'll be a little more careful in future. To encourage you, I've brought you some condoms, all in pretty colours.' I walked out smiling, and showed Arthur the box of 144 multicoloured condoms from USAID.

Something strange happened at Entebbe airport, as I was filling out the alien's departure card. A man in plain clothes, obviously some sort of security man, started asking odd questions. 'Ah, Mr Hooper,' he said, even before he had seen my passport, or the departure form. 'How is your writing going? And the BBC?'

I was immediately suspicious. 'The writing's going very well thank you, and I'm not so busy with the BBC now. And how do you know I'm a journalist?'

'We know such things, of course. We always read your pieces with great interest. And what about Lucy? Is she well?'

I didn't like the tone of all this. I had been going out with Lucy for the latter half of 1982, and hadn't seen her since. This security man, with his wide, laughing mouth, had obviously done his homework, and wanted me to know it too. I began to get angry.

'I don't know why you're asking all this, but quite frankly I think it's none of your business. Now, I've already spent half an hour going through airport security and NRA security, having my bags searched and my hand-luggage searched. Is there anything else you'd like to search? Any other checks you'd like to make?'

He was laughing. 'No, of course not, Mr Hooper. You don't know who I am, do you?'

'Should I know? Who are you then?' I began to realise that it really would have been better if I had controlled my temper.

'No, it doesn't matter. Perhaps we don't know each other after all. Have a pleasant flight, Mr Hooper.' And he turned to the next person in the queue.

It was a short flight over the corner of Lake Victoria, and through the turbulence of the warm air currents above the Rift Valley, to sweep in past the Ngong Hills to Kenyatta Airport, Nairobi. I sat next to Sally Fegan, the UNICEF representative in Uganda. We talked about the visit by the WHO people from Geneva, who had been helping the Health Ministry draw up a national plan for dealing with AIDS. 'Really, Uganda should get the WHO regional office, as a reward for the work they've already done in fighting AIDS. They've got a very progressive approach over here,' she told me, in her customary forthright manner. 'But I expect in the end it will go to Zaire. They got their request in two months back.' Sally always had a great love for the internal political machinations of aid and relief work.

'And how bad do you think the AIDS situation really is here?' I asked. She did not waste a moment on reflection.

'Well, ninety-two per cent of Ugandans live in small rural areas, and tests in Mukono district – which is rural, although it's admittedly not that remote from Kampala – showed that four per cent of the adult population was seropositive. In Kampala, by contrast, about fifteen per cent of the sexually active age group is positive. So overall, the virus is probably affecting about five per cent of the adult population of Uganda, and maybe half that many of the total population.'

Later, she asked why I was travelling to Nairobi. I gave her a brief résumé of my ups and downs with Sue, and finally told her about the good news of my HIV test. I explained how nervous I had been, and then added that Dr Carswell had seemed rather edgy as well.

'Well, that's not entirely surprising,' said Sally, giving me a funny look.

'Why's that?'

'Well, I think Wilson may be in some sort of trouble with the government at present. I certainly don't think he'll be wanting to have any more dealings with the press.'

Sally obviously knew something, but she refused to be drawn further. What she knew and I didn't was that earlier in February Dr Carswell's picture had appeared in the *Guardian* in London, beside a quotation printed in large letters. 'Next year we'll see the apocalypse,' he had been quoted as saying. 'Come back to Kampala then . . . there'll be plenty of parking space.'

But something else had happened to Dr Carswell at the beginning of February, something else which I hadn't heard about. There had been an attack in the middle of the day on his Tank Hill home, in the course of which his cook and gardener had been brutally beaten to death with a *jembe*, an African hoe. It was rumoured that the attackers had been soldiers in uniform. Dr Carswell had reported the attack to the local police station, immediately after his return home, but apparently no investigation was ever mounted by either police or government.

'One might as well have been reporting a lost pup,' was how he put it to me, months later.

14 · INSTANT SNAPS

'And Jonathan as well,' she said, almost as an afterthought, from where she sat over on the other bed.

'You're kidding. But you always told me that you hadn't done anything with him.'

'I know,' she sighed; then all was silence. 'I don't think you can ever trust me again, can you?' she said, finally. It was more a statement than a question.

For the previous hour, Sue had been telling me about the other men she had slept with since she had first met me nearly a year before. Jonathan was the last on the list. And somehow he was the hardest of all to accept, possibly because I had felt it in my bones all along. In fact, my constantly anticipating it had in all probability helped it to happen. In the end it had all been rather prosaic, with Jonathan returning to Dorothy's Place late one January night, after a party, while I was still busy kicking nicotine and licking my imagined wounds down on the coast. Sue – still nursing the black eye – was alone in the flat, they drank some whisky together and ended up making love. In the morning she regretted it, knowing that even though Maria and Jonathan had split up, her cousin would never forgive her if she found out. 'And I am not feeling very nice afterwards. It is like I am going to bed with my brother,' she added. And even though what Sue got up to after I attacked her on Christmas Eve was none of my business, I still felt jealous. Brothers, after all, are sacrosanct.

There were ten men altogether, although Sue had previously mentioned only two of them. In Nairobi, apart from Jonathan and the diminutive Frenchman Jean-Michel, there was Rolf, the tall blond German with whom I had seen her ten days before, and a couple of Kenyans – one black and one white. There had also been two or three one night-stands in Kampala, as well as Patrick, the French diplomat whom Catherine had tipped me off about on Christmas Eve. Sue had seen him a number of times when I was out of town, as well as on the night of the 'Rwandese dinner party'. In addition, she had slept with Nigel Beale, who had treated her cheaply, giving her a *malaya*'s tip when she left in the morning. Knowing Beale's nature, I could imagine how he must have enjoyed taking his revenge on my own philanderings with his girlfriend Helen – and, of course, it was a fair cop. Sue had also, during my absences, been having a quiet affair with the kid brother of one of her Ugandan friends; it didn't help very much when she explained in mitigation that 'he is very good-looking you know; very nice for girls'.

After she had finished telling me, it was three in the morning, and I sat on the other bed with my head in my hands. The room was in darkness. Periodically, I would come up with the name of another mutual friend, and ask 'What about him? Did you sleep with him too?' And she would answer quietly, 'No Eddie, I think I am telling you, everybody.' But even as I finished the last of the bottles of Tusker, and felt the room swaying, I knew what courage it had taken for her to come clean.

'Come on,' I said finally, my mouth thick with the taste of beer. 'It's time we went to bed.'

In the narrow single bed we held each other tightly and said nothing, though each knew that the other was awake. I was thinking how long ago it seemed that I had got the thumbs-up from Dr Carswell, although in reality it was just twelve hours before. And then I thought back to touching down in Nairobi, and taking the taxi straight to Dorothy's Place, sitting down with Sue and telling her the good news about the test. Then asking her angry questions about the blond man I had seen her with, and getting sullen, non-committal replies. Later, telling her that I wanted her to come back to Kampala with me, to be with me and no one else, and her refusing, again and again. In the end, taking out the air ticket I had bought her, and throwing it down on the bed as I walked out. 'You might as well have it, since it's in your name. Throw it in the bin if you want, it's up to you.' And walking off down the hill, that same walk I had taken so many times in the preceding weeks, down to Buffalo Bill's to drown my sorrows.

Then some time later, shortly before closing time, Sue's friend Rosemary coming over to my table to tell me that Sue was waiting outside. Feeling quietly elated, but saying I didn't want to see her; demanding, in fact, that she go away. Rosemary asking me again, pleading over and over. And going outside to find Sue waiting in the shadow of a tree, away from the lights, dressed hurriedly in a T-shirt, a *khanga* and a pair of flip-flops, and my asking her what she wanted, and she crying and saying she wanted to be with me, and the long silence which continued for the taxi ride back to the hotel. It was only when we were up in my room that I told her my terms: that she tell me about all her other sexual contacts, making sure that none were missed out.

And so, afterwards, I lay there holding her, our bodies both slightly chilled despite the crush in the small bed. I could feel her ribs pressing hard against her skin, and remembered how whenever I came back from abroad, and we went to bed that first time, she was always so thin, and when I asked her she would say, as if it was not important, 'Oh, I am not eating so much these days.' How after a week with me, she was always that little bit plumper, more filled-out. Yes, I thought, whatever she does do when I'm away, she doesn't get to eat very much *matooke*.

There was, of course, another potential explanation for her slenderness. But had we not been tested together, only two months before in December, and both found negative? But of course that test had been meaningless, given the fact that she had certainly had other partners in the weeks preceding it. And then all that talk of Amboseli, all that 'I don't care, we can have AIDS together' nonsense, when, in fact, she had been taking more risks than I during the month we had been apart. And that, really, was the crux of it. Sue was not a *malaya*, but she did like to have a good time, and she still hadn't realised how dangerous it was to sleep around, even with a relatively small number of men. All my explanations to her, and the photographs I had shown her of people dying horribly because of Slim, had failed to get through. Or rather she had been shocked, but only on an emotional level; she still didn't associate having different boyfriends with what she saw in those pictures. I cursed the fact that our limited mutual vocabulary made some subjects so difficult to discuss. And yet I knew that, over the last six years, I had been a lot more promiscuous than Sue. The problem was that I had finally seen the error of my ways, whereas Sue had not. At the beginning of 1986, of course, it had taken me several weeks before I really got the message; perhaps, therefore, I should not be quite so hard on her.

And so, as first light started to seep under the curtain, and the throb of the Hollywood disco near by was replaced by the early morning sounds of the wakening city, I began, slowly, to explain to Sue what I was feeling, that over and above the jealousy and possessiveness, I was really worried that one of us was going to get the virus, and give it to the other, and then that would be the end of the story. 'I know that,' she told me. 'And if I sleep with someone else, I make him wear a Durex. I tell him that I go for a test with you, and I am OK. I don't want anyone to spoil my test.' I began to put her on the spot, asking her about this time, and that; and soon she was telling me she 'didn't remember'. I realised that whatever the good intentions, the question of whether or not a condom was used on a particular occasion was finally a matter of chance, dependent on a myriad of random factors.

And then I remembered the day with Emma, and the time at Amboseli when I threw away the Durex, and I realised how easy it was to be irresponsible, and that if she had the virus then I probably had it too by now, that it would have been too early for any antibodies to show on the blood test which I'd just had, and then I shouted 'Oh God' and held her to me, and finally we made love.

We spent the next few days fooling around. Suddenly I remembered that it was quite impossible to look at her without smiling. No thoughts of work now; it was just a question of getting our relationship back on the rails. I allowed myself to forget that in a few weeks we would have to pluck up the courage to have ourselves tested all over again.

We went everywhere together. One day, I took Sue into the Press Centre, where she made a big hit with the Voice of America correspondent, who was henceforth forever enquiring about my 'beautiful girlfriend'. The VOA man also happened to mention that some time before, a Ugandan called Mike Rukeba had tricked him into making an advance of 200 dollars, after which he had disappeared.

'That sounds like Mike,' I said, laughing. 'But surely he was working for VOA as a stringer at some stage? That's what he told me when we met in Luzira in 1983.'

'Maybe he was; I don't know . . . that was before my time. Anyway, after he got out of prison, he began turning up here in the office with all sorts of hard-luck stories, and eventually I lent him two hundred bucks, which he said he'd repay at the end of the week. And I never saw him again. I tell you, if I ever get hold of him, I'll put him straight through the wall.'

'Yes, he does seem to get up people's noses,' I said.

While in the Press Centre, I got hold of a photocopy of the first article in Peter Murtagh's three-part series on 'AIDS in Africa', which had appeared in the *Guardian* at the beginning of February. Entitled 'A present from Buffalo Bill', and sporting a large photograph of punky Nancy and Afro-haired Susan, two of BB's regulars, smiling full-face at the camera, it was a vivid reconstruction of Murtagh's evening at the wild west bar, and later at the New Florida disco ('a flying saucer-shaped night club suspended over a petrol station'). Early on there comes a description of an Englishman at Buffalo Bill's with a girl on each arm, who shouts in answer to Murtagh's question: 'AIDS? I couldn't give a fuck.' Murtagh comments that if the raucous *muzungu* ended up sleeping with one of the girls in the bar, he had a one in four chance of having sex with an HIV carrier.

As it turned out, Murtagh's article had an immediate impact on the lives of Nancy and Susan, and I was the unwitting catalyst. I was reading the article at Sue's house, when one of her visitors saw the photograph (captioned, 'For £25, Nancy or Susan will give a British soldier a good time ... and possibly more'), and insisted on borrowing it for five minutes. In fact, I did not recover it until two hours later, by which time local legend had it that the two of them had been photographed because they had AIDS. I argued till I was blue in the face that this was nonsense, and not what the article said at all. Meanwhile, Nancy and Susan, by all accounts, were angry because they had been told it was just a quick snap, with nothing being said about publication in a British national newspaper. Whatever, their reputations were ruined, and very soon they stopped calling at Buffalo Bill's; apparently some of the other women had begun referring to them as 'The AIDS girls'. I don't know why I still find this particular twist of fate so upsetting, and this despite the fact that Peter Murtagh and I may even, quite unwittingly, have helped save Nancy and Susan from the very infection which they were suspected of having.

Other Western papers and magazines, incidentally, proved to have greater understanding of the potential implications of such photographs, at least for their own kind. The *Sunday Telegraph*, for instance, printed an action photograph from Buffalo Bill's only after taking the precaution of blanking out the eyes of the British servicemen in shot, to prevent identification; the black girls' faces were left untouched. The West German magazine *Stern* went one better, by obscuring the faces of white men and white women in two of its photos, but not those of the black women and men who (respectively) accompanied them. The front cover of this particular issue, emblazoned with the words 'AIDS und tourismus', featured a white man (face hidden, of course) standing behind a naked black woman, and cupping one of her breasts with his hand.

Kenyan press coverage of the region's AIDS epidemic was equally variable in quality. The local media response tended to wobble alarmingly between fine, provocative journalism and head-in-the-sand denial, with the pattern largely determined by responses to the government's own position – as demonstrated by ministerial press conferences, speeches in parliament, and announcements from the President's Office. Questioning the official line was permitted, but only within bounds; veering too far from it could be disastrous, for Kenya is not a country which tolerates substantial criticism in the pages of its press.

In December 1985, commendably, Kenya became the first country in black Africa to report AIDS cases officially to the World Health Organisation (six Kenyans, and four other Africans), but sadly the official stance underwent dramatic change during the year that followed. Reports in foreign newspapers and journals which mentioned the incidence of AIDS in Kenya were often excluded from the country, as was an Associated Press report about the arrest of 275 women from the towns of Eldama and Kisumu, who were then forcibly 'tested for AIDS' by police. What little domestic coverage there was tended to adopt a tone of scandalised denial. A not untypical report was that concerning Prince Charles's decision to carry his own blood supply when he visited Africa, which appeared in the official party newspaper the *Kenya Times* under the scornful headline: 'Prince Charles scared of AIDS'.

By early 1986, the local rumour factory was working overtime, but it was not until August of that year that the Kenyan government decided to issue an official statement. It acknowledged that there were now 109 AIDS cases in the country, 65 per cent of them from the two western provinces bordering Uganda, and that four new cases were being diagnosed every month. In an editorial published two days later, the *Daily Nation* loudly praised the statement, but then concluded with an ominous, and strongly-worded, warning: 'We in the press . . . have been faced in recent years with a situation in which it has become increasingly difficult to get people in key government situations to talk to us about things which it is their duty to talk about . . . Do they know that, if the issue concerns something as serious as AIDS, this cageyness with public information can land a country in very serious trouble?'

In December 1986, there was uproar in the Kenyan parliament following the publication of a dossier entitled 'AIDS and the Third World' by the London-based Panos Institute which, in the midst of a wealth of pertinent information, had claimed that 88 per cent of certain groups of Nairobi prostitutes were now HIV carriers. In response, the Health Minister announced that the report was inaccurate, misleading, and perhaps 'loaded' against Africans. The *Kenya Times* was less equivocal, ending an angry editorial, 'We categorically reject such half-baked research findings that reflect the current racial tag on the disease.'

The issues became further polarised in January 1987, with the so-called squaddies saga. The whole sad story was in fact something of a storm in a teacup, but served graphically to illustrate how emotions are unreasonably aroused by the subject of AIDS. The *Daily Nation* reported that the British Ministry of Defence had banned the servicemen of the Parachute Regiment from visiting the coastal resorts of Mombasa and Malindi, after forty out of 600 Queen's Own Highlanders, the previous British unit to have visited Kenya, had contracted venereal diseases (rather than HIV) following Christmas R and R on the coast. The *Daily Nation* said that an adviser to the Highland Health Board, Dr James Dick, had erroneously claimed in a British paper that 65 per cent of the prostitutes in the Malindi area were HIV carriers.

Kenyan reaction to the reports was swift and extreme. Shariff Nassir, an assistant minister from Mombasa, said, 'We have never seen or heard about AIDS in Mombasa or Malindi, as AIDS is mainly a homosexual disease, and homosexuality is not practised here but in Europe.' The Minister for Foreign Affairs, Elijah Mwangale, spoke of a 'smear campaign, intended to stop tourists from coming to Kenya', while the Minister for Health, Peter Nyakiamo, stated more soberly that 'there is no scientific basis for the hysterical and alarmist media presentation that Mombasa and Malindi constitute a source of AIDS in Kenya.'

The embarrassed British High Commissioner, John Johnson, took the unusual step of calling a press conference exclusively for the African press, where he back-pedalled furiously. He described the Ministry of Defence ban as 'illogical', and blamed the scandal on opportunistic speculation following AIDS Week in Britain. 'Kenya is one of the healthiest tourist resorts in the world,' he announced. Meanwhile, the paratroopers, who had also been banned from Nairobi after dark, showed what they thought of the restrictions by regularly flocking to places like BB's and the New Florida in numbers even greater than before. Two months later, it was announced from Britain that blood tests had been carried out on the Highlanders, and that none had been found to be HIV-positive. Nevertheless, when a Royal Navy vessel docked in Mombasa for two weeks in April, the wives of twenty of the 230 sailors on board flew out to join them, presumably as a precautionary measure.

Later in January, an informative and visually-striking poster featuring the slogan, Spread Facts Not Fear: Help Crush AIDS, emblazoned over a giant hand which was doing just that, appeared in the streets and as an insert in the pages of Kenya's dailies. The campaign was devised and implemented by the Kenyan Red Cross Society in conjunction with its Norwegian counterpart. Although the campaign was remarkably successful, with posters and a million pamphlets in English and Kiswahili achieving blanket coverage of the country, the government seemed more concerned with trying to take credit for the Red Cross initiative than with mounting an effective health education campaign of its own.

At around this time, the *Weekly Review*, a Kenyan magazine of news analysis and commentary, printed a lengthy appraisal of the AIDS situation in the country, and voiced its misgivings about the limited nature of the government's response. It concluded its report in forthright manner, as follows: 'From the remarks of the country's leaders, it appears that it is fear that adverse publicity in the foreign press will put Kenya's tourist industry in jeopardy that is at the centre of the government's ambivalence towards combating the dreaded viral disease ... This raises the question of what takes precedence over the other: promotion of tourism ... [or] the health of the people.' (Kenya had 650,000 foreign visitors in 1986, and tourism was the country's second leading earner of foreign exchange.)

The much-respected editor-in-chief of the *Weekly Review*, Hilary Ng'weno, was also the brains behind an imaginative and innovative fourteen-part drama serial called 'Usiniharakishe' ('Don't Rush Me') which had just begun on Kenyan television. The programme sought to provide basic sex education, in the course of which it tackled the question of teenage pregnancies, a perennial problem in a country with one of the highest birth-rates in the world. The second episode depicted a teenage boy and girl, both clothed, embracing on a bed. This so offended Omar Soba, the Assistant Minister of Information and Broadcasting, that he personally called at the Voice of Kenya studios to have the third episode stopped, even though the series had been made with the full approval of the health ministry. There was great controversy for some days afterwards in the press, until President Moi announced that all debate on the matter must cease and that 'respectable methods of educating youth, especially through elderly men and women with a more traditional approach, should be utilised.' The rest of the series was never shown.

One can only surmise whether Ng'weno received (or discerned) an official reprimand over 'Usiniharakishe' and the AIDS coverage in the *Weekly Review*, but it soon became clear that he was incensed about some of the articles about AIDS in Africa which had appeared in the Western media. In March, he devoted the whole of his occasional column in *Newsweek* to the issue. Under the heading 'AIDS in Africa: A Racist Taint', Ng'weno produced a diatribe that said more for his powers of expression than for his journalistic balance. He maintained that medical experts knew and that 'any well-meaning commentator on the African scene' ought to know that AIDS ranks 'very low on the ladder of health priorities for the continent at the moment' compared with malaria and other poverty-related diseases. He went on to ascribe the 'apparent obsession in foreign lands about AIDS in Africa' to the low standard of competence of foreign correspondents and foreign AIDS researchers working in Africa, and to the ever-growing amounts of money 'to be made in the AIDS business'.

It is my belief that in this particular article, Ng'weno utterly failed to address the true significance of AIDS in Africa in the year 1987: that of a problem which, like Kenya's high birth rate, contained within itself the seeds of potential disaster for the future. He offered the sort of placebos which one would perhaps expect from a defensive minister of health, instead of the bitter medicine that one would hope for from a man spoken of by many as the leading African journalist of his age.

On the other hand, he did undoubtedly present a case to be answered, for there had indeed been several reports on Africa's AIDS epidemic in the international press which were sensationalist or even racist. But equally, there had been responsible and well-researched pieces – such as those by Lawrence K. Altman of the *New York Times* – which incurred the wrath of African governments simply because they came out with facts and figures which were too accurate for comfort. Feeling that such articles bore enormous damage potential for areas such as tourism and business investment, the governments in question simply panicked, and information about AIDS swiftly became restricted material in a manner unprecedented with other diseases. Researchers and doctors, both nationals and expatriates, were often made aware that they should not speak further with the press. Many of them chafed at the restrictions, feeling that greater issues were at stake than 'protecting the honour of the nation'. Such persons continued to brief reporters, but only in private and off the record.

Both sides were right, in their different ways. The unchecked figures, incorrect hypotheses and wild claims which have appeared in some Western newspaper articles have caused profound offence and anger in Africa – and also on occasions economic loss, as when a Malindi hotel had over half its bookings cancelled in the space of a week, as a direct result of the squaddies saga. But overall, the propagation of accurate information about AIDS in Africa has helped rather than hindered the fight against the epidemic. In the end, responsible journalism has as important a role to play as have condoms, clean needles, and health education campaigns.

It was quite by chance that as soon as I entered Buffalo Bill's, I spotted a tall blond man walk up to Maria, and realised that it was Rolf, Sue's German friend. I walked closer, and heard Maria say, in her graphic English, 'She at home now. She sick on the bed.'

As soon as Rolf turned away, I went up to him and introduced myself. 'I think we have a mutual friend,' I said.

'Yes, and what of it? Does that mean you are going to go up there and beat her again?'

I assured him I was not, and instead we ended up sitting down together for a drink. It turned out that he was back once again from Germany, but this time on holiday, and with his wife and kids. He had left them at their hotel, and had been on his way up to see Sue, to give her the photographs of their last day out together, by the waterfalls at Thika. It was the same day that I had met them as they returned to Dorothy's Place.

Soon I realised that this Rolf was rather a nice guy. Later on, I asked him if he would mind telling me about how it was between Sue and himself. He was quite happy to recount the story.

'Well, I met her first when I came to Kenya about two years ago. And I like her very much; I find she is different from all the other girls you meet in a place like this. And I started to take her out places, mostly in the countryside, and then each time when I came back from Germany I would bring her something – a dress, a pair of jeans, something like that. And for a long time I didn't even go to bed with her, it was funny. Mainly I enjoyed her for her company; as you know, she has a very nice sense of humour. In the end, I think I have been going out with her perhaps five or six times before we go to bed together . . .'

'As a matter of interest, did you use condoms?' I broke in, rather betraying my preoccupation of the moment.

'Of course I use condoms. Don't you? You're not telling me that you're a journalist and you've been sleeping with the women here without them?'

I smiled rather ruefully. 'Well, actually, except for one occasion, I've only been with Sue over the last year. Before that I wasn't being so sensible, but it seems I got away with it.'

Later, he started apologising to me for our unfortunate meeting three weeks earlier. 'Look, I am happy to leave the two of you alone, really. You seem to be a nice man, though you shouldn't keep on hitting her. It becomes a little easier each time, you know. Anyway, you obviously care about her, and that's the main thing.'

And he pulled out the photographs, asking me to deliver them to Sue. I started to protest, but he was adamant.

'Look, Mister Ed. I have my wife and my kids waiting at the hotel, and I said I'd only be away for an hour. I'm glad that we meet. Now you go up there and say hello to her from both of us.'

She was sitting up in bed, unwashed, unbrushed, and rather smelly. It was obviously not a good time. She started crying when I walked in, and just carried on doing so when I took her in my arms. What I hadn't had a chance to tell Rolf was that, after the reunion between Sue and me, and the very loving week that followed, things had started going wrong again for us while we were visiting friends up in Kisumu. The day after we got back to Nairobi, we split up once more, but this time in an almost lazy way, as if we were both exhausted by the endless rounds of melodrama and recrimination. She left her pullover behind in my room – an accepted tactic between us – so I dropped it in at her place the following day, stopping for five minutes to chat, but saying I was too busy to stay for tea. I knew that I must get back to Kampala and start working, for I had done very little in the past three months, and I began gearing myself up to leave her behind for good. But somehow a week passed, and I got involved in some rather open-ended negotiations with the SPLA about going over the border into their zone of control in southern Sudan, and suddenly I found that I was missing her like a tooth. Earlier that evening my resolve had finally cracked, and I'd sprinted out of the house to flag down a taxi and search her out at BB's.

'I think that you are not coming back,' she said and then cried some more, her tears staining one of the photos. A worried-looking Anna came in, to check that we weren't having another row, but I told her we were OK, and that Sue would be staying with me for a few days. Then I chivvied her out of bed, and hastily packed some of the piles of neatly-ironed clothes in the famous red suitcase. Later, in the tiny bedroom of the guest bungalow at my friend's house, we lay awake until well after dawn, talking about this and that. I could never understand how, with our limited common vocabulary, we always had so much to discuss.

That Saturday night we went out together to the Carnivore, to help Catherine celebrate her birthday. Sue had not even really wanted to go – I noticed that recently she was talking about her friends less and less when she was with me – but I insisted. It turned out to be a good evening; everyone got a bit drunk, and Sue and I had a long session on the floor, dancing to the live band and then the disco. 'You two look like you've been together for years,' said Catherine, when we came back up for some air. She meant it kindly, I think.

The next day, we didn't get up until the late afternoon. By that time, the sun was casting long, sharp shadows across the lawn, so I fetched my camera and called Sue. She took my arm; I held the camera, one-handed, to my eye, and took what turned out to be the last shot on the film. I have the print in front of me now, its right-hand side tinged just slightly with orange. The two of us are silhouetted perfectly on the grass, our heads inclined slightly towards each other, her hand clearly resting in the crook of my arm, and the shadow of a banana tree off to one side. The perfect instant snap.

I don't know quite what happened later that evening, but within two hours of that photograph being taken, we had both reached unbelievable levels of anger. After some time, and still arguing, we stormed off towards Westlands, one of Nairobi's wealthier suburbs, where we spent the rest of the evening at a particularly unlovely open-air bar on the edge of a busy highway. There we continued the argument, with me hissing pure vitriol at her whenever the waiters were out of earshot, and her just laughing softly and bitterly, and shaking her head. I can't remember many of the ugly details, except that she told me that she'd never really wanted me as her boyfriend, and I told her that if she'd given me AIDS through her messing around, I'd come back and take my revenge. That night we lay side by side in bed, our bodies never touching. In the morning I went to the kitchen and made an omelette, while she packed her things up, slowly and carefully, and then walked off down the drive. Another instant snap. I would never have to call on her at Dorothy's Place again.

15 · THE INTERNATIONAL PERSPECTIVE

By the time I flew back to Uganda in mid-March, there was only one topic of conversation in the country: the assassination a few days previously of Andrew Kayiira, the former UFM leader. A fortnight before his murder the treason charges against him had been dropped, and he had been released from Luzira prison, although shortly afterwards President Museveni gave an address to the Uganda Law Society in which he made the pointed, and disturbing, assertion that too many guilty people were being freed by the courts. Despite the fact that he was now apparently viewed as a right-wing opponent of the regime (a supposition only reinforced by the persistent rumours that he had been groomed for leadership by the CIA), Kayiira elected not to leave the country to join his wife in America. Instead he applied repeatedly, and without success, for an audience with the President. One night in early March a group of armed men broke into the house where Kayiira was staying, and shot him three times. Despite the government's prompt denials of involvement, most people felt that the killing had either been officially sanctioned, or that someone had taken the independent initiative of ridding Museveni of his 'turbulent priest'. Military involvement was also suspected, with some villagers apparently testifying that soldiers had been seen waiting near the house since earlier in the day.

The case was never satisfactorily resolved. Even detectives from Scotland Yard, who were called in by the government to assist in the investigation, were apparently baffled. Three petty criminals who were former members of the UFM were eventually arrested and charged with the murder, but they were acquitted a year later. The fact that they were redetained by security personnel as they walked from the courtroom only added to popular misgivings about the case.

*

Meanwhile, since late 1986, civil war had broken out in earnest in northern and eastern Uganda. It was no longer possible to gain access to the north past the Nile crossing at Karuma Falls on the Gulu road, or past Soroti in the east, and even the roads to the south of these points came under occasional attack. Since February, independent observers like missionaries and relief workers had been ordered to leave many of the affected districts, and journalists had been tacitly denied access, so that information was increasingly restricted to the contents of official NRA statements, and the horror stories of those fleeing the area. Neither source was reliable. In the midst of the propaganda, there were unconfirmed claims about the existence of a new 'Triangle' of killing, like that of Luwero in Obote's times, but this time to the south of Kitgum in the Acholi region. Although such reports seemed greatly exaggerated, it did appear that since the failure of attempts to pacify and win over the population of the north, a new, much tougher official policy was being implemented. Museveni himself, in an uneasy echo of his predecessor Milton Obote, even threatened to 'annihilate' those who opposed him.

'They are fighting a dirty war, but trying to hide the fact,' a relief official recently returned from one area told me; 'there was no torture or killing in the first phase, but now they act like any army waging acts of terror under stress.' Despite this, most of the information coming in clearly suggested that the worst examples of army misbehaviour were not unleashed entirely gratuitously, but came in response to prior rebel attacks. It also seemed that the NRA's excesses were not in the same league, at least in terms of scale, as the orgy of violence and killing in which the armies of Amin, Obote and Okello had participated. On the other hand, there were quite simply too many reports, and too much evidence, for these incidents to be merely the aberrations of individual commanders or rogue military units.

The new NRA policy in the war-zone appeared to be to hold the garrison towns, but to withdraw from the countryside in between. Sometimes the army's attempts to restrict the operations of the various rebel groups such as the UPDM, Alice Lakwena's Holy Spirit Battalion, the Uganda People's Army, and the improbably-named FOBA (Force Obote Back Again), involved using similar tactics to those which had been used by the UNLA in Luwero. Fields and grain stores were burnt, mission hospitals evacuated, and their water pumps and supplies of food and drugs, destroyed. Effectively, a free-fire zone was being created. Sometimes, especially after rebel attacks on garrisons or convoys, more specific counter-measures were deemed necessary. In one case, the thirty women of a village near to the scene of an

1 A pile of skulls assembled by villagers from the Luwero Triangle – a testament to Uganda's violent past

2 The funeral of Charles Ssemujo – one of twelve held in Kyebe sub-county during the first week of August 1986

3 Roland Neveu at the funeral of a Kyebe man thought to have died of Slim

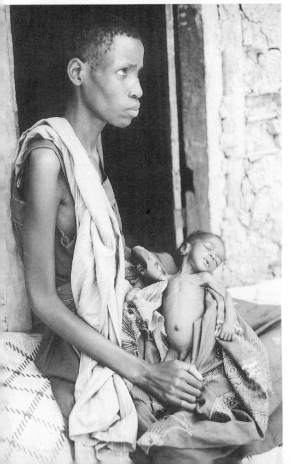

4 Florence and Ssengabi, sitting outside their hut in Gwanda. Florence died one month after this photograph was taken; her baby, Ssengabi, died four months later

5   The main street at Kasensero, leading down to Lake Victoria

6   Aida and John Bosco, both HIV-positive, in hospital in Kampala. Babies frequently fall sick long before their mothers display any of the symptoms of AIDS

7   Nsambya Hospital's Sister Nellie Carvalho spotting serum samples with reagent prior to testing for HIV antibodies on ELISA

8   John, the fisherman, and Proscovia, the barmaid, at Kasensero

attack were apparently gang-raped by a group of soldiers. Another time after an ambush, ten men were allegedly taken at random from a village and three-piece-tied with such ferocity that four of them died, while five of the others later had to have one or both arms amputated after gangrene set in. On other occasions, cattle-camps and villages suspected of harbouring rebels were bombed indiscriminately from the air. In addition, there were now widespread reports about the army exploiting the prevailing insecurity by misappropriating large herds of cattle.

The authorities were also resorting to other extraordinary measures. In particular, there was a new class of prisoner, the 'lodger', held either in official prisons like Luzira Upper, or else in police cells or military barracks. Lodgers were not, however, covered either by formal charges, or even by detention orders. They were held at the pleasure of, and as the direct responsibility of, the NRA. Numerous sources testified to there being between 2,000 and 5,000 lodgers held under lock and key in various locations around Uganda, some of them, especially those from the north, being kept naked and without blankets. There were several unsubstantiated reports of deaths in detention. It was also clear that at least one section of the NRA felt that enquiries about the status of such prisoners, whether by journalists or human rights organisations, constituted gross interference in Uganda's domestic affairs.

The embassies and relief agencies seemed to be content, at this stage, to maintain a watching brief. But one official assured me that protests would be made if the situation got any worse: 'This government, quite exceptionally in Africa, has made human rights one of the cornerstones of its policy. So there's some basis for putting pressure on it.' I wondered, however, if the NRA's almost puritanical zeal and sense of rectitude, forged in the course of the five-year battle against Milton Obote and the UNLA, would actually prove susceptible to external pressure if the level of internal opposition increased.

At this stage very few reports about the civil war, and the deterioration in NRA behaviour, were reaching the outside world. I decided that it was about time that somebody put pen to paper.

I also managed, within a few days of arriving back in Kampala, to find a new girlfriend. Gertrude (the colonial influence is still strong when it comes to the naming of Ugandan children) was a university graduate from West Nile in the north-west of Uganda; she was tall, black, graceful, and a marvellous conversationalist. She was still living at home with her parents, and had given up her 5-dollar-a-month secretarial job to become a member of what the World Bank would call 'the informal economy'. Like many Ugandan women at that time, even those who retained their jobs for the respectability that employment conferred, Gertrude survived by living on her wits, by doing some *magendo* (buying goods at official prices, and reselling on the black market), and through the generosity of her male admirers.

It did occur to me that living on one's wits might, in Gertrude's case, include doing some intelligence work for the government. She had a friend called Robert, who had perfected a sort of bored lounge-lizard style which often involved his sitting down with us in the Baraza Bar at the Imperial, indulging in idle political gossip, and cadging drinks. He always seemed to be hovering in the background, and I began to wonder if, despite his allegedly being an aspiring business agent, he was actually more of an *agent provocateur*.

Looking back now, I recognise that Gertrude and I never really clicked. This applied socially – I had put on a lot of weight since giving up nicotine and splitting with Sue, and so I never felt like taking Gertrude out dancing – but also in the bedroom, where the multicoloured condoms turned out to be something of a passion-killer by persistently splitting in the middle of the final act. Not only that, but I kept finding that when I held Gertrude in my arms at night, I would quickly drift away into other thoughts, and that by the time I drifted back, my face would be wet with tears. Appalled by this behaviour, I began to wonder what on earth I was doing with Gertrude and, more particularly, what she was doing with me. We spent less than a month together before a trivial incident gave me the excuse to end the relationship. She couldn't believe that I was reacting so strongly. But in reality, of course, I was still settling old scores with Sue.

Meanwhile, Wilson Carswell had rather more to think about than splitting condoms. He and his wife Margaret were suddenly told by the authorities that they would have to leave Uganda, and they named 1 April as their day of departure – presumably with irony intended. They had been working in the country for nineteen years, and both appeared to be profoundly shocked by the events of the previous two months. One evening just before their departure I met Dr Carswell as he was leaving the Speke Hotel. I asked him about the February edition of the *Health Information Quarterly*, which he had been promising to give me. 'You may as well come and wave me off at the airport – everyone else seems to be doing so. I'll make sure I bring a copy for you,' he promised.

He was in fine fettle when I greeted him at the airport two days later. He was sporting the tweed jacket and kilt that I had always known would suit him, and he and his wife were sitting with a circle of friends and colleagues, including several of the nuns from Nsambya. He gave me the promised copy of the *HIQ* as if it were the crown jewels. 'You'll find it all in there,' he said, in an echo of eight months before. I wanted to ask him so many things: about why he had been expelled, about the attack on his house, about what he had actually said to Peter Murtagh, about the HIV tests which I'd heard he had just done on another group of pregnant women. But it was hardly the time. I thanked him, wished him well, and left him with his friends.

Not long afterwards, I was back in the UK myself. I was finding it hard to settle in Kampala, and decided quite suddenly that I would be better off back home. I had material from over a dozen sources about the civil war in northern and eastern Uganda, and I also had feature stories to write about Lamu and, of course, Slim. My friend with the big smile was once again at the airport when I left. 'We seem to be travelling up and down rather a lot,' he said, and I restricted myself to nodding agreement.

Following the British government's 'Don't Die of Ignorance' campaign, with its icebergs and tombstones, there was considerably more awareness about, and interest in, the AIDS problem than I had detected during my previous visit back home. I spent a fortnight busily writing articles, after which I managed to sell a 3,000-word piece on the insecurity in Uganda to *New African* magazine, and a Lamu feature illustrated with several colour photographs to *Intercontinental*, the house-magazine of the hotel chain.

After waiting the customary eight weeks since my last unprotected sexual contact (with Sue, for I had decided to ignore the condom-related mishaps with Gertrude), I paid another visit to the Hospital for Tropical Diseases and gave some blood for testing. The following day I set off to visit Helge in Hamburg. In all, I spent nearly a month in Europe, including a fortnight in Helge's attic flat, feeding his cats, and writing a cathartic short story about Sue; I also made an unexpectedly large amount of money from the sale of various versions of the AIDS story to Swiss and German papers. Flushed with my suddenly bulging bank balance, I invested in a phone call back to London, and found, to my relief, that I had been pronounced seronegative once more.

By the time of my return to England, in early June, the Third International Conference on AIDS was being held in Washington; it attracted over 7,000 participants, nearly 1,500 of whom were from the press. Probably the greatest significance of the week-long meeting was that it marked the emergence of AIDS as a vital political issue. The night before it opened, President Ronald Reagan delivered his first major speech on AIDS, fully six years after the illness was first detected in America. Most observers felt that the entire emphasis of the speech was misguided. Instead of announcing a huge public education campaign (something which most European countries had seen as their first priority, and had embarked on long before), he told his audience of glitterati that there would soon be routine (meaning mandatory) testing for all prisoners in American gaols, together with all immigrants and aliens seeking permanent residence in the US. He thus expressly rejected the advice of his own surgeon-general, Everett Koop, who had previously warned that such enforced testing would tend to drive the disease underground. As he spoke, sixty-four protestors, many of them PWAs (People With AIDS), carried off a publicity coup by getting themselves arrested outside the White House by police wearing long yellow rubber gloves, presumably intended for warding off the virus. The following day Vice-President George Bush reinforced Reagan's message, and shocked the conference, by announcing that the US government would be advising individual states to test couples seeking marriage licences, and attenders at drug-abuse and STD clinics.

Numerous studies presented at the conference confirmed that HIV was spreading fast into the heterosexual population. It was pointed out that while only 4 per cent of the 1.5 million Americans who were estimated to be HIV carriers were classified as having been infected by heterosexual contact, a further quarter to a third of them had caught the virus by sharing needles to inject drugs; since most of this group were heterosexuals, they might well transmit the virus to the opposite sex. There was further evidence of the potential for heterosexual spread from the US army, for half of the servicemen and women found to be seropositive were married; the army was also predicting that 90 per cent of all HIV carriers would die of AIDS or ARC within ten years of infection, the highest forecast thus far. It was reported that HIV was now spreading faster among heterosexuals than among homosexuals, many of whom had radically changed their behaviour in the face of the epidemic, and that heterosexual contact was now the leading cause of transmission around the world. Many researchers believed that this state of affairs would also obtain in the US before long; already, incredibly, AIDS was said to be the leading cause of death among women in New York City between the ages of twenty-five and thirty-four.

Neither were there any signs of an imminent breakthrough in the development of an effective AIDS vaccine or drug treatment, although there was much optimism voiced, especially from scientists eager to generate funding for their research. Already roughly a dozen different drugs which to some extent blocked the progress of the virus in the body had been developed, but the best-known and most widely-used, AZT, was still prohibitively expensive at 10,000 dollars for a single year's treatment, and likely to cause dangerous side-effects in some patients.

The highlight of the conference was felt by many to be the keynote speech delivered by the director of the WHO's Special Programme on AIDS, Dr Jonathan Mann. He told the conference that as many as 10 million people had already been infected with HIV worldwide, and that up to 3 million of these could expect to develop AIDS within the next five years. (Many observers felt even these figures to be conservative.) And in an apparent reference to the measures announced by Reagan and Bush, Dr Mann told the conference, 'Sometimes bewildered, sometimes frightened peoples and their leaders are seeking answers, perhaps simple answers, to complex disease control and ethical questions.' He decried such mooted responses as cards certifying that the bearer was free of HIV, tattoos for confirmed carriers, or a self-imposed quarantine, whereby seropositives would be allowed to retain their freedom in return for a promise not to work, marry or travel. 'How our societies treat HIV-infected people will test our fundamental values, and the moral strength of our culture,' he said.

He warned that after the first epidemic of silent HIV infection in the mid to late 1970s, and the second epidemic of AIDS itself which began in the early 1980s, there was now a third epidemic – 'the epidemic of economic, social, political and cultural reaction to HIV infection'. He said that there was 'a rising wave of stigmatisation' against homosexuals, prostitutes, haemophiliacs, Westerners in Asia, Africans in Europe, and so on.

Mann made particular reference to the problem of AIDS in African countries. He compared Western expenditure of up to 100,000 dollars for a single patient with annual health budgets in Africa which often amounted to less than 1 dollar per head of population. 'What political system,' he demanded, 'could withstand for long the destabilising impact of a twenty or twenty-five per cent, or higher, HIV infection rate in young adults?' Pointing out that, as with the smallpox campaign, the Western world would undoubtedly gain more than it spent on global AIDS control, he called for an investment of billions of dollars to help the Third World fight the disease.

'The alternative is to abandon Africa as if the world was not one,' he said. 'The epidemic cannot be stopped in one country until it is stopped in all.'

PART TWO

The Response

16 · ZERO GRAZING

Arthur Stern had become a good friend in the year since I had recorded that hurried interview with him in Moyo, and by the time that I flew back to Uganda in the middle of June 1987, I was looking forward to seeing him once more. That evening, I walked across town to the restaurant where his girlfriend, Christine, was working, and I remember hoping that I would find him there, rather than absent on one of his up-country trips. But as soon as Christine saw me entering the restaurant, she burst into tears; it took some time to calm her down. Eventually we moved to a table in the corner and ordered some beers. Then she told me the whole sorry tale. Apparently a week earlier Arthur, together with Christine and several other of his Ugandan friends, had been arrested at gunpoint in the middle of the night, and taken to the Military Intelligence headquarters at Basima House. Although all his friends had been released the following morning, Arthur himself was still being held. Christine told me that she knew of no reason for his arrest.

I did what I could to investigate the case. The first step was to contact the people at his embassy, who knew that he was being held at Basima House, but not much more. The second was to locate his friends who had been arrested that night, and who could perhaps cast some further light on the affair. This proved difficult since those who were not too frightened to speak tended to be overwhelmingly angry with Arthur, on the dubious, but understandable, grounds that befriending him had caused them 'problems with the government'. But eventually, after two days of chasing and coaxing, I managed to piece together the bare bones of what had happened.

Apparently, after my departure for England, Arthur had set off to the Sese Islands, situated 30 miles south of Entebbe in Lake Victoria; there he had spent some idyllic days fishing and exploring the region by dug-out canoe, before falling foul of the local DA, who demanded that he return to Kampala and get official clearance. Against all expectations, Arthur managed to procure all the necessary documents and letters from the US embassy and the Ministry of Tourism, and he returned to the islands armed with a typewriter with which he intended to record some of his Ugandan experiences. But once again he was out of luck. After a few weeks he went down with a particularly severe bout of hepatitis, which necessitated his return to the mainland, and his isolation at Nsambya Hospital for the better part of a fortnight. Two days after his discharge from hospital came the arrest. In fact, Ugandan law does not provide for the arrest of civilians by members of the army, but such is the turbulent nature of Uganda's recent history, and such is the persuasiveness of a brandished gun, that nobody in their right mind would have dreamt of arguing.

I went back to the US embassy to fill them in on what I'd discovered, and later accompanied one of their consular officials to interview a couple of the witnesses to the arrests. The official told me that a formal representation had been made to the Ugandan government about the case, and that nothing more could be done until an answer was received. This reminded me of the passive response by the British High Commission to my own detention in Luzira four years earlier. I decided that it was down to me, as a friend, to help get Arthur out. It never really occurred to me that I might be creating problems for myself.

I called on various well-placed people, none of whom were able or willing to help, but eventually went to see Jack Maumbe-Mukwana, the Deputy Minister of Information and Broadcasting, who had been a fellow detainee in Luzira in 1983. Despite his apparently lowly cabinet position, Jack was said by many to be an important man in the NRM hierarchy, and in addition a close friend of Museveni himself. (Several important NRM functionaries were deputies or ministers of state in their ministries, but were nevertheless suspected to be the men wielding the real power.) I felt that our shared experience of incarceration might render the minister more approachable on the subject of another detainee, and so it proved to be. He emphasised that it was not for him to interfere with intelligence matters, particularly among the military, but he then gave me a letter addressed to Patrick Karegeya, another fellow detainee from Luzira days, who was now an officer with Military Intelligence, based at Basima House. I recalled Karegeya as one of a group of four students picked up from Makerere University for suspected anti-Obote activities, with whom I had shared the same cell (actually the old prison chapel, at that stage housing over a hundred prisoners). We had talked several times during the month I had spent inside, and had got on well; I was overjoyed to discover that he was now in MI.

Later that afternoon I headed off to Basima House clutching Maumbe-Mukwana's letter. I was already half-way there when I decided that it would be wise to inform someone about where I was going, so I stopped the taxi by a hotel, and eventually got through to the American official on the phone. To my amazement, he told me that he had just discovered from the US embassy in Nairobi that Arthur had been released and driven to the Kenyan border three days before, in fact on the very day that I had flown back to Uganda from Britain. I was pleased and relieved that Arthur was free, albeit a bit fed up about having wasted so much time and energy. Later, I went down to tell Christine the good news.

What with all this excitement, I did not have much time to review the AIDS situation until about a week after my return to Uganda, when an article in the government newspaper *New Vision* brought me back to earth. It reported that 'Slim has claimed the lives of yet another two students at Makerere University.' After some minutes of rummaging around in the cardboard box which served as my AIDS file, I managed to dig out the most recent edition of the *HIQ*, which the bekilted Dr Carswell had given me on his April Fool's Day of departure. It contained a twenty-two-page review entitled 'AIDS in Uganda', edited by Carswell himself. The conclusion of the report gave a breakdown of the 1,011 AIDS cases which had been confirmed up to the end of 1986, and attested that 'about 100 new cases of AIDS are now being seen every month in Kampala hospitals'.

There was also a lot of interesting serological data, much of it highly alarming. One hundred and eighty-six barmaids had been sero-tested at Lyantonde, a small town of 5,000 people on the edge of Rakai district, which served as the major truck-stop on the road between Masaka and the Rwandese and Zairean borders. Seventy-six per cent of the barmaids, it was claimed, had antibodies to HIV. Even though the author of this study, a young Ugandan post-graduate named Warren Namaara, later amended the figure to 67 per cent, and though Dr Carswell, in a subsequent medical paper, wrote that each barmaid had 'admitted to having more than twenty sexual partners a month', this was still a horrendous figure, being only slightly lower than the HIV levels encountered among prostitutes working in the capital cities of Kenya and Rwanda.

Meanwhile, further east along the road in Masaka itself, 30 per cent of adults attending an out-patients' clinic had been found to be seropositive. In Kampala the given figures for blood donors and pregnant women were still around the 12–13 per cent mark. In Mukono, the next district to the east of Kampala along the main highway, some 4 per cent of adults tested had HIV antibodies, but significantly they all came from the rural part of the district, rather than from Mukono trading centre.

If all this serological data was entered on a map of East Africa, it was possible to trace a clear pattern of transmission that followed the main passenger and trade route from the central African hinterland, through Uganda and into Kenya, where doctors were reporting seropositivity levels of roughly 2 per cent among the adult population in Nairobi, and slightly higher levels in the western part of the country, near the Ugandan border. The *HIQ* provided further evidence for this route of HIV transmission by reporting that 33 per cent of long-distance truck-drivers and their turnboys had proved seropositive (Dr Carswell had carried out tests in one of Kampala's lorry parks). In Carswell's subsequent medical paper on HIV infection in Uganda, he explained that all the truck crews did regular runs along the trans-African highway linking Kenya and Uganda to Tanzania, Rwanda, Burundi and Zaire; that half of them claimed over fifty lifetime sexual contacts; and that 80 per cent of the remainder claimed over ten. Once again, the number of sexual partners was linked to HIV susceptibility. Between them, Namaara and Carswell had provided statistical proof that the trucking network, with its attendant 'service crews' of prostitutes and barmaids, constituted probably the most efficient amplification system for HIV in Africa.

The theory of transmission along the truck routes had first appeared in the press in Peter Murtagh's *Guardian* series in February, and again in an article in *Time* magazine later that month which declared that 'huge reservoirs of infection exist along trade routes connecting the hard-hit countries of the AIDS belt'. The article went on to ascribe the rapid rate of spread to promiscuity combined with a higher incidence of venereal diseases among Africans. As evidence, it claimed that African AIDS patients in Rwanda and Belgium had had a lifetime average of thirty-two sexual partners, and quoted figures from the Panos report to the effect that 10 per cent of the Kampala population and 7 per cent of the Nairobi population had experienced gonorrhoea, as compared to just 0.3 per cent in London, and under 1 per cent in New York City.

The gravity of Uganda's situation was really brought home to me some days later, when I received an aerogramme from Dr Carswell. He had written it just after his return from the Washington conference, and he commented that too many African countries were still playing down the extent of the epidemic. He closed with the almost casual remark that 'the Ugandan authorities are hesitant to accept that 24 per cent of women attending one of the antenatal clinics in Kampala this year were HIV-positive.'

It did not take much detective work to find out that this awful percentage applied to 170 pregnant women from the clinic at Nsambya Hospital, whom Carswell had sero-tested in February 1987, shortly before his departure. He had previously undertaken two similar studies at this clinic: in October 1985, just over 10 per cent of the antenatal mothers had proved seropositive, and between February and April 1986, 13 per cent. If this group of expectant mothers was taken as representative of the sexually-active population of Kampala, then the level of seropositivity in the capital appeared roughly to have doubled in the space of a year. On the basis of that admittedly small sample of 170 pregnant women, it could no longer be said that one in ten of sexually active adults in Kampala was seropositive, the ratio generally accepted by all parties, for one in four now appeared to be closer to the truth. And, by inference, many of the next generation of Ugandans were also doomed to be HIV carriers, before even leaving the womb.

The following week, when I was up in West Nile reporting on the repatriation of tens of thousands of Ugandan refugees from Zaire and Sudan, I discovered that Slim had appeared even in this most remote of Uganda's regions. Every hospital I visited in the area had a few cases to report, including that at Yei, over the border in Sudan. In the course of the safari I also came across several individuals who, like me, had found that the multicoloured condoms were prone to rupture during use.

There had been several other significant developments in Uganda during the two months I had spent in Britain and Europe. Most obvious was Museveni's acceptance of an economic package backed by the IMF and the World Bank, which involved devaluation, the issue of a new currency, and the reassessment of official buying and selling prices for such vital commodities as coffee and oil. The NRM moderates had won their battle with the hardliners who believed that such terms constituted a shameful surrender to the pressures of international capitalism. The net result was that the IMF was appeased, and agreed to provide a loan of 24 million dollars for 1987; the World Bank also released 100 million dollars. On the other hand, Uganda was obliged to service 70 million dollars' worth of debts, most of which stemmed from the profligacy of previous regimes; this sum, equivalent to 30 per cent of all external income, represented a crippling burden for an already shattered economy.

The new monetary system meant that 1 dollar now exchanged for 60 new Ugandan shillings, as compared to 1,400 of the old variety (or 15,000 at the black-market rate). But the exchange rate had still not found its true level. Before a month had passed 1 US dollar was buying 100 new shillings in the Asian shops where the real market values were set, and after three months the rate had risen further to 180. There was one encouraging sign, however. For the first time in many years, the presidential profile was not emblazoned all over the bank-notes. And most Ugandans, despite losing 30 per cent of their cash when the banks converted their notes to the new currency, were genuinely pleased to be rid of their bundles of grubby, almost worthless 'Obotes'.

Another important development was that Uganda had become the first country in the world to initiate its own national AIDS Control Programme, or ACP. A donors' conference held in Kampala in late May, and jointly organised by the Ugandan Ministry of Health and the WHO, had rewarded the Ugandan initiative by pledging over 6.9 million dollars for the ACP's establishment and first year of operation. A further 14 million dollars was pledged for the remaining four years of the five-year programme.

The money was specifically earmarked for a massive public education programme; the rehabilitation of blood banks and screening services; the supply of protective materials, medical equipment, condoms and therapeutic drugs; the rehabilitation of Entebbe's once-renowned Virus Research Institute; the establishment of a national surveillance system; the training and orientation of health workers; and the conducting of serological and KAP (knowledge, attitude and practice) surveys. Roughly a quarter of the 20-million-dollar total was to be undesignated, to allow maximum flexibility in implementation. The government had continued, by and large, to be open about the epidemic, and this policy had apparently paid off handsomely.

The WHO team which had visited in February also deserved much of the credit for the success of the donors' conference. The seventy-four-page ACP 'medium-term plan' which they produced was so comprehensive, with its lists of objectives, methods of implementation, and in-built progress indicators, that it even touched on such issues as the contribution that could be made by traditional healers, and the particular problems faced by village midwives. It also relied heavily on Wilson Carswell's various epidemiological surveys, so it was doubly ironic that its official publication date should have been 2 April 1987, the day after the Carswells' departure from Uganda.

More cynical observers commented that a price had been paid for all this foreign assistance, namely a franker numerical acknowledgment of the scale of the problem. Just before the donors' conference began, Uganda had reported 1,138 cases of AIDS to the WHO, which at the time represented the third highest per capita figure in the world after USA and Haiti, and over a quarter of the official WHO total for the entire African continent; it was even conceded that this might be 'only a fraction' of the true total. Meanwhile Jonathan Mann, the director of the WHO's Special Programme on AIDS (SPA), called the approval and funding of the Ugandan plan 'a landmark', and added: 'we all owe a debt to Uganda for its leadership in openly confronting the AIDS problem. This is historic for us because this is the first of what we expect to be many such similar meetings and examples of international co-operation on behalf of AIDS control in a given country.' And sure enough, shortly afterwards, Tanzania announced a total of 1,130 AIDS cases, and the approval of its own five-year AIDS plan. By the end of July, Rwanda and Kenya had followed suit.

The first physical evidence of this massive funding was the provision of brand new office accommodation for the ACP in Entebbe. This was important, in that it provided the leading figures of the National Committee for the Prevention of AIDS, which had already been in operation since October 1986, with a proper, centralised work environment. The committee's chairman was Dr Okware; its secretary was Dr Lwegaba, the man popularly credited with the 'discovery' of Slim; Dr Sezi was chairman of the publicity sub-committee; Dr Mugerwa chairman of research; Peter Kataaha chairman of laboratory work; and Louis Ochero was perhaps the key figure as chairman of health education. Also due to move into the new building was a four-man team which had been seconded to the ACP from WHO in Geneva, one of whom was the virologist Bob Downing, an appropriate choice in that he had been testing Ugandan blood samples at Porton Down for the past two and a half years, and had been a central figure in the drafting of the ACP five-year action plan.

I had already met and interviewed Louis Ochero, the head of health education, on the day I left Uganda for England in April. He was an older man, balding, with a gentle and dignified manner. He told me about the national 'Love Carefully' campaign, with its 400,000 posters and 500,000 leaflets which had already been printed in English and three Ugandan languages, and he added that it was hoped eventually to extend coverage to fifteen of the country's indigenous tongues. The *Love Carefully* pamphlet equated Slim with AIDS, explained what the disease was and the major symptoms to look out for, discussed how people caught the disease, and suggested the best ways of avoiding infection. There was a companion pamphlet, *Work Carefully*, which was intended for health workers, and both pamphlets were illustrated with sketches by Ochero's own daughter, Grace. These pamphlets superseded another series entitled *Everything You Need to Know About Aids* which had been issued as early as July 1986.

Ochero was well aware that such initiatives would not reach the entire population. He explained that the pamphlets and posters, together with broadcasts on radio and television, were all very well, but that there was a great need to reach the majority of Ugandans who lived in rural communities, far from the impact of such facilities. Therefore, he said, the most important component of the health education campaign was the spread of information by word-of-mouth, through, for example, theatre groups, singers, and the local resistance committees. 'We have made ourselves open to tell the public the truth about this disease,' he told me proudly. 'You will find the behaviour has changed. While men used to run so much in public places, used to have so many women around, they are now narrowing to zero grazing.' This last was the catch-phrase of the moment in East Africa, and an effective one too; health officials in both Kenya and Uganda were later to claim authorship of the expression. Its tongue-in-cheek adaptation of an agricultural metaphor, and its exhortation to stay in one field, stick to one partner, went down very well in Africa, even if some Western doctors thought it too euphemistic.

Since I had a plane to catch, I did not enter into a debate with Ochero about whether or not the health education message was really making an impact where it mattered most, among the sexually active. Certainly on my travels, I had encountered a small number of educated people who were fully aware of the dangers of Slim, if not always fully sensible in terms of their response, together with a much larger number of people who were bewildered and frightened by it, and who therefore often demonstrated wholly inappropriate reactions. Examples of the latter group had been featured in the Panos report: the prostitute who maintained that 'if AIDS was here, all the bars would be closed'; the bus driver who slept only with fat women, because they could surely not have Slim; the AIDS-affected men in Zambia who believed that they would be cured if only they had sex with a 'fresh', uninfected partner. It was still, for instance, the tradition in many areas of Africa – including apparently parts of Buganda – for the brother of a dead man to take over responsibility for his widow, and to have ritual sexual intercourse with her on the night of their marriage. Unless people quickly became better informed, such traditions were liable to have horrible repercussions in the age of AIDS.

The days spent making contacts in Europe began to pay off when, at the end of June, the picture desk of the German news magazine *Der Spiegel* telexed me, asking for pictures on the theme of fighting AIDS in Uganda. Overjoyed at getting my first formal photo assignment, I spent the next two days rushing between Kampala and Entebbe with cameras slung round my neck. As it happened, it was a piece of good timing, for a USAID consignment of 2 million condoms had just arrived in the country, and it was almost impossible to move that week without tripping over a box or two. I photographed condoms on sale at 15 shillings each (25 US cents) in the big pharmacies, condoms on sale beside the herbal medicines in the open markets, condoms being handed out at family-planning clinics, and condoms being rolled on to a plastic demonstration penis (pink, not black) by a matronly matron at Makerere University Hospital, who told me that she was giving each student applicant a 1-gross box 'to be getting on with'. I even contemplated shooting the much-rumoured distribution of free condoms by NRA soldiers on roadblock duty at the Owen Falls dam over the Nile, until someone pointed out that I would probably get myself arrested for photographing a potential terrorist target.

Later I visited the by-now famous Sister Nellie Carvalho at Nsambya Hospital, and photographed her and her laboratory assistant William as they centrifuged, and added reagent to, the latest batch of serum samples, and then waited for the computerised read-out on ELISA. Sister Nellie told me that since the *Guardian* articles she had been warned not to speak further with the press, and so I didn't even attempt to find out about the latest seropositivity figures. In any case, her report on the first three months of operation of the Nsambya ELISA machine, in late 1986, had already appeared in the last edition of the *HIQ* – she had tested nearly 1,000 units of blood donated by apparently healthy persons for transfusions, and nearly 16 per cent had proved to be positive. The seropositive donors had been noticeably young; 66 per cent of the male carriers and all the female carriers were below the age of thirty, and half of the female seropositives were actually twenty years or younger. It was soon after this that Nsambya initiated a policy of taking blood only from young teenage girls at mission boarding schools, though even then some donations still turned out to be infected.

Nellie mentioned nothing to me about the gift which she had received just a fortnight before from Tom Rayner, a farmer and health care researcher from Norfolk. Rayner had read about Nellie in Peter Murtagh's *Guardian* articles, and had been so moved by her plight that he had set about converting a spare long-wheel-base Land-rover which he had on his farm into a mobile AIDS unit. He stocked the vehicle with a village hospital kit, together with bedpans, a stretcher, sheets, towels, and medical supplies, shipped it to Mombasa, cleared it through customs, and then drove it up to Kampala to hand over to Nsambya Hospital. Perhaps Nellie felt that an independent initiative of this type might arouse jealousies and ill will among other members of the NCPA, even that the gift might be taken away from her. Whatever, she merely repeated to me her earlier comment to Peter Murtagh: that many journalists had come to fill their notebooks, but few had helped them in real terms with the crisis they were facing.

Next I went down to Entebbe, to photograph the blood-screening equipment which had just been installed at the Virus Research Institute. One of the technicians there told me that they had been experiencing some teething problems, especially with the dilution of specimens; he also let slip that very high levels of seropositivity were being encountered in Uganda's hospitals, though it was to be some weeks before I would discover just how high he meant.

Afterwards, I called in at the Ministry of Health headquarters, where I managed to locate most of the principal figures from the NCPA. I photographed Louis Ochero beside some of his daughter's dramatic posters ('In the paradise of loving, beware of AIDS ... it is the flower of death', and 'Beware of the sweetness and splendour of sex: it could prove hazardous to your health and life'). Dr Samuel Okware, it transpired, was in an important meeting, but after I sent a note inside asking when he would be free, he came straight out to be photographed. I explained briefly who I was, and that I was currently wearing two hats – one as a photographer for *Der Spiegel*, the other as the prospective writer of a book about the AIDS epidemic in East Africa. It was the first time that I had met the chairman of the NCPA, and I was impressed both by his amenability, and by his relaxed manner. Before he went back into the meeting, he gave me the number of a private clinic in Kampala where he worked in the afternoons and early evenings. 'Contact me there,' he said.

I called on him as suggested at the Pilkington Medical Centre a few days later. He was still full of smiles and handshakes, but this time much less welcoming of questions. He was just leaving, he said, and was shortly setting off for a conference overseas. By this stage we were already standing outside the clinic and he had his car keys in his hand, so I said that perhaps I should come and see him the following month, when he was less busy. But this seemed to make him even less helpful. 'I wonder what sort of questions you'll be wanting to ask me. You're very dangerous people, you know, you journalists.' He was grinning, but a point was being made.

'Look, Doctor. I don't want to ask you any tricky questions. Just the policy of the national committee, how much money you've received so far, how many AIDS cases you have in the country, that sort of thing. In actual fact, the main thing I'd like to ask you, right at this moment, is whether you can give me permission to speak to some of the other doctors and nurses like Sister Nellie, who are specialising in AIDS work.'

'Even if I wrote a note to Nellie, she would not agree to speak to you,' he said, as he unlocked the car. 'Anyway, you're going to be here for several months, so we don't have to rush, do we?' He was smiling again as he drove away.

Back in February, Dr Okware had been quoted in *Time* as saying that in Uganda 'in the year 2000, one in every two sexually active adults will be infected'. Perhaps he'd got his tail singed on that one; whatever, it appeared that these days he was being far more cautious. I would have to tread softly, I decided, if I was going to make any headway with the chairman of the NCPA.

It was a weekday morning, and I was the first customer of the day for the Baraza Bar. The Baraza occupies that part of the ground floor of the Imperial Hotel that overlooks the Standard Bank roundabout: on two of its sides it is open to the elements, and is thus effectively an open-air café. It was a fine morning, so I chose a seat beside the balcony, and ordered a plate of scrambled eggs on toast and a pot of coffee. Suddenly, I detected a presence behind my right shoulder.

'Hello,' said Mike Rukeba. 'I thought you might like to buy me breakfast.'

When the waiter came, Mike scanned the menu, and then ordered the most expensive breakfast available, all sausages and bacon imported from Kenya. He had with him that morning's copy of *New Vision*, purchased from one of the many newspaper-sellers who were already out on the pavements, their titles displayed on cardboard sheets, each pile weighed down against the wind with a piece of broken glass. Uganda is one of the few countries in the world where the shortage of newsprint, and the thirst for news, decree the existence of a healthy black market in the sale of newspapers.

I listened as Mike made smalltalk, which was not the sort of thing that improved one's breakfast.

'I was sorry to hear that you broke up with that nice girl ... what was her name?'

'Sue,' I grunted.

'Yes, that's right. The one that used to stay with that other girl, Barbara. What went wrong then?'

'We finished, that's all,' I said, while I tried to remember if I'd ever introduced Mike to Sue. Surely I hadn't. But I must have told him about her on that ride down to Kyotera. 'Anyway, you're out of date, Mike. I've won and lost another woman since then.'

'Oh, I see,' he said, as he watched a maribou stork take off from one of the lamp standards, and glide down over the roundabout.

Conversation lapsed for a while. Our breakfasts arrived, and Mike picked at his in desultory fashion. Clearly his visit had not been motivated by hunger. 'Have you seen today's *New Vision* then?' he asked, suddenly.

'No, Mike, I haven't, but I see that you have a copy there.'

He opened the paper at the front page, and laid it down beside me. There it was, the main headline, and below it the byline 'Mike Rukeba'.

I started to congratulate him. I was amazed, and genuinely pleased for him despite myself.

'But I didn't even know you wrote for *New Vision*,' I said. 'When did you start?' I recalled that only once before had I actually seen his byline in any of the papers for which he apparently worked.

'Oh, some time ago,' he said, casually. He prodded the paper with his finger. 'You can read it if you want.'

It was an incomprehensible piece, spread over two pages, about Barry Baxter, the new WHO administrator with the AIDS Control Programme. The gist of the story seemed to be that, in the days before his employment with WHO, Baxter had been working on the rehabilitation of Luwero district, and, it was claimed, had stolen seventy-five bags of cement. It was a very unusual article, in that nothing had come to court, and the only evidence consisted of rather vague allegations made by two of the Luwero district officials. I was astounded that the editor had printed it. But I didn't have the heart to voice my reservations.

'Well, that looks great Mike. Star reporter for the government newspaper, eh? Now, just explain to me, because I've only had a chance to skim through: how are you sure that it was Baxter who did it? What's the proof?'

He pointed to a couple of paragraphs, but I was still no clearer as to what it was all about. I had no idea whether Baxter was guilty or not; I hadn't even met him. But, as it stood, he appeared to be in a spot of trouble.

'So what do you think will happen after all this? Will he be charged? Taken to court?' I enquired.

'Oh, I expect that he'll have some problems with the security authorities once they've read this,' said Mike, almost yawning now. 'Anyway, I've got to go now. Thanks for the breakfast.' And he was off, leaving the half-finished meal behind him.

A short time afterwards, the Ministry of Health announced that Barry Baxter did not have satisfactory credentials for the job of ACP administrator, and he was obliged to leave Uganda at short notice. It was apparent, however, that the WHO felt that Baxter had been falsely accused, for he was promptly invited to take up the Geneva-based post of SPA desk officer for East Africa, including Uganda.

When I heard about Baxter's departure, I was reminded of a time, shortly after the Museveni takeover, when I had been walking in Kampala, and had come across Francis Odida, a large, friendly, albeit rather naïve Acholi who had just started up a newspaper called the *Sunday Review*. Francis was peering under the bonnet of a car, and beside him was Mike Rukeba. Odida was a well-known supporter of UPC and Obote, and was somewhat sparing in his encouragement for the new regime. I was therefore surprised to see him and Rukeba together. I gave them a generalised greeting, and carried on down the road. But Francis came out from under the bonnet, and insisted on introducing me to Mike. I explained that I already knew him of old, and asked Francis if Mike was now one of his employees.

'Oh, he's a very good journalist, Mike,' said Francis with warmth. 'You really should take him with you on one of your up-country trips.'

I just laughed, and carried on walking. 'Yes, Eddie. Take him with you one of these days,' Francis shouted after me. When I think back to that afternoon again, I can almost hear a note of pleading in Francis Odida's voice.

At the end of the year, Francis Odida was arrested and charged with seditious publication, and the publishing of false news. One year later, after putting out another contentious article, he was charged once again with sedition, to which was subsequently added a charge of treason. Treason in Uganda, technically at least, carries a mandatory death penalty.

17 · THE GUERILLA COMMANDER

'Are fish eaters safe?' ran the headline at the top of the letters page in the *Focus* newspaper. 'Dear Editor,' the letter began. 'The emergency of deadly AIDS has forced the general public to examine every aspect of their life in a bid to avoid contracting AIDS. And the question arising out of such examination is: Are fish eaters safe from AIDS? Observers have established that rain-water washes human waste into lakes and rivers. Since AIDS victims are responsible for part of this waste, then the waters must already be abounding in AIDS infection. Automatically the fish can't be spared by the disease. In light of this hypothesis, how safe are the consumers of this fish?' The letter was signed 'Fish Eater, Kampala'; there was no editorial comment below to assure the writer that such fishy fears were unfounded.

I was in the Imperial's main restaurant, a huge, murky cavern full of rickety chairs and threadbare carpets. It was renowned in Kampala for the slowness of its service, which was largely due to the fact that all cooking was done on charcoal braziers resting on top of the great, derelict ovens in the kitchen behind. Unfortunately, however, this was the only place in the hotel to get breakfast before the Baraza Bar opened at half-past nine in the morning. On this particular morning, one of the waiters sidled across to my table, and asked me to come to the phone: I thought it was probably the manager asking me to pay off my hotel bill, or some similar irritation. Instead, it turned out to be Arthur, phoning from California.

'Hello matey,' he crackled down the line, in that awful cockney accent he sometimes assumed when talking to me. It was great to hear his voice.

'Hello you old bastard,' I replied.

We spoke for some twenty minutes, though I did not find it easy to relax with the great hall of discreetly chinking crockery at my back. We kept tripping up on the half-second delay as well. After some time, the conversation turned to his departure.

'Look, Ed, thanks for your letter. And I really want to thank you for all you did, even if I was already out by then.'

'That's no problem, Arthur. And if there's anything else I can do over here that won't get me into trouble, then just say the word.'

'Well actually mate, there is one thing you might be able to help me with. The boys at Basima House never gave me back my diaries and notebooks. And I was really thinking of writing up some of my experiences, you know, a book of travel stories or something.'

I was a little horrified. I really didn't want to be getting involved with Military Intelligence at all. My previous unpleasant experience with Commander Joseph Musoke had only served to reinforce the realisation that MI officers, of whatever regime, were more or less laws unto themselves. I didn't mind going to Basima House to try to rescue Arthur, but his notebooks were another matter.

'Arthur, I really think that perhaps you should go through your embassy on that one . . . it could be a really delicate matter. And wasn't there some rather sensitive material in some of those? Or had you already sent those notebooks from the north back home?'

'No, there's no problem about those. But I see what you mean, Ed. You're quite right. I'll see what the embassy can do.'

Just before putting the phone down, I told him that if I had a sudden brainwave, I might just be able to help out, and he carried on protesting that it really didn't matter. But I'd remembered that I still had the letter from Maumbe-Mukwana to Karegeya.

I had never been to Basima House before. It was an ugly modern brick building on the hillside opposite the army headquarters at Republic House. A friend had given me a lift, and he drove off pretty smartly after dropping me at the entrance to the car park. I made my way to reception and asked for Patrick Karegeya.

I was escorted to an upstairs office, and then left there to wait for five minutes or so. He entered almost without a noise, and looked more familiar that I'd expected, as if I'd been talking to him only yesterday. He had slightly protruding eyes which made him look unfriendly at first, but after we'd greeted each other a large, ready smile took over, and I felt more relaxed with him. After we had shared some reminiscences from the Luzira days, and congratulated each other on our new positions, I explained the purpose of my visit, and gave him the letter that the minister had written a month before. He read it in silence.

'And why do you think that we'll want to give you back these notebooks?'

'Oh come on, Patrick. The guy's a friend of mine. He wasn't doing anything wrong here – he just enjoyed your country, that's all. He wasn't a spy, he was a traveller, with a rucksack. You remember those don't you, from the days before Amin started scaring everyone away?'

'Eddie, I can assure you that we wouldn't have arrested him if he hadn't been doing anything wrong.'

'What was he doing then? Tell me that.'

'I'm not at liberty to do so. But he was arrested quite properly, and for sound reasons.'

'Was he though? He was just a nice, open guy who used to get himself into scrapes occasionally; he was up north for a while, and some of your people probably came across him there, and then you found out he was on the Sese Islands and you didn't know what he was doing there, and you decided that since he was American, he was probably a spy. He was picked up for nothing, on suspicion, just like I was and you were under Obote. Otherwise, if you had something on him, why didn't you charge him? No, Patrick, you got the wrong man, and you just won't admit it.'

'Is that what you think?' Patrick Karegeya was not looking happy now; I realised that my attempt to bluster my way through, to force him into acknowledging that a mistake had been made, what the hell, never mind, here's his diaries back and send him our best wishes, had backfired. I decided on a last-ditch gamble to convince him that Arthur was innocent.

'OK, Patrick, I got this letter from him in the post a few days back. I want you to read this, and then tell me he was a spy.'

He picked his way slowly through Arthur's spidery handwriting, while once again the room fell into silence. The letter consisted of Arthur's attempt to sum up, to furnish an explanation for, what had happened to him: it was stunned, rather than recriminatory, in tone. Despite this, I began to feel nervous. I grew aware of my lungs breathing in and out, more heavily by the moment. After a while I got up from my seat and started pacing the room; then I began pointing out significant passages in the text. Still Patrick said nothing. Eventually he turned over the aerogramme, and I took it from him, before he could read the return address on the back.

'He says that the arresting officers had guns with them. That's a lie,' was his only comment. I began to wonder if he himself had been one of those present at the arrest. If so, I was in trouble. Either my other witnesses were all lying, or he was. I started thinking that intelligence boys are the same the world over, never mind the country or regime: looking to protect their own species first, and worrying about the rights of their suspects at some stage after that. I had been wrong to come here, I realised. Now to get out again, as painlessly as possible.

'OK, Patrick, let's leave it. I just thought you might be able to help, that's all. I'll go to the embassy, and ask them to make a formal application to you for the return of the notebooks and diaries. Will that be better?'

'You won't get them, Eddie. Evidence, you see. Anyway, why are you so interested in this Arthur Stern? What is he to you?'

'A friend, Patrick, just a friend. You recall those, don't you, people you like and trust? A friend for whom I'm willing to lay my position on the line, just as you presumably were for people when you were mobilising at the university, or fighting in the bush, or whatever. OK?'

We made mutual protestations about how good it was to see each other again, and finally I left. But I was feeling bad as I walked off down the road to find a taxi. The meeting had not gone well.

The following morning, at nine o'clock, I was arrested. There was a knock on the door of my hotel room, and when I answered it there were two policemen standing there, and that was that. I was asked, quite politely, to bring my passport, and to come with them. I demanded to know what it was all about, and one of them told me, quite bluntly, that since it involved my passport, I was probably about to be deported. 'Oh no,' I said. 'You're kidding. Not again.' They made no objections when I insisted that I be allowed to phone the British High Commission, to inform someone there of their names and ID numbers, and the fact that they were taking me to CID headquarters at Impala House. As they were leading me out of the hotel, I also told the people at reception, and everyone else within earshot, what was happening. The more people who know where you're going, the safer you are. The only problem was that they didn't take me to Impala House at all.

The police Land-rover drove up the road past the CID headquarters, and then into the courtyard of the old Organisation of African Unity building next door. The OAU had closed its Ugandan branch a few months earlier and since then, although the sign remained outside, the building had apparently been discreetly taken over by one of the security organisations. I was escorted from the courtyard into an office behind, and invited to sit down. And there I sat for the next hour. Nobody answered my occasional half-hearted enquiries about why I'd been arrested, and why I'd not been taken to a police station as promised.

Eventually my spirits picked up again, and I began to get shirty.

'What are we all waiting for?'

'You are waiting for the big man,' one of my three guards informed me; the two policemen had now been joined by a man in plain clothes.

'Which big man?' I demanded to know, but nobody answered. This made me less nervous, and more angry. 'I could be waiting here all day, couldn't I? Well, I think you'd better bring me some breakfast.'

'You'll get some food after you've spoken to the big man,' I was told.

'No way. I know my rights. You arrested me before I had a chance to have breakfast, and you have a duty to keep me fed and watered. Now, I'll provide the money if need be, but I want someone to go and fetch me something to eat.' There was a short discussion, in Luganda I think, and then one of the policemen disappeared out of the door. Half an hour passed, and he hadn't returned. I demanded to go to the toilet. I was told to wait. I asked whether they wished me to relieve myself on their big man's carpet.

'Ah, Mr Hooper, you are very funny,' said the remaining policeman. But there was some more discussion, and eventually the door was unlocked, and then I was escorted down the hall to a far from hygienic lavatory. When I finished, nobody was waiting for me outside, and I did a quick recce to the end of the corridor, and across the deserted court-yard, before I went back inside the room. Shortly afterwards, another man came in, but he was not Mr Big either, just a replacement for the official in plain clothes. When the latter left the room, nobody bothered to relock the door. I tried my luck with this new man.

'Look, with all due respect, I am starving hungry, and I want some breakfast. A policeman went out nearly an hour ago, allegedly to buy me food, but he has apparently disappeared, and unless I am brought food in the next five minutes, I am going to walk out of here to the kiosk under Impala House, and I am going to buy myself some *sambusas*.'

'I'm afraid that you can't do that, Mr Hooper,' he said. But he seemed a pleasant man, and I decided to continue to assert myself and see where it got me. I knew from the bitter experience of 1983 that if one went along meekly with events, then one's adversaries grew all the more secure and dangerous.

'Oh can't I? Look, you may have me under arrest, but you don't have the right to starve me.'

'Well, strictly speaking, you're not under arrest . . .'

I didn't even let him finish the sentence. I was already out of the chair and walking to the door. 'Fine, if I'm not under arrest, I'm walking out of here right now, and I'm going to get myself some food.' My hand was on the doorknob now, and nobody else had moved. 'If your boss wants me, he can contact me any time through the British High Commission. Goodbye.' I walked out of the door, and set off briskly down the corridor. Never for a moment did I think that I'd get away with it.

I could hear them rushing out of the door after me, but they were already arguing in Luganda or Kiswahili. I realised that neither the policeman nor the other man was sure who should take charge of the situation. I was already half-way across the courtyard by now, and I could hear one of them clapping his hands, and first hissing at me, and then shouting softly at the soldiers guarding the exit, presumably telling them to stop me. I suddenly realised that he was scared that his boss would hear him, so I kept walking. If one of them had just run up behind me and put his hand on my arm, I would have stopped. But nobody did.

I turned into the short tunnel that led to the exit, and saw that the two soldiers were still lounging against a low wall bordering the side of Impala House. Another four or five seconds, and I was past them, and out in the street. They were still calling after me, and clapping their hands, but I resisted the temptation to turn round. The next hundred yards were perhaps the most frightening, because I was half-expecting a bullet in the back. But a few passers-by had seen what was happening and stopped to watch, which made me feel safer. I couldn't believe I had done it, but then I was past Impala House, past Chez Joseph, and trotting down the steps to the lobby that runs under the UN building. As the steps turned I looked up above me, and could see no pursuers. There was someone I knew in the lobby, waiting for the lift, but I called out that I couldn't stop, and carried on out the other door, turned right into what used to be called Obote Avenue, and finally pushed open the glass doors of the British High Commission. It had been the longest 200 yards of my life.

It wasn't until I was admitted through the inner locked door and upstairs into the office of the Third Secretary, Gordon Brown, that I felt completely safe. And it wasn't until I started talking to him and to the press officer, Dougie Kerr, that I realised just what was going on. My visit to Karegeya was only the half of it.

'You weren't responsible for this, I suppose?' asked Dougie, chucking the latest copy of *New African* at me. I had been up in West Nile when the July issue first hit the streets, but now Dougie told me that it had caused something of a sensation. The entire supply had been sold out in the course of a single day, and after that, copies apparently began changing hands at up to ten times the official price. Which, given the lurid nature of the cover, was hardly surprising. It sported the figure of Yoweri Museveni, in camouflage fatigues, looking out over a scene of devastation. A pall of smoke and a helicopter were outlined against a sky of pulsating yellow, below which a group of soldiers had congregated around a bus. In the foreground were two particularly loutish-looking specimens, their shirts open to the waist, one of whom was carrying a rifle loosely by his side, and the other, rather incongruously, a spear. All around them in the bush were mangled and bloody bodies. Printed over part of Museveni's forehead were the words 'Uganda's Killing Fields'. 'Oh God,' I said. 'That's my article.'

It wasn't my title, though – the only killing fields in the article being those attributed to the UNLA in Luwero in 1983 – and neither was the cover my idea of responsible artwork. Nevertheless, with the exception of a few inserts, the omission of a number of qualifying 'apparently's' and 'allegedly's', and the attribution of some of the misbehaviour and poor judgment to Museveni personally, rather than to the NRA in general, it was surely my article. And what's more, it was accurate, even if most of it was already some four months out of date.

'Oh well,' said Dougie. 'You've got some problems then.'

They were as helpful as they could be, Gordon and Dougie, letting me phone around town in an attempt to make contact with somebody in the intelligence services, to tell them where I was, and the fact that I was ready to be interviewed in the presence of an official from the High Commission. Eventually I managed to get through to the police corporal who'd escorted me from the Imperial, and who was now back at Impala House, quite beside himself with fear. He pleaded with me to give myself up, saying that the big boss was blaming him for my escape. I pointed out that I hadn't escaped, but that things hadn't been done in a proper, or legal, fashion. I told him to tell the boss man that I was ready to speak to him any time, that he only had to contact me at the BHC. 'And you'd better tell me his name, so I know who I'm dealing with.' There was a long pause at the other end, and then the corporal whispered, 'He's called Commander Katsigazi.' I relayed this information to Gordon and Dougie, who told me that I was dealing with the deputy head of Military Intelligence. 'They say he was a great fighter in the war; he's supposed to be quite a tough character,' someone added.

We all went out for lunch at the Nile Grill, an open-air restaurant in Kampala's main street; I felt quite confident that I would not be rearrested since I was with Gordon, Dougie, and a visiting reporter from the *Independent*. The latter was fed up because he had been expecting to link up with Catharine Watson, the paper's stringer in Kampala, but she had instead taken off for Dar es Salaam, leaving him in the less than capable hands of Mike Rukeba. 'He's utterly hopeless,' he told me. 'I've run around with him, paid for all his meals, taxis, everything, for the last two days, and I haven't even had a sniff of a story. I got fed up this morning, and told him to bugger off.' I laughed, and recounted a few Rukeba stories to make him feel better.

In the afternoon, the journalist drove me up to the Speke Hotel, and let me use his room there to file a story for the BBC. The previous night, *Focus on Africa*, which many people in Africa treat as a bible when it comes to news developments on the continent, had featured a story about a West Nile guerilla group which claimed to have taken over large parts of the region, and to have surrounded Moyo, one of the major towns. I had just flown down from there two days before, and knew the story to be untrue, so I was eager to file a refutation. It was also a good opportunity to inform the BBC about my adventure with MI, just in case there was more trouble to come. I sent my story, which was used, but got short shrift from my former BBC colleagues regarding my problems with Katsigazi.

'I'm afraid we can't really do anything to help unless you actually get arrested,' I was told by one of the producers.

'I'll let you know when that happens then,' I said as I rang off.

For the next six days, I was effectively on the run, with the clothes I stood up in, and my passport, which I still had with me. I soon discovered that the police had returned to the Imperial, to order that my room be double-locked so that I could not sneak back inside for my luggage without their knowledge. So at night I stayed at the houses of various friends who were good enough not to make a fuss about the potential risks to themselves. And in the daytime, I returned to the relative safety of the British High Commission, and tried to reach Katsigazi by phone. But Katsigazi proved to be quite unreachable. And soon the Acting High Commissioner, Peter Penfold, still jumpy after Ugandan allegations that the principal witness to the Kayiira murder had spent two nights at his official residence prior to fleeing the country, ordered that no phones should be put at my disposal, either in the High Commission itself, or at the British Council which was housed under the same roof. His directive must have been fairly explicit, because people who had been helping me one minute were summoned to the phone the next, after which they became too busy, or too scared, to speak to me further. The diplomatic cold shoulder is not a lovely thing.

In the end I grew tired of washing the same clothes every night, and trading on my friends' goodwill. My various attempts to sneak into the Imperial unnoticed and persuade someone on the staff to unlock my room having failed, and both my NRM 'friends in high places' being out of the country on official business, I decided to call on a senior policeman of my acquaintance, tell him my story, and ask him to phone the deputy manager at the hotel and instruct him to open my room. How he managed to swing it without giving his name I shall never know, but he did. And so I returned to the Imperial, where the manager in question at first attempted delaying tactics through the lunch hour, but eventually gave the order for my door to be unlocked when I pointed out that neither MI nor the police would be likely to cover my hotel bill.

Before even changing my clothes, I checked through my notebooks. They were all there, apparently untouched, which said a lot for the integrity of both the hotel staff and the investigating authorities. I gathered them together, and sneaked out via the back stairs to drop them at a friend's house: now at least nobody would be interrogating my sources. And I was only just in time, for when I returned to the Imperial, my two police friends from Impala House were waiting once more outside my room, having clearly been tipped off by someone in the hotel. 'I'm sorry, Mr Eddie,' said one of them (the shared drama of the previous week had somehow got us on first-name terms). 'We've got to take you in again. But it really is Impala House this time, I promise you.' I phoned the BHC once more, packed a bag of clothes just in case, and went along quietly. But before leaving, I also phoned a fellow journalist, Jengo, the Ugandan stringer for Agence France Press. To his enormous credit, he dropped everything, and went down to Impala House to meet me.

I was taken to the office of the deputy director of CID, who seemed quite a pleasant chap. He said that he knew nothing of the matter in hand, but that someone else would be coming to speak with me in a short while. We made smalltalk for twenty minutes or so, but presently I heard voices down the corridor, and then the noise of a man walking, but unevenly, as if dragging his foot.

Commander Katsigazi was clearly very impatient, and very angry. He began his tirade even before he had turned the corner and swung his useless leg into the room.

'So you're the man who dares to escape from me when I summon him for investigation,' he screamed.

I never had a moment's doubt that counter-attack was going to be the best defence. 'And you're the man who uses policemen to make his arrests for him, and then has me held illegally in an office of the military.' This was the best I could do under the circumstances. I was preoccupied with trying to keep my voice quiet and calm.

'Illegally? What do you mean illegally? Do you know who you're talking to?'

'Yes, I believe that I'm talking to the second-in-command of Military Intelligence.' I actually began to feel high on the battle of wits that was about to take place.

'Then I would have thought that you would have been well advised to do whatever I asked of you.'

'Commander, with all due respect, your two policemen came for me, told me they were taking me to Impala House, took me next door instead – where my high commission had no knowledge of my being . . . failed to feed me, and then eventually let it be known that I was not actually under arrest at all. Now that's the sort of thing I'd expect in Obote's times, but not now . . .'

By this time, he was spluttering with rage. 'And do you think that if you walked out of there in Obote's times, you would have made it in one piece?'

'No I don't, I'm fairly sure they would have shot me. But it's not his regime any more, thank God, and I think it was quite reasonable, under those circumstances, for me to leave. Besides which, I said that I'd be contactable through the British High Commission, and I was. I've been there waiting for your call for the last six days.'

'You expect me to phone you to ask for a meeting, do you?'

I tried to tone things down a little. 'Well, perhaps that was a bit cheeky, but you've got to understand that I was frightened as well. I've already been arrested and detained once, in 1983. I know how things can get out of hand.'

He was apoplectic once more. 'Things don't get out of hand in this country any more. If you know anything at all about this country, you wouldn't compare now with 1983. And I know all about your past history.' He was tapping a file with my name on it, which he had thrown down on the desk as he entered. Oh my God, I thought, this is serious. At least I had managed to mention my detention before he did.

We continued like this for the next two and a half hours. Talk bounced between us as in a ping-pong rally where both players have got fed up with loopy topspin, and are just trying to bury the ball on the opposite side of the table. Except that we'd bypassed the first stage entirely.

'You journalists, you know nothing about Uganda.'

'Do we hell. Just because you fought in the bush against Obote doesn't mean you're the only one who understands what's been going on here. I've followed your war against the UNLA. I went into Mbale with the first of your units, and saw the bodies of those that Ojuku had murdered lying in the streets where he left them. And I went into Gulu soon after you took that, and saw that there hadn't been any revenge, that not one Acholi had been killed.' This was blatant appeasement, but it also happened to be true.

'Well, if that's the case, why don't you print the truth, instead of all these lies?' Increasingly, it looked as if the *New African* piece was behind all this, and that my visit to Basima House had been merely the catalyst that had started the process. Once more, I made a conscious effort to moderate my voice, which had been getting louder to match his.

'What lies are those, Commander? Come on, why don't you tell me what all this is about? Why have you had me brought here today?'

He threw it back at me: 'What do you think it's about?'

Bull-by-the-horns time; pre-emptive strike. 'My gut feeling is that you suspect me to be the author of the article in "New African".'

He laughed, for the first time. And for the first time I could see that he was a handsome man, fit and slender, slightly rakish in his battle fatigues. I began to like him, despite myself. And the injury to his leg, presumably sustained during the fighting, was something of a badge, a testament to the sincerity and commitment that underlay his fury and his rush of words.

'Is that what you think?' he asked. 'Well, did you write it?'

'No, I didn't. In fact, I haven't written anything for the magazine for almost six months now.' I explained to him that during my last trip to London, I had had a substantial row with the editor, Alan Rake, who had accused me bitterly of siding with the strikers against himself during an industrial dispute at the magazine, and of failing to supply him with articles which I had offered to write. This was quite correct, but equally there seemed little point in resurrecting the issue when the strike had just been settled. In the end I had become so irritated by Rake's self-righteousness that I simply told him that I was sorry he felt that way, and walked out of his office.

I told Katsigazi about all this, but didn't bother to vouchsafe the fact that, at the time of my argument with Rake, my long article on insecurity in Uganda's north had already been accepted by the magazine's deputy editor for publication in the next issue.

9   Graves amidst the *matooke* trees in Katongero village, Kyebe. Six of the ten occupants of this household died in the space of eighteen months, all apparently of AIDS

10   Dick Ssentamu, a former Kasensero fisherman. When this photograph was taken Dick had already been sick for four years with symptoms suggestive of AIDS Related Complex

11   Jimmy Ssemambo outside Kyebe Health Centre. The condoms were part of a consignment which had arrived two years earlier to be sold at subsidised rates to the public

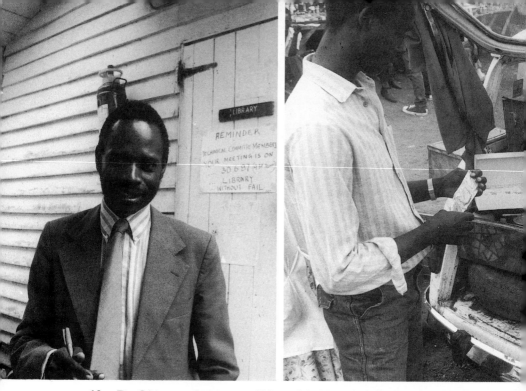

12   Dr Okware, chairman of Uganda's National Committee for the
Prevention of AIDS, and director of the national AIDS Control Programme

13   An open-air market, Kampala: herbal medicines and USAID
condoms are sold from the boot of a car

14   An AIDS Control Programme mini-bus at Kasangati

15   Taking a blood sample at Kasangati

16   Out-patients queue outside Kagando Hospital in a rural part of western Uganda

17   On the main road from Masaka to Kampala, a husband transports his wife's body, wrapped in bark-cloth, to a burial place

18   The TASO project in Kampala, where people can meet, eat, and learn skills such as tailoring. It is this contact that helps relieve much of the feeling of hopelessness and isolation that HIV-positives and AIDS patients share

'I see,' he said, at the end of my story. For almost the first time, he paused to draw breath. 'As a matter of interest, what do you think about the article, then? Is it true, do you think?'

Time for me to draw breath as well. 'Well, quite honestly, Commander, it's difficult for me to say. I've applied to your people in Republic House several times – on three occasions at least, since February – to be allowed to go up north or east into the war-zone. And each time I call, I find that Commander Tumwiine and Dr Bata are up-country, or are busy in meetings. So I leave messages with their secretaries, but nobody ever rings me back. I believe that this is not just the case with me, but with my colleagues as well.'

He was as quick as a ferret. 'So if you admit that neither you nor your colleagues have been up north, how can any of you have written the lies in this article?' And he was brandishing the offending mazagine, which had appeared from inside my file.

'Come on, Commander, that's not fair, and you know it. Whoever wrote that piece quite clearly went to sources who had recently been up north. Whether that information was correct or not is another matter again, but the author had clearly done some homework.'

We carried on batting to and fro. I told him about my Gulu mistake of the previous year, which I don't think he knew about, but I also explained that I had been the author of the Minority Rights Group report on Uganda, which, together with the Amnesty International report, had helped mobilise international opinion against the excesses of Milton Obote's regime. 'Those were the real killing fields,' I said, 'and those reports went a long way towards persuading various Western governments, notably the British, to acknowledge that fact.' I was enjoying my own rhetoric by this stage. The longer we argued, the more confident I became of winning.

It was then that Commander Katsigazi delivered the *coup de grâce*. 'What would you say about this, then, Mr Hooper?' he asked, all innocence, as he pulled a single sheet of paper from my file. It was a letter from Alan Rake to his regular Ugandan stringer, Epajjar Ojulu. On the back of the letter, in a different type-face, was the postscript: 'Won't be able to run your piece in July, because we have a long cover story on Uganda by Ed Hooper. Will try to fit yours in next month.' It was signed, 'Alan'.

'Ojulu didn't give us that,' commented Katsigazi. 'We found it when we searched his office.'

I almost gave up on the spot. I couldn't believe Rake's stupidity, his lack of professionalism. It was a wrench to make myself go on, to at least come up with some visible response. I decided to carry on with the bluster, to buy more time to think.

'Well, quite honestly, I don't know what to say to that. I must admit, it looks genuine enough. But it's just not true.' My voice didn't sound very true, either; not enough conviction. I realised it was time to project a bit, as when recording one's copy into a microphone from a prepared script.

'I can only think – and I know this doesn't seem very convincing – I can only think that either Rake wrote this himself in an attempt to make problems for me after our row ... but I know that's not likely ... I don't think he's a very good editor, but I don't think he'd stoop to something like that either. Or – and again it seems a bit far-fetched – that someone forged the postscript and the signature on the back of this letter. As you can see, it's been typed with a different typewriter, though I must say that the signature' (and here I made a great show of comparing the signatures on either side of the letter), 'yes, I must admit that the signature looks genuine enough.'

Amazingly, it worked. Or rather, it didn't really work, because ten minutes later, after further argument, I decided that my defence was too absurd and was about to confess everything, and lay myself at the commander's mercy, but, incredibly, Katsigazi blew it at what should have been his moment of triumph. In the middle of the interrogation, he suddenly reverted to a furious tirade against me for walking out of his office the previous week. Twice, I tried to interrupt him ('Commander, I have something to tell you') and twice he carried on obliviously. When he eventually finished, almost five minutes later, I realised that he was spent, that he'd shot his bolt. I kept my mouth buttoned from then on. Twenty minutes later we were looking each other in the eye and firmly shaking hands, the two policemen and the CID deputy director were laughing and, slowly, we walked back down the corridor together to where Jengo, bless him, was still sitting on a bench outside, waiting to learn my fate.

Katsigazi took me back to his office in the OAU building, and changed into his civvies. Then he drove Jengo and myself and the two policemen up to the Imperial, because by this stage I'd promised to lend him my copy of the book, *CIA – Dirty Work in Africa*. He took the opportunity to have a quick rummage through the rest of my books, but it was nothing like a search, and in fact I complimented him on his restraint, for not forcing his way into my room during my six days' absence. Finally, I took the party downstairs again, to buy everyone a drink in the Baraza Bar. The policemen ordered beers, but Commander Katsigazi insisted that he would take only a soda. As an army man, he explained, he felt it was important to remain teetotal.

When he eventually left, it was after seven o'clock, and I returned to the Baraza, ordered another beer, and sat back with a wonderful, joyful feeling of relief. I had survived. Various friends and members of the management, who had been discreetly following what was going on, came over to offer their congratulations. Before going up to bed, I popped in to the telephone switchboard behind reception, to tell them that I was taking calls once more. 'Well done Eddie Hooper,' said the telephonist with a grin. 'We're glad to have you back.'

Despite calling on him several times at the OAU building in the days and weeks that followed, I never saw Commander Katsigazi again nor, come to think of it, did I see my paperback. So I'd like to take this opportunity of telling him that I'm sorry I lied to him. My only real excuse is that right then I had a particular reason for wanting to stay in the country, namely to research the rest of this book. I'd also like to say, belatedly, now that I can finally acknowledge authorship of the article, that I stand by every word of it. Not the cover, nor the title, both of which constituted a cheap attempt, for whatever reasons, to sensationalise. But the content, Commander, was well researched, was checked wherever possible, and was stated to be hearsay in the cases where it was not. It was, in short, what you would describe as 'truth' rather than 'lies'. Except that what you really mean by truth is actually something else again, for you have surely grown to confuse that concept with your own personal political beliefs.

And I'd like to add that, while I still believe that the NRA is not abusing the people of Uganda to the same degree as its predecessors, I also believe that it is steadily falling into the same traps of compulsion, tribal discrimination and repression. And that one of the surest indicators of such a tendency is the inability to tolerate any criticism, whether it be made by political opponents or by independent observers. Too many in the NRM regime seem to take the line that 'if you're not with us, you're against us'. And by so doing, they serve only to polarise opposition to, and criticism of, their actions.

18 · GOOD NEWS, BAD NEWS

Probably never before in human medical history has there been a killer of such insidious efficiency as AIDS. The causative virus is so evolved that it attacks the very device – the immune system – which is itself designed to combat disease, so sophisticated that its outer protein coat keeps changing, rendering the development of an effective vaccine highly problematical. Unlike many other viral conditions, AIDS typically takes eight or nine years to develop, during which time a carrier may feel quite healthy, but may transmit the virus to others. And this evolutionary excellence applies not just to the ability of the virus to escape detection, to survive counter-offensives, and to effect the destruction of its host in the most horrible of ways. It seems to apply even to the emotive impact of the disease on those whom it threatens, be they individuals or communities.

AIDS fuels mankind's most deep-seated and primal fears. It passes from person to person through the most basic and intimate of activities – the act of sex, the act of birth, and the mingling of blood – all of them symbols of shared experience since the earliest days of the species. It can also be transmitted through injection – a more recent symbol of health and wealth in the 'developing' world, of hedonism or dependency in so-called 'developed' countries.

In Africa, AIDS strikes at the most valuable sector of society: women in their twenties, the childbearing years, and men in their thirties, the most productive years at work. By contrast, in the West, three of the groups which AIDS seems to favour the most are ones which have traditionally aroused widespread prejudice and victimisation: homosexuals, drug addicts, and blacks. Small wonder, then, that all around the world people have been attracted by AIDS-related conspiracy theories, or talk of Armageddon. Especially when the list of scapegoats has included such hardy perennials as the CIA, the KGB, God and Africa. Members of the press, of course, have been as guilty as any. Much of the foreign coverage of the African epidemic has been hysterical and ill-informed; much of Africa's domestic coverage has been chauvinistic and absurdly defensive.

A good example of the former genre is the infamous article that appeared in September 1986 on the front page of the London-based *Sunday Telegraph*, under the headline: 'African AIDS "deadly threat to Britain".' The article claimed that the British High Commissions in Uganda, Tanzania and Zambia had presented 'a series of alarming reports' to Whitehall about the potential risks to Britain posed by AIDS in Africa; ministers were apparently describing them as 'The Doomsday [sic] Reports'. Apparently, the diplomats had warned that African visitors to the British Isles 'could be a primary source of infection and should be subject to compulsory tests'. An 'Opinion' column adjoining the article alleged, 'The government has been aware of this danger for some months but has not yet acted. This is folly. No one must be admitted from these countries where the incidence of AIDS is much higher than anywhere else in the world without first undergoing stringent medical checks. It would be monstrous if ministers were to hold back from action lest they be accused of racial discrimination. For in this instance there is a positive duty to discriminate.'

The following day, in the *Daily Telegraph*, a slightly more sober follow-up article appeared in which Foreign Office officials were reported as saying that no immediate action was likely. It was acknowledged that 'effective regulations would present huge difficulties' since 'AIDS tests normally take about three months to produce'. (HIV antibody tests actually take more like thirty minutes, but the writer probably meant that to be sure of not admitting any carriers, it would be necessary for travellers to be tested, put in solitary confinement for two or three months and then retested, to ensure that none were in the 'serological window' stage of carrying the virus but not yet displaying antibodies.) The article went on to forecast that decisions would have to be taken about whom to test, and where. 'Would testing stop at black African visitors, or would it be extended to businessmen and holiday-makers returning from these countries? Should testing also be extended to visitors from California . . .?' it enquired tremulously.

On the other side of the coin are features which have appeared in the African press, like the extraordinary piece that was put out by the *Weekly Topic* in January 1987. The headline read: 'Propaganda: Uganda a new breeding ground for racist-sponsored AIDS', and the article was ascribed to 'A Special Correspondent'. The piece claimed that Dr Carswell (described as 'an American citizen') and Dr Goodgame were both CIA agents who, with the collaboration of such as Blaine Harden of the *Herald Tribune*, Cole Dodge, the former UNICEF representative, and even Uganda's minister of health (unnamed), were staging an 'attempt to turn Uganda into a new AIDS belt' by claiming that over 10 per cent of sexually active Ugandans had been infected with the virus. The article went on to assert that 'the energetic and Ugandan President Yoweri Museveni [has] denied any outbreak of AIDS or any epidemic in Uganda,' and added that the 'so-called experts' and collaborators (which by this stage of the piece included 'agents parading as journalists on *New African* magazine' – was this meant to be me? – were 'working as missionaries to prepare ways for the New Colonisation of Africa and possible genocide on behalf of US and Western imperialists struggling daily to put down the African people.'

After the Katsigazi episode, I felt I needed a break from Kampala, so when the SPLA began a new wave of attacks on Ugandan refugee camps in southern Sudan, I decided to go back up to West Nile to cover the situation. I travelled by road, in a relief agency vehicle, and the thirty-six-hour safari made me realise that less had changed in the up-country districts than might have been hoped for. Our vehicle was searched exhaustively at a number of roadblocks – reasonable enough, in that there was a civil war going on – but many of the searchers conducted themselves in that old, unfriendly, truculent manner of people who were looking either for trouble or a bribe. Also *en route*, we witnessed an army lorry which, under its tarpaulin, was carrying a full load of coffee, clearly bound for illegal export to Zaire or Sudan, and, more disturbingly, we saw several trucks bound for Kampala and loaded with new NRA recruits from West Nile, some of them just children aged twelve or thirteen. A group of parents had apparently approached the local army commander in a bid to 'unvolunteer' their children, but had been refused permission to speak with them. When I finally reached Arua, I encountered simmering resentment against the NRA: there was talk of locals being arrested and tortured, of vehicles being commandeered by the army for long periods without explanation, of there being one law for the soldiers, and another for the local populace.

On my last morning before flying back to Kampala, I decided to pay a visit to the famous smugglers' market at Aliwara, situated 5 miles across the border in Zaire, where coffee, gold, dollar bills, even brand-new trucks, were all available for the right price. It was a bad mistake. First I was effectively arrested by Zairean immigration for not having a proper visa (by contrast, the Ugandans were all allowed to cross without papers); then I was taken to Aliwara where the army wanted to arrest me too; and eventually, after paying an exorbitant bribe for a one-day pass, I was escorted back to the Ugandan border by a customs official. On the way, however, I was ordered from the vehicle at gunpoint and lengthily harangued by a local militiaman – his face distorted with drink and *bhang* like a blown brussel sprout – who, it transpired, was just having a little joke for the benefit of his colleagues on roadblock duty.

And there was more to come. That evening, back in Kampala, a wing of the Speke Hotel burnt down in a fire, and I went out to record the drama with camera and tape recorder. I was promptly arrested again, by two plain-clothes security men, and though I protested that I was a reporter, the only thing that saved me from being carted off into the night was the fact that I shouted loudly to the other bystanders and then, as the security boys paused, wrestled myself free and ran back to the Imperial. Later, a local paper reported that much of the furniture which the NRA had helped rescue from the fire was quietly loaded on to army lorries later that night. Meanwhile, I decided that I had better calm down a little. Three attempted arrests in two different countries in the space of twelve hours might be something of a journalistic record, but it was considerably more excitement than I needed.

A couple of days after the Speke fire, I bought a motor-bike. I had been thinking about it for some time, telling myself how it would pay for itself in a matter of months; how I could spend an entire day down at Entebbe interviewing the ACP people, and not have to worry about finding a taxi for the journey home; how I could leave it safely in the Imperial's guarded car park at night. So by the time that I actually saw it in the showroom – a reconditioned Honda 250 trail bike, bright red in colour – I was already half in love. Then when I took it out for a spin, and felt the warm wind in my face as it accelerated along the dual carriageway, and skipped over the potholes, and swerved round the cars lumbering along Kampala Road, I knew that I couldn't live without it. Never mind that it was absurdly overpriced. Never mind that friends with a bit of technical knowledge told me that the forks were bent, that it had obviously been turned over quite drastically in the past. Here was freedom, and I couldn't wait to have it.

To reassure myself that it was money well spent, I upped my work rate. And certainly the bike meant that I could get more done in a day than when I'd relied on a combination of taxis, feet and *matatus* (boxes on wheels, which would cram in as many as twenty unfortunates, and then hare off down their pre-set route at breakneck speeds). My work benefited, but everything else did so as well, for life in Kampala is always something of a hustle, a question of how close one keeps one's ear to the

ground, how quick one is on one's toes – or wheels. Within a week, I'd
received a large sum still owed me in travel allowances from my time
working with WFP in 1981. Over the years, I'd tried to get the payments
reapproved on no fewer than four occasions. Now suddenly there was a
new, helpful representative in charge of the office, a secretary who was
willing to push the forms through quickly, and suddenly I'd covered the
cost of the bike.

Der Spiegel, meanwhile, had phoned once more, and was asking me
to supply background material on four different subjects, ranging from
child-marriages to the refugee repatriation programme. More running
around between different relief agencies, more buying people meals,
and following up of contacts. In addition, there was a veritable flurry of
stories about cattle-rustling, people displaced by the civil war, impending
famine in Karamoja, and the reorganisation of the police force, which
at one stage involved its being disarmed by the army; even the police
chief had his car stopped, and was forced to surrender his weapon. I
kept very busy.

The next time I met Mike Rukeba, it was entirely my fault. I had
spent a liquid ninety minutes at the BHC Club, and had left with
Ron, a British engineer, who was going to pick up his girlfriend and
her sister and take them on to a party at the US Marines' House. He'd
asked me if I wanted to do escort duty, and I'd agreed. We duly collected
the sisters from their flat on Nakasero Hill and, as we returned to Ron's
car, a figure emerged from the gloom on the far side of the street.

'Hello Hooper,' said Mike Rukeba.

It was partly the fact that he had shocked me, coming out of
the shadows like that, and partly that I had already consumed a large
number of White Caps. Whatever, I really went for him.

'Well I never, it's Mike Rukeba. Can't I ever get away from you,
even for an evening? Do you spend your time following people, or
what?'

He ignored the attack completely, and instead continued with his
own special brand of matey obnoxiousness.

'So, Hooper. What are you doing here? Picking up your new girlfriend,
I suppose?'

Suddenly I felt that I'd had a bellyful of Mike, of his artful
artlessness, of his parasitic nature, of his continued appearances in
my life.

'Look, Rukeba,' I said, almost spitting his name out. 'I want you
to know something. Where I come from, at least, it's bloody rude to call

someone by their family name. You don't do it unless they're in school, or in the army. I'm not in either, so I don't want you to address me like that again. Not ever. You can call me by my Christian name, like you normally do when you come round to hassle me over the breakfast table, or if you can't manage that, you can call me Mr Hooper. Have you got that?'

'So you want me to call you Mr Hooper?' he asked, angry himself now.

'I tell you this, Rukeba. From the first time I met you, you haven't stopped whingeing, or wheedling, or trying to get something or other. And now I've had enough; I don't want you hassling me any more. Go off and bother someone else, if there's anyone else who'll put up with you. But stay out of my way; get off my back.'

Mike Rukeba said something under his breath, then turned and walked away. I got into the car, still seething.

'You don't like him very much, do you?' said Ron who, like the girls, was amazed at the outburst.

'No, not a lot,' I grunted back. 'He makes my flesh creep.'

At about this time, 'the energetic and Ugandan President' Yoweri Museveni, far from denying any outbreak of AIDS in Uganda as the *Weekly Topic* had claimed, was actually holding rallies in Masaka and Kyotera in order to advise the populace about the dangers of Slim. His basic message was that the disease was spread through sexual contact, rather than through witchcraft or any other more esoteric route, and that people should limit themselves to one partner. He recommended that young people should get themselves tested for HIV before they got married. He also criticised the use of condoms which, he said, tended to encourage a false sense of security, and perhaps even a corresponding increase in sexual activity. The condom distribution campaign promptly ground, quite spontaneously, to a halt. And less than a week later, Dr Okware, who had flown to Sydney to address a three-day Pacific Forum on AIDS, was stressing that condoms were a problem because of Uganda's cultural beliefs and traditions, that they were 'associated with prostitutes', and that people 'believe it is like eating a boiled sweet with the wrapper on'. Again, on his return, the good doctor assured the local press that condoms were considered 'simply a desperate extra-precautionary measure ... nobody has any intention of flooding the country'.

The chairman of the NCPA evidently had a good sense of where the butter lay on his slice of bread.

*

I decided that it was high time that I paid a proper visit to the people at the AIDS Control Programme in Entebbe. I arrived at the brand-new building one day soon after lunch, but in spite of the fact that all the key officials had by now transferred into their new offices, the place was almost deserted. I did, however, bump into one of the senior figures from the Ministry of Health who was not directly involved with the ACP, and he showed me something I hadn't seen before. It was a Goods News Bible, supplied and distributed free by the Baptist Mission of Uganda. Pasted inside the front cover were two inserts, entitled 'Medical Science Answers Five Questions Relating to AIDS', and 'God's Word', doing likewise. The scheme, I was told, was the brainchild of Rick Goodgame, who as well as being a senior physician at Mulago, was also chairman of the Baptist Mission in Uganda. In this, his latest project, he appeared to be on much firmer ground than when giving interviews to the BBC and the *Herald Tribune* the year before.

The first insert, being the medical answers, detailed the nature of the disease, its presence in Uganda, the lack of a cure or a vaccine, and the ways in which it was possible, and not possible, to become infected. Quite rightly, it stressed the risks of multi-partner sex, but some of the answers were ponderously non-controversial, such as this on the epidemiology: 'In some parts of the country an increasing number of healthy young people are infected.'

But it was God's answers to AIDS which were more interesting to a layman like myself. The questions concerned such issues as God's plan for sex and marriage, the individual's responsibility towards those having the disease, and eternal life for those dying of it. Each question was followed by a number of pieces of advice, each referenced to an appropriate passage in the Good News Bible. The first answer, for instance, read, 'Sex is only for husband and wife together; sex outside of marriage is foolish and deadly. Proverbs, 5.' And the biblical passage in question included the following: 'The lips of another man's wife may be as sweet as honey and her kisses as smooth as olive-oil, but when it is all over, she leaves you nothing but bitterness and pain ... Keep away from such a woman! Don't even go near her door ... She will take you down to the world of the dead ... You will lie groaning on your deathbed, your flesh and muscles being eaten away, and you will say, "Why would I never learn? Why would I never let anyone correct me?" ' In view of the fact that over 90 per cent of Ugandans are regular church-goers, this seemed an important initiative in the process of familiarising people with the risks of AIDS, though I did rather miss the wormwood and two-edged sword of the Revised Standard version.

Since the ACP building was still virtually empty, I decided to pay another visit to the once-renowned Virus Research Institute on the far side of Entebbe. It is beautifully situated on a grassy slope overlooking one of the bays of Lake Victoria, and I was lucky enough to find the director, Dr Sempala, present and willing to give me an immediate interview. I presume that he had not, at this stage, heard about the *Sunday Sport* article which had appeared some six weeks earlier; if he had, I'm quite sure that he would probably have refused me, or any journalist for that matter, an audience. But that little tale comes later.

With some pride, Dr Sempala told me that the VRI was to be set up as a national reference centre for AIDS, and that there were hopes of developing it as the headquarters of a regional network. He told me that the institute already had two different ELISA machines installed, together with a Western blot for confirming presence of the virus. Results so far, he told me, indicated 'one hundred per cent correspondence' between the results gained on the various tests, even with different technicians carrying out the work. This was an unheard-of claim, for such testing nearly always involves a small proportion of false positives, false negatives and 'borderlines', and it also conflicted with what his technicians had told me on my previous visit, when they had voiced concern about procedures. But for once I didn't argue.

He also told me about the serological surveys. Firstly there was one just beginning at Kasangati, which would be completed by the end of August; to find out more, I should contact Dr Konde-Lule at Mulago's Institute of Public Health. Secondly, a series of sero-tests had been completed just three weeks before at hospitals all over the country, at the behest of the ACP. And lastly there was a national sero-survey due to start in a few days' time, which would involve the taking of 10,000 blood samples from all over the country. The VRI and ACP were already training technicians in the correct sampling techniques, and tests would take place in a hundred different clusters subdivided into appropriate strata (capital, urban, semi-rural, rural and suchlike) and substrata (western, central, eastern and northern). The whole process was expected to take between six and eight months, so that by early 1988 the ACP should have a fairly accurate idea of where HIV was present on a countrywide basis.

Dr Sempala then told me about the plans for constructing a P3 laboratory, where the immunodeficiency virus could be isolated, grown, purified and characterised. A P3 lab is only one step down from the sort of isolation facility available at Porton Down, and I have often wondered exactly why Uganda would be needing such a thing: presumably it was important to test the HIV strains found in Uganda against those being encountered in Europe and America. He added that game wardens around the country were being asked to collect chimpanzees, so that a colony could be started at the institute. I later heard that the primates were to be artificially infected with HIV, and then used as an animal model for the testing of vaccines and herbal preparations. President Museveni was known to be personally interested in the research, and Uganda itself was financing it, which would help divert criticism from bodies such as the World Wildlife Fund.

As I rode back from the VRI, I thought just how pleasant it was to come across someone like Dr Sempala who didn't treat every bit of AIDS-related information as if it was marked Top Secret. And the success of the interview persuaded me to try once more at the ACP building before heading back to Kampala. As I walked in, I caught Dr Okware just leaving his office. He was unusually helpful, providing me on request with dates and venues for various forthcoming conferences and seminars on AIDS control. When some of these later turned out to be incorrect, I merely put it down to the changes of arrangements that are always happening in Uganda, and usually for very good reasons. It is only now, when I check back through notebooks and diary, that I find that just about every piece of information that he gave me, including dates, venues and durations, was comprehensively wrong.

After Museveni's statements about AIDS in the south-west, I decided that it might be a good time to apply for a formal interview with His Excellency, or 'H.E.', as African presidents tend, respectfully, to be known. I duly phoned the Presidential Press Office at State House, and got through to Hope Kivengere, the President's press secretary. I explained who I was, and she told me, rather coolly I felt, that I should submit my questions in writing, through the Ministry of Information. So I spent half a day drawing up questions, until I had arrived at what seemed an acceptable balance between gentle lobs and nasty googlies; I went over the wording half a dozen times, until it felt just right. I particularly liked the one which read, 'Mr President, you were formerly renowned as a guerilla leader, and you have now been Head of State for over eighteen months. Are compromises inevitable on the way from the bush to State House? If so, which ones have you had to make?' I finished typing, and hopped on the bike to see if I could catch Jack Maumbe-Mukwana at the ministry.

He was just leaving for home, but instead he called me straight through into his office. Firstly I told him about my unpleasant experience with Commander Katsigazi. I explained that in the end nothing untoward had happened, but that I had been very close to being expelled from the country 'over a mistake'.

'I kept phoning you up, Jack, but they told me you were out of the country.'

'Yes, that's right. I was away for ten days on official duties. How unfortunate that it should have happened just then,' he commiserated. I had already learnt that his trip had taken him to eastern Europe, and wondered once again why ministerial visits to the East were almost never mentioned in the press, or openly acknowledged.

Time was drawing on, and his brief-case was clearly packed and ready for the off, so I handed over my questions for H.E. Then I asked him if he would mind taking a quick look to check that I hadn't been too strong, hadn't gone over the top, diplomatically speaking. He glanced through and, rather to my surprise, ignored all the telling questions about Slim disease, three-piece-tying, the illegal detention of lodgers, the continuing recruitment of young teenagers into the NRA, and the perceived existence of a tribal élite in army and government. Instead he homed in on my question about the alleged divisions between radicals and moderates in the NRM.

'What have you heard about that?' he asked.

'Nothing very much apart from rumour,' I answered.

'I was just wondering. Being a deputy minister, one doesn't always hear about these things,' he said, still fishing. It was the first time I had glimpsed a little guile beneath his friendly exterior.

'Why, do you think that the question will cause me problems with the President?' I asked, concerned.

'No, not at all. I'm sure he'll be happy to answer all your questions. We are an open regime; we have nothing to hide. Just wait a week or two: I'm sure you'll receive a call to State House.'

But all of a sudden, I had the very strong presentiment that I would not.

I had always, I thought, enjoyed a friendly relationship with the staff of the quasi-Marxist journal, the *Weekly Topic*. Shortly after the NRM takeover, I had given them a lengthy feature I had written about the first month under the NRM regime, which included some dramatic reports from the front line, and from the former torture chambers in Nile Mansions; they had used it as a centre-spread. And later in 1986, when I had been writing a feature article about the Ugandan press, I had featured the *Topic* and its deputy editor, Charles Onyango-Obbo, both prominently and favourably, describing the newspaper as probably the most intelligent in Uganda. However, having been with Sue in Kenya at the time, I had completely missed the 'AIDS propaganda' article of six months earlier, and was thus blissfully unaware of the minefield I was entering when I invited the *Topic*'s editor and his deputy to join me for lunch that Sunday at the Imperial. They arrived with another man, an Asian, whom they described as 'one of our regular correspondents'. As I led them through to a table in the Baraza Bar, I was expecting a nice lazy lunch and an opportunity to exchange views about a number of pressing issues.

But it was not to be. From an early stage, the conversation became polarised along racial lines, something which I'd hardly ever before experienced in Uganda. I happened to mention the anticipated famine in Karamoja. The editor, Wafula Ogutu, promptly asked me what I thought that the international aid agencies were up to in that area. I asked what he meant. Eventually it transpired that he was referring to the gold that was being panned in the streams of the Karamojong hills; European relief officials were involved in smuggling it out of Uganda, he claimed. I asked him what evidence he had, and he refused to elaborate.

'Have you been up there to see for yourself?' he demanded.

'No,' I answered, 'I haven't been up there since 1982, but I know several of the Europeans now working in Karamoja, and I'd be very surprised if any of them was involved in smuggling.' But Wafula was unmovable: 'I know they're doing it,' he insisted.

Soon the conversation turned to the subject of AIDS. There had been a lot of coverage in the local press at around that time, relating to three individual issues. A Ugandan travelling on an invalid diplomatic passport had been arrested whilst attempting to smuggle 80 pounds of marijuana through Gatwick Airport, but subsequently released without charge and deported back to Uganda when it was learnt that he was an HIV carrier. And, at around the same time in early August, the Ugandan Commissioner for Immigration had announced that henceforth, foreign nationals found to be suffering from 'infectious diseases like AIDS' would be required to leave Uganda; this followed the announcement at Washington, two months earlier, of similar immigration restrictions for the US, and the first deportations of HIV-positive African students from countries such as India. But the actual timing of the Ugandan announcement seemed to have been prompted by the much-publicised arrest of an Australian construction worker 'on suspicion of spreading AIDS in Mbale town'. Local papers described luridly how girls known to have been consorting with the man were being shunned by family and friends; how the town's bars were nowadays 'deserted'. Eventually the man was tested for HIV at Mulago, and found to be seronegative.

He was released amidst vague threats that he would sue both the Ugandan government for false arrest, and *New Vision* for libel.

The third issue had sparked an even more heated controversy, though it was clearly destined to lead up a blind alley. An energetic debate had begun in the pages of several newspapers as to whether HIV could be spread by such communal activities as drinking from the Holy Communion cup, or sharing drinking straws while imbibing local brews like *tonto* and *malwa*. Dr Okware had entered the debate, only to get himself into hot water. First of all, he had refuted an earlier report to the effect that saliva could not transmit the virus. 'The fact is that saliva may contain the virus and as a result could possibly transmit the AIDS infection,' he was quoted as saying. On the same day the Anglican Bishop of Namirembe was reported in another paper as advising his congregation that until such time as the saliva issue was resolved, each piece of communion bread would in future be dipped individually in wine.

The following day, Dr Okware gave a fuller explanation of the medical evidence in the *Topic*. He explained that the AIDS virus theoretically existed in all bodily fluids, but that there was no epidemiological evidence that either saliva or sweat, which contained only very small quantities, were means of transmission in practice. 'If it were true that Slim can be transmitted by saliva, why is it that the elderly believers above sixty years, who rarely miss Holy Communion on Sundays, are not vulnerable to the disease?' he was reported as asking. 'Because the AIDS viral dose in sweat is also very small, one will not catch Slim by shaking hands with a sweaty infected person,' he added. Unfortunately, the piece appeared under the misleading headline: 'No "Slim" in saliva or sweat says Dr Okware.'

This caused even more problems, so Dr Okware wrote a letter to the *Topic* which appeared in the following week's edition – and which actually served to complicate the debate even further. In it, Okware repeated that theoretically the virus could be transmitted through saliva, and then added that the presence of abrasions, cuts and mouth ulcers would increase the likelihood of such transmission. 'In view of the high prevalence of infection by the AIDS virus in urban areas the risk through the oral (mouth) route could be potentially significant,' he wrote. He went on to say that the Ministry of Health had therefore advised against the sharing of the communion cup, and that he himself would advocate the principle of 'one man, one straw' during *malwa* sessions. It was apparent that once the chalice had become an issue, Okware and the ministry were inevitably manoeuvred into a failsafe position that only added unreasonably to people's fears.

The chalice issue also served to raise temperatures around the table that Sunday lunch-time. After the first article appeared, I had communicated Okware's concern about the headline to Wafula and his colleagues, and it was now apparent that my intervention had been viewed as interference. Suddenly the Asian, who had hardly spoken up to this point, turned to me and asked where I thought AIDS came from. Sensing a trick question, I replied that nobody had any proof about its origins, just as nobody could say when or where syphilis, or influenza, had first appeared on the planet. But my three lunch companions would not accept this as an answer; they insisted that I should say how and where I thought AIDS had started. Eventually I said that the body of current medical opinion appeared still to favour the theory of an African origin for HIV, possibly as a result of crossover from a similar immunodeficiency virus in a creature like the green monkey. It was just what my colleagues had been waiting for. I had failed the test of the ducking-stool: I was a heretic.

Suddenly all three were speaking at once. All the old arguments and objections came flooding out: but their basic content was that I was a racist, looking to scapegoat the people and the continent of Africa. The Asian, in particular, was quite beside himself with fury. Although he was sitting beside me, not 2 feet away, he was by now virtually screaming, and droplets of his spit were splashing in my face. On the other side of the table, Wafula and Charles were also shouting to make themselves heard. People at other tables turned around to see what was going on. It took some time before I managed to break in long enough to ask them what their own theories were.

Again, there was uproar, but the major ideas that emerged were that AIDS had emanated from America, where it had first been identified; that it had probably originated from a germ-warfare experiment which had gone disastrously wrong, or which had involved the deliberate release of the virus amongst certain target populations by the CIA; that it had started as a homosexual disease which had then been spread to the heterosexual African population via the promiscuity of Western tourists; and that a lot of the Africans now being diagnosed with AIDS were actually 'false positives' who were sick with other diseases. I pointed out that even if as many as half of those diagnosed seropositive in East and Central Africa were actually false positives, the levels of infection being found strongly suggested that the virus, however it originated, was now travelling outwards along the trucking routes to the main ports like Mombasa and Dar es Salaam, rather than inwards from the coast. 'And that's the sort of thing you're going to be writing in your book?' Wafula demanded. 'They'll never let you out of the country with it.' The others laughed in approval.

For the purpose of this argument, it was clear that I, as a *muzungu*, was felt to be on the side of America and the CIA, of the baddies who were trying to blame Africa. I resented this implication, as I resented the accusation that I was racist, and now my voice was growing as loud as the others. The four of us were getting out of control. Nearby diners were making shooshing noises, and urging us to calm down. The head waiter, clearly eager that we should leave, came across very promptly with the bill; by this time, we had fallen into an angry silence. Wafula, perhaps a little embarrassed, suggested that we should all pay for ourselves, but I insisted that it had been my invitation, and that I would pick up the tab. 'Oh well, if you can afford to pay . . .' he began, as if this in itself was evidence of iniquity. 'Well gentlemen, I think we've all had enough,' I said, as I pushed back my chair and headed off towards the exit.

Since the argument with the *Topic* journalists, I have taken the opportunity of looking into the question of the origin of HIV and AIDS more closely, and on one level I have to agree with Dr Pinching that the subject tends to lead up a blind alley. The debate has prompted some of our battier scientists to insist that the virus was engineered in a laboratory, or brought to earth by a meteorite, and that HIV's rapid spread in Africa was caused by the WHO Smallpox Eradication Programme (a claim rapidly disproved by the fact that Uganda's smallpox programme began in 1972, and that by 1987 near-zero seropositivity had been encountered among Ugandan children up to the age of fifteen, save for those born to already-infected mothers).

In addition, the suggestion that HIV 'began' in Africa has caused enormous defensiveness and anger on that continent. However, this response is hardly appropriate in that no reasonable person can blame a particular group or race or nationality for a virus or disease. Fecund tropical climates happen to be more successful at spawning life-forms, including viruses (and including *Homo sapiens*), than are temperate ones; this does not, however, mean that people living in tropical areas are responsible for this evolutionary process. The important point here, of course, is that some Africans, rightly or wrongly, have *felt* themselves to be stigmatised, and that perhaps one should be sympathetic to such sensitivities (which, with my colleagues from the *Topic*, I failed to be) even if one does not defer to them.

On other grounds, however, African anger is entirely understandable, for some of the early AIDS research done by Western scientists in

Africa was both inaccurate and misleading. In 1984 a team led by the American, Bob Biggar, tested a number of Kenyan tribes, and discovered very high levels of HIV-positivity among all of them, notably over 50 per cent among the Turkana, in the remote north-west of the country. Meanwhile another American, Carl Saxinger, was announcing that blood samples taken from children in Uganda's West Nile region in 1972 revealed that some two-thirds had been HIV-positive. The implication of both studies was that HIV was endemic to Africa. Only later was it revealed that almost all these apparently infected sera had actually been false positives, in Biggar's case because the testing method used (direct ELISA, rather than the competitive ELISA commonly employed nowadays) also reacted positively to malaria and other parasitic infections, and in Saxinger's because blood samples had become 'sticky' due to frequent thawing and refreezing. Whatever the subsequent explanations, the fact remains that the scientists in question failed to carry out sufficient checks, and ignored circumstantial evidence – such as the lack of any actual AIDS cases from these areas – that should have made them suspicious of their findings.

After the publication of these medical papers, and prior to their being discredited, all sorts of theories were put forward to explain why so many Africans apparently had HIV, including the proposal that this was a result of widespread but clandestine homosexuality, or the frequent use of anal intercourse as a contraceptive method and a means of protecting female virginity. In actual fact, doctors working in Africa report an almost total lack of anal sores or lesions among African populations, which effectively disproves such theories. But in the light of such flawed research and half-baked conjecture, it is hardly surprising that some Africans doubted the veracity of later, more reliable work which found high levels of HIV among urban adults.

However, there is another level at which the debate about origins is entirely valid. For if scientists could determine, even approximately, the environment in which HIV 'began', if they could locate a species which carried an immunodeficiency virus without getting disease, or a human community which had acquired a degree of resistance to HIV, then such discoveries might have important implications in the search for a therapeutic treatment for AIDS, or even an HIV vaccine.

The best clues to the history of the virus are those provided by epidemiological research. The earliest blood sample to give convincing HIV-positive reactions to a variety of retrospective tests was drawn from an unidentified subject in the Zairean capital of Kinshasa in 1959. But this is just a single sample, which could conceivably have been tampered with or mislabelled. Of greater significance are the thirteen blood samples taken from both urban and rural parts of Zaire between 1970 and 1976 which have since given reliable HIV-positive reactions to two different testing methods. Also of interest is the case of the Norwegian sailor who, together with his wife and youngest child, died of AIDS in 1976; the man had first fallen sick as early as 1966, prior to which he had visited several African ports, where he had contracted STDs at least twice. It must be noted, however, that there is also conflicting epidemiological evidence, notably that provided by the case of Robert R., an American teenager (and presumed homosexual) who died in St Louis in 1969, and who is the earliest confirmed AIDS fatality from anywhere in the world. Robert had no known African connections.

With the exception of Robert R., the earliest certain cases of AIDS cropped up seemingly independently in the United States, Haiti, Europe and Africa at around the same time in the second half of the 1970s. However, other circumstantial evidence is strongly suggestive of an African origin. Firstly, many of the early cases of AIDS in Europe involved people who had been born in, or resident in, Africa. Secondly, HIV infection is more widespread in Africa than in any other continent, with higher seropositivity levels encountered in the centre of the continent than around the coastlines and other ports of entry. And most compelling of all is the fact that the human immunodeficiency virus actually consists of a range of slightly different viral strains, of which Africa presents a far greater number than do the other continents; it would therefore seem likely that the virus has been present there longer.

It can therefore be said with reasonable confidence that HIV, while neither endemic nor widespread, was already present in different areas of Zaire during the early 1970s and probably before that. So how did it get there? HIV is a member of the family of retroviruses, whose genetic material contains RNA instead of the more usual DNA; because of the high error rate during replication, they evolve perhaps a million times faster than normal viruses. Numerous other mammalian species are carriers of similar retroviruses. At some point in time there must have been an ancestral virus, a 'protovirus', from which these present-day retroviruses subsequently evolved. Different scientists propose different family trees. Some believe that the protovirus must have existed in a primate species, perhaps the African green monkey, or the sooty mangabey monkey, both of which are host to strains of simian immunodeficiency virus (SIV) that do not cause actual disease in those species in the wild, though they do cause an AIDS-like illness when artificially introduced into another monkey species, the macaque. Others think that the protovirus host could have been another non-primate mammal, such as a cow, cat, horse, goat or sheep which was close to man in physical rather than evolutionary terms.

Most scientists seem to believe that the HIV we see today first appeared fairly recently, though opinions differ as to how it achieved its present form. It could have involved the fusion of two other retroviruses to create a new virus which affected humans; it could have been a gradual process of mutation from a harmless 'passenger' virus; or mutation could have occurred when the animal host of another retrovirus either bit, or was eaten raw by, a human, thus allowing the virus to 'cross over', or adapt, to a human host. Given the faster evolutionary capacity of retroviruses, mutations could well be occurring all the time.

For instance in 1985 came the discovery in West Africa of a slower-acting, less pathogenic human immunodeficiency virus, which soon became known as HIV-2. Most scientists would agree that the geographic distribution of the HIV-2 epidemic means that this particular virus did originate in Africa. But in terms of genetic structure HIV-2 is only distantly related to HIV-1 (as the 'original' HIV is now known), and neither is it very closely related to any of the SIVs (despite an early American report to the contrary, since discredited after it became clear that there had been viral contamination in the laboratory). There are thus still some missing links, or missing branches on the family tree.

So much for the likely origin of HIV; but why the sudden explosive worldwide epidemic of AIDS? An interesting medical study published in 1988 showed that HIV-prevalence in an isolated rural population of northern Zaire remained constant, at 0.8 per cent, for the ten-year period between 1976 and 1986. Using this as an example, one can visualise how a strain of HIV could exist undetected in a remote human community for some time, causing a few unremarked deaths from opportunistic diseases, but basically held in equilibrium by conservative sexual mores which hampered its onward transmission. And one can then imagine what would happen if the virus encountered a change in its habitat – perhaps because one infected person moved from a village to a town, or perhaps because the remote region was opened up by the building of a road. Whatever, the viral 'seed', to use Dr Pinching's metaphor, might then find a new, richer 'soil' in which to grow, perhaps in the local town or city. Thereafter, it may be imagined that the explosion in cheap air travel which began in the early 1960s could have played a crucial role in propagation. The next stage would come when a number of seeds found their ways to ideal patches of fertile ground such as those provided by the gay bathhouses of San Francisco, the back-street 'shooting galleries' of Edinburgh, and the trading centres and battle-zones of post-independence Africa. Such amplification systems would simply toss the seed skywards, to allow the winds and breezes of the planet to do their work.

In the latter scenario, however HIV 'began', it is the two new factors which are introduced to the equation almost three decades ago (cheap air travel, and the relaxation of sexual and behavioural mores in the 'swinging Sixties') which spark the global epidemic of HIV. It is worth noting that, over the last thirty years, SIVs have also been spread around the world. In this case the culprits have been the international medical laboratories, which require ever-increasing supplies of monkeys for research purposes.

And having written this, I must defer to the wisdom of the Zambian President, Kenneth Kaunda, when he says: 'What is more important than knowing where this disease came from is knowing where it is going.'

19 · THE FIRST SURVEY

Although I had known for over three days that she was on her way, it still hit me like a stomach-punch when I saw Sue sitting, smiling at me, from the other side of the Baraza. I had spent much of those three days devising ever-crazier plans for avoiding her, from flying down to spend some weeks in Kenya or Tanzania, to (in the depths of the night, this) going to the border and bribing an immigration official to keep her out of the country. Nevertheless, as soon as I saw that smile, I couldn't help but smile back. I walked across to her table, shook hands and asked how she was, before explaining that I was busy, and would have to go; I would see her around. My reticence had the desired effect, for she seemed upset.

But that was about as far as I got with the arm's-length plan. Later that evening, I went back downstairs and invited her to join me and another friend for dinner; she said she'd love to if we ate there, in the Baraza, so that she could stay with the friends who'd brought her up from Nairobi. I said that I'd already arranged to go to another restaurant, which was true, and so we parted. But the following evening, as I was returning from a long day of buzzing around town, she came running up the hotel steps just behind me. I repeated my dinner invitation, and this time she accepted.

We went to the Palace, which had always been our favourite restaurant. It was situated on the first floor of an office block, but to get there in the evening one had first to negotiate a series of corridors illuminated only by candles stuck to the cement floor. Upstairs, however, the large room was well lit and pleasantly decorated. Indeed, the very acceptable Chinese and European cuisine made this the leading restaurant in Uganda, better by far than any similar establishment of the previous ten or fifteen years, since the collapse of the economy during the time of Amin.

We had not been seated ten minutes before we started the old game.

Sue seemed to think that we could simply begin where we'd left off, five months before. I felt that we had first to establish a few ground rules.

'Eddie, I want to get married,' she suddenly announced.

'Well, that's nice for you. Anyone I know?'

'What are you saying?'

'You haven't said who you want to get married to,' I said, emphasising the long vowel sounds, and suddenly feeling in very good humour.

'You are joking with me . . .' (the eyes downcast now) '. . . you know who to.'

'No, I don't know who to, Sue.' It was impossible to escape those owlish vowels, and I felt like laughing. But I resisted the impulse, and instead carried on sternly, pressing home the advantage. 'And quite frankly, I'm amazed that you can come back to Kampala after we haven't seen each other for five months, and just come out with something like that. Because I tell you this, I don't mind having one more try at you and me living together, but this has really got to be the last. If it goes wrong this time, then that's it. Finish. What do you say? One more trial run.'

She was still looking down at the table. 'Yes,' she whispered.

'I'm sorry, I couldn't hear you,' I bullied.

'Yes, Eddie. I want to try again.'

A deep breath. 'Fine. Good. But if you start messing me about like you did before, telling me stories and seeing other men and all of that, then I've got news for you, because you and your bags will be outside my door before you have time to sneeze.' I didn't know who had written the script for all this, but I was certainly enjoying playing it.

'I won't mess around. I promise,' she said, and her eyes were wet as she looked up from the table.

I looked at her for some time. 'OK, then. We'll give it another try. Let's see if we can do better this time around.'

Presently she raised her glass in the air, and touched it to mine. 'Hello, Eddie,' she said, pushing her face forward across the table, so that I was forced to look at her. I couldn't help smiling, despite myself.

'Yeah, yeah. Hello Sue.'

I had already decided that, for the rest of the year, I would leave my other feature work, and devote my time to researching the AIDS book. And the next item on my agenda was to follow up on Dr Sempala's suggestion, and monitor the progress of the first large-scale HIV sero-survey and questionnaire on AIDS to be conducted in Uganda. Generally known as 'the Kasangati survey', it was being co-ordinated by Joseph Konde-Lule, a courteous and capable Muganda doctor from the Institute of Public Health at Mulago. I arrived at the institute, as directed, at eight o'clock in the morning, and was escorted by Dr Konde-Lule on to the AIDS Control Programme mini-bus that was just about to leave.

It was a mere half-hour journey to the trading centre of Kasangati, along a tarmac road that, despite its occasional potholed sections, was generally in excellent working order. Dr Konde-Lule explained to me that the study would actually be undertaken in two different rural locations, at Kasangati 10 miles north-east of Kampala, and at Nsangi, a similar distance to the south-east, on the Masaka road. Some 2,000 interviewees were to be asked, at each location, a total of twenty-six questions concerning their *knowledge* of how AIDS is transmitted, their *attitudes* to the disease and to those whom it infected, and their *practices*, either cultural or sexual, which might influence transmission. In addition to this so-called 'KAP study', a sample of blood was to be taken from each person interviewed. In all, there were five teams of three people conducting the survey, and each interviewer was expected to complete up to twenty questionnaires and take a similar number of blood samples every day.

Soon after leaving the hospital, we passed a few shops, a cluster of potholes, and the bustle of activity that denoted a small trading centre. Despite the early hour, a number of predominantly young people, who from their clothes and general mien appeared to be mainly *magendo* hustlers and bar-girls, were hanging around with no particular place to go; disco music was fuzzing out from somewhere, through speakers which had long passed their prime.

'We haven't taken blood from there,' commented the doctor, 'but let me make a generalisation. Wherever you have an area which is inhabited mainly by young people who are just renting rooms, rather than living at home, then this is quite commonly an area of high promiscuity. And wherever you have a lot of promiscuity, you are likely also to have a high infection rate.'

I asked Dr Konde-Lule about the recent debate about condoms which had been prompted by the President's statements in Masaka and Rakai.

'Well, the President feels that the AIDS Control Programme has been rather sluggish at controlling the disease, and he has stated that he is opposed to the use of condoms. He has not gone out of his way to ban them, but he wishes to go on record as being not in favour of them. He says that we haven't done enough research to ascertain their usefulness, and that we don't know how protective they actually are. And I think he's probably right.' The very fact that Dr Konde-Lule was able, within earshot of numerous colleagues, to discuss and analyse the views of the President, was a telling indication of how much more free the man in the street, or the mini-bus, felt since the overthrow of Amin and Obote – particularly if the street or the mini-bus was situated in southern Uganda. But the doctor was not finished.

'He feels – as someone was jokingly saying – that for a condom to really protect, it should maybe cover the whole of the body!'

'What does he suggest as an alternative, then?' I asked.

'Well, he advocates more health education, and says that people should retain their known cultural values, and stop copying the Western habits of promiscuity, which are not so common in traditional African culture.'

'Is that entirely fair, though, Doctor? Don't you think that urban areas – like the trading centre we've just passed – would be promiscuous places whether or not Uganda had once been a British protectorate?'

'Some people here would actually classify AIDS as a colonial disease. In African traditional culture, boys and girls were never able to play around, because they had to get married: boys when they reached eighteen years, girls at around fourteen. In the colonial culture, people don't get married until much later than this. This in itself tends to encourage promiscuity, and when copied in our culture, it has had the same effect.'

As we rolled into Kasangati trading centre, and stopped outside the New Tex Night Club And Lodging, I was still thinking about the great divide in Ugandan society. The great majority of God-fearing, church-going Ugandans, the old and the middle-aged especially, still tended to their *shambas*, or dutifully sat at their desks in the ministry or wherever, and then, dignity intact, collected their paltry salaries at the end of the month. But the young, those who had grown up during the past twenty years or so, had received a host of free and memorable lessons about the transience of human life and the impermanence of possessions. And after such a practical education, many of them did not want to hear about the new minimum wage of 300 shillings a month; they knew that it represented just 5 US dollars at an official rate that was never obtainable when one wanted to purchase at the bank, or, more realistically, just three bottles of beer or loaves of bread in the market-place. They knew that this amount could be made many times over in a black market deal, or tucked quietly into a girlfriend's hand as one walked from her door in the morning. And so they left their family homes in the village, and decamped to the big city, or at least to the local trading centre, where they could do *magendo*, rest and play to their heart's content.

The colonial influence, the introduction of a monetary system, the desire of the colonial authorities to attract pools of cheap labour to the towns (African men, but not their families), the corresponding growth in prostitution, further contact with Western ideas from James Bond movies to Coca-Cola, the collapse of the official economy, the boom in the black economy – all were factors in the new rootlessness, the easy-come-easy-go lifestyle that, twenty-five years after independence, seemed to permeate not just urban Uganda, but the urban areas of the greater part of sub-Saharan Africa. But had such factors made Africans more promiscuous than other people? Some Western observers had raised eyebrows when a survey of African AIDS patients in Rwanda and Belgium had revealed a lifetime average of thirty-two sexual partners; in Uganda a similar study had come up with a figure of eighteen. And yet, in terms of promiscuity, such figures were probably far lower than those of many gay men in the West (where a study of twenty-seven US homosexuals with AIDS reported an average of 120 sexual partners in the twelve months preceding the onset of symptoms), and perhaps equivalent to those of many heterosexuals in their mid-twenties in New York, London or Hamburg. In the end, I thought to myself, there was almost certainly no hard statistical evidence to back up either the Third or the First World version of the promiscuity myth, for accurate sexual data was notoriously difficult to procure. But it seemed possible that promiscuous behaviour was pretty much the same the world over.

The mini-bus stopped outside a small brick house in the parish of Seeta. In front was the *oluja*, the mandatory Kiganda front garden, a patch of bare earth which is swept clean each morning with a twiggy broom. At its three corners, the interviewers and their subjects were sitting facing each other on wooden chairs, the questions and answers flowing quietly to and fro like smalltalk. Another group of people waited patiently on the *baraza*, or front balcony of the house. Birds were moving in the trees, and chickens scratching the red earth. We seemed a hundred miles from Kampala, rather than ten.

Dr Sozi agreed to let me ask her a few questions as she took a blood sample from a middle-aged woman. The doctor was working quickly: already she had completed ten of the questionnaires in two hours, at a rate considerably faster than the thirty minutes officially allowed for each interview. She said that most of the adults in the village were amenable to taking part in the survey, and that many had been waiting their turn in the queue since early morning. The interviewers could give medical assistance to interviewees when requested so to do; they could also supply condoms to any of the boys and young men who asked for them, and who were already familiar with their use. It appeared, however, that no condoms were handed out to women, lest their husbands should suspect them of adultery, and sue for divorce. The only real problem they had encountered, said Dr Sozi, was that some people feared that they might be infected with the virus through the very needles used for the extraction of blood samples: that the researchers might be reusing the needles, and pocketing the surplus. It was a very Ugandan neurosis. (Later on in the survey, to allay such fears, each interviewee was apparently given his or her own needle to dispose of as they chose, the pit latrine being the suggested method.)

About half an hour later, there was a torrential rainstorm, and I took shelter on the *baraza* with Dr Konde-Lule; we watched as the downpour subsided into a soft, persistent plashing of the small pond that now covered the russet-coloured forecourt. Presently I asked him if he was learning anything interesting from the preliminary results. How many sexual partners, for instance, were people saying they had had in the last half-year? He told me that most of the older people, especially the married women, said that their spouse was their only partner, whereas the young people in the survey had had, on average, between two and five partners in the previous six months. Some of the young men, in particular, were laying claim to over ten partners, while a few alleged that there had simply been too many to count. And, since they had discovered that some of the girls were sexually active at the age of thirteen (there had been several local cases of girls giving birth at fourteen), they had had to lower their age limits for respondents accordingly.

Most of the people interviewed, the doctor added, were not using condoms.

'Generally, they're not available, or have not been encouraged in the past, though in the few areas where they've been introduced, the young people have really gone for them. What it's shown us is that if they have condoms they'll use them, but if they don't have them, they'll do it anyway without. I suppose this advocates for the distribution of condoms,' he added, 'especially for those young people who cannot desist from playing sex.'

Later, the whole team of interviewers, as well as myself, were invited into a local home to take lunch. The food was good and wholesome: steaming-hot *matooke* and chicken portions in a rich sauce of onions and tomatoes. We ate with our hands, a pleasant change after the endless servietted niceties of the Baraza Bar. As ever in Africa, there was laughter and easy conversation as we stood around the dining-table, dipping our nests of *matooke* in the thick gravy. As ever I, as a foreign guest, was treated with especial kindness and solicitude. The choicest cuts of chicken were always being nudged in my direction.

The next day, I rode back up to Kasangati trading centre to get some photographs of the interviews and the blood-letting beneath the trees. Later I attempted to interview a young man who had just completed the questionnaire, but was prevented by a local cow which proved that this was indeed a rural area by nudging me repeatedly in the back. Eventually I had to admit defeat, but I decided to repair to the local restaurant for some refreshment before the ride back to Kampala.

I ordered tea and cakes, and then got talking about Slim with Joseph, the man sitting at the next table. It turned out that he was a proof-reader for a local newspaper. My recorder was still out on the table, so I invited him to join me for some tea, and for 'a chat into the microphone'. Joseph surprised me by declaring that engaged couples were now getting tested before they got married, or staying faithful to each other for six months, and then getting checked; I began to suspect that he was saying the things he thought I wanted to hear. But when I asked him about condom usage, he gave an interesting reply:

'If a woman hears that a man is using condoms, she is scared.'

'Why is that?'

'They say it can remain in the body, and one can die. So there is a fear of using these things.'

Before this had fully registered I heard a snort of laughter from the waitress, who had obviously crept closer to listen to the conversation. When I turned to speak to her, she promptly retreated into the gloom at the back of the café. But slowly I enticed her closer, though she still held a hand up shyly to cover her mouth. Then, amazingly, she blurted out a question.

'I'm asking you, sir, why don't you keep those people who have Slim in one place?'

It took a couple of moments before I realised what she meant.

'You mean so they can't come into contact with anyone else? But how would you feel if your brother got Slim, and was taken away and locked up? He wouldn't be able to see you, or his wife, or the family, until the day he died. Would that be fair?'

But the girl was unimpressed by this shameless appeal to sentiment. 'It's good because if that person knows he's got Slim, he just keeps on loving those girls and just giving them Slim, because he doesn't want to die alone.'

'Do you know any boys who have done that?'

'No – I've just read about it in the newspapers ... that there's a certain man who gave ten thousand shillings to a girl, and after they had finished playing sex, he told her that ...' (and here she dissolved into giggles once more; we calmed her) 'he told her, "I have got Slim, and now I have given you Slim. That's why I gave you so much money." '

But for all her gaucheness, the seventeen-year-old waitress was better briefed than Joseph about matters like condoms. She had a boyfriend, she told us, just the one. She didn't know if he had other girlfriends. She didn't use condoms, but she didn't fear them either. 'I've heard that if you use them, you won't be attracted to Slim,' she explained, her delightful grammar and the egocentric thinking of the young now coalescing. If only it was like that, I thought: if it was we humans who could decide if we were attracted to Slim or not. Instead of which, it's all down to a virus, to the smallest of organic particles.

'They say your girlfriend is having Slim,' said Sue, when I got back to the hotel that afternoon.

'Which girlfriend is that now?' I asked, trying not to nibble.

'I think she is calling herself Margaret. She is Rwandese, like me,' she added helpfully.

We soon established who we were talking about. Her name was indeed Margaret, she was Rwandese – or at least Munyarwanda, and therefore from a people who had formerly lived in that country – and she had indeed been an occasional lover of mine in 1983, and again on one occasion in March 1986, a couple of weeks before I met Sue. She had a classically beautiful face, a small, erotic figure, and she was totally unreliable, being quite unable to keep a date. Much questioning elicited the information that Margaret was said to have Slim because she was thin, and because she had suddenly gone back to her village some months before and had not been seen since. I pointed out that Margaret had always had a 20-inch waist and the litheness of a ballet dancer, and left it at that, feeling that Sue was probably trying to wind me up a little about my past affair. I didn't take the gossip too seriously, for slender women, traditionally less sought after by African men than their plumper sisters, were these days also the butt of some fairly heavy-handed jokes.

My less sceptical side, meanwhile, kept nagging me with the thought that there might be, as was so often the case, some kernel of truth in the rumour. And if there was, then there were obvious implications for both myself and Sue, never mind the negative HIV tests that we had both had since. Later that night in bed I told Sue that, in order to be on the safe side, we had better get ourselves tested once more. By chance, I was already due to see Dr Konde-Lule the following morning, and he readily agreed to give me a letter to the Nsambya Hospital laboratory. Before lunch, Sue and I had both transferred 5cc of our finest red to a syringe held by Sister Nellie Carvalho.

The days passed busily enough as we waited for the results to come through, and I realised that things between Sue and me were better this time around. We were happier, we gave a lot more to each other, trust seemed to be building up again. Then one morning, I think it was about ten days after her return from Kenya, Sue refused to get out of bed, despite the fact that I had explained that between eight o'clock in the morning and six o'clock at night, my room was an office rather than a meeting-place or a boudoir. Eventually, after the third time of asking, I pulled back the covers, and lifted her, gently but firmly, into the bathroom. She spent the next hour in there, while I got on with some writing, but she was still seething by the time she emerged. I let her complain for some ten seconds, and then I blew.

'OK, Sue, that's enough. You know we agreed that this time we were going to do things my way. I told you that I wouldn't have any messing around. Well, a few days have gone by, and it seems that we've started all over again. So, I think you'd better just pack your bags and get out of here. Your friend Patrick is still here at the French embassy: perhaps you can go and stay with him. Maybe he's fool enough to put up with all this nonsense. But I'm not. I've had quite enough of it.'

'All right, I will,' she snapped back at me. 'He never tries to make me get up when I don't want to.'

'Well, that's nice for you. I'm going to go out now. Make sure that your bags are out of here by the time I come back tonight. And leave the keys at reception, please.' As I walked out the door, it crossed my mind that Sue might take her revenge by disappearing with some of my belongings. And yet I knew that it would never happen; it was just not her style. The only item that I would lose, I realised as I whistled my way down the front steps, was my much-loved girlfriend.

All day, I was preparing myself for the awful emptiness that I would feel when I got back to the hotel. The keys were waiting for me at reception, and I unlocked the door to find her bags all packed, and stacked neatly against a wall. Presumably someone was picking her up later, I thought. But then there was a knock at the door, a very tiny knock, and immediately I knew what had happened. As I pulled back the bolt, I felt a great burst of excitement. She was standing in the corridor looking sad; without a word, I waved her into the room.

'So what about Patrick?' I asked, cruelly. 'Wouldn't he have you back this time?'

'I am not seeing Patrick. I am here all day waiting for you,' she sniffed, and then she began crying in earnest. I took her in my arms, and her small shoulders heaved as I held her tightly to me. I felt that uneasy conflict of emotions that a weeping woman always evokes in me; that odd blend between tenderness and triumph, emotion and cold calculation.

Later, I had to phone *Stern* magazine about a story I was doing for them, and when I'd finished, I saw that Sue was examining one of the 'Zero Grazing' posters which I had left on the table. It was a very literal interpretation of the message, one of Grace Ochero's early efforts, I assumed. It showed a long-horned Ankole bull tethered to a stake, and munching away at a landscape of luxuriant grass, which was cropped short to the ground in a circle around him.

'What does it mean?' asked Sue. 'The cow makes pee-pee on the grass, so we mustn't eat it, or we'll get Slim?'

'What a disgraceful suggestion,' I said. But although she was joking, I'd heard enough misconceptions about AIDS at Kasangati to realise that too many things which seemed obvious to those in the know are anything but obvious to those who aren't. So I carefully explained the zero grazing message; Sam Okware would doubtless have been proud of me.

'So that means,' said Sue, moving closer against my shoulder, 'that I have to stay with you, and you have to stay with me?'

Oh well, I thought, as she nuzzled my chest, and I rubbed my chin against the top of her head: I always was a sucker for the corny bits.

'Yes, that's about the size of it,' I said.

'I'm not going to leave you, Eddie,' she said, after a while.

The last time I saw Mike Rukeba was for just a few seconds, as I was parking my bike in a busy street in the town centre.

'Hello Mister Hooper,' said someone from a few yards further up the pavement. The sarcasm that underlay the word 'Mister' left me in no doubt as to who it was.

'Hello Mister Rukeba,' I replied in kind.

'I feel sorry for you,' he said. So, at least he's decided to hate me, I thought; that's a definite improvement on being his friend.

'Well, that's just fine, Mike, because I feel quite sorry for you too.' Again, there was the unmistakable ring of the playground about all this, but nothing else sprang readily to mind.

'You'll see,' he said, walking past me now, and off down the hill. 'But I pity you. I really pity you.'

He was round the corner by the time I had finished locking the bike. My first instinct was to go chasing after him, to grab hold of him, ask him what the hell he was talking about. But in the end I decided to let it go; making a scene in the street can only cause problems. But I also felt a twinge of fear; he must have felt pretty sure of his ground to have threatened me in that manner. But that, clearly, was his intention, I reasoned; he was just taking revenge for my unpleasantness of the other night.

It was only later, when I looked at the papers, that I saw that he was front page on *New Vision* once more, this time reporting from Soroti, which no other journalist had managed to reach for several months. So, he clearly had friends in the army, friends who were ready to take him up to the war-zone as reporter for the official government newspaper. Times had certainly changed. The article itself told of another attack by members of Alice Lakwena's Holy Spirit Battalion on Soroti railway station, some 4 miles outside the town. Of a total attacking force of 750, over 400 rebels had been killed and four captured. The NRA, by contrast, had suffered two fatalities and six injuries.

Over the past few months, the Holy Spirit Battalion had become well known throughout Uganda, largely due to the army's press briefings. Alice herself was a twenty-seven-year-old Acholi, the daughter of an Anglican catechist, who had apparently received the gift of second sight in late 1986. She and the spirits who spoke through her had such powers of persuasion that as Alice passed through the villages of Gulu, and down through Lira and Soroti, she was able to enlist thousands of young men, and boys as young as even six years of age, to join her messianic crusade against the NRA.

She told her followers that the oil and ashes with which they covered their bodies would make them invisible to bullets, and that the stones they clutched in their hands would explode like bombs when they threw them. They believed her, and with each new attack, hundreds more of them chanted hymns, clapped their hands, and ran straight at the NRA's guns. A few of her fighters had proper guns; others carried sticks, knives, or axes; but many were completely unarmed except for the magic stones. In the course of one year, over 5,000 of them were mown down by the army. Lakwena claimed that those who died had been those whose faith was weak, and astonishingly, she always seemed able to persuade more recruits to take the place of the dead. It was the sort of extraordinary story which could only be told in Uganda.

And it was no mere Radio Katwe stuff. Alice did indeed exist; an American contract worker had once met her at Karuma Falls, and had even driven her and two of her followers part of the way to Kabalega, the next waterfall downstream, where she apparently had to dip her Bible in the water before starting on her divine mission. Her followers existed too, whether alive or dead, as Mike Rukeba's report made abundantly clear. But many of us were beginning to wonder why the NRA did not simply move in and capture the remaining rebels, or even destroy them from the air with helicopter gunships. It seemed so convenient that the most active rebel movement in the north was apparently intent on a constant round of recruitment and mass suicide. And yet, even when one's opponents were running into battle largely unarmed, the figures of 400 dead and just four prisoners testified to some quite remarkable marksmanship from the NRA ranks.

The only clue in Rukeba's article as to the real sequence of events comes in paragraph seven, where a Tanzanian rebel who has already provided him with six whole paragraphs of quotable material subsequently dies 'of bullet wounds'. Rukeba, who was presumably invited up to Soroti by the army as a usefully compliant pair of eyes and ears, deserves credit for daring even to mention the incident. But it was the only hint he gave of what really happened: that NRA soldiers walked around the battlefield shooting dead the wounded rebels, even those with only minor injuries, where they lay. The NRA's Eastern Brigade Commander, Tom Kyarigonza, was apparently present at the time. Rukeba, I have been told since, was 'quite shocked' by the executions.

20 · THE MAN IN THE WHITE MERCEDES

A few evenings later, Joseph Konde-Lule called on us at the Imperial. Our part of Kampala was experiencing one of its periodic power cuts at the time, and we had already passed him in the candle-lit corridor before he recognised my voice, and called out. 'I've got some news for you, Eddie. And, I believe, for your friend,' he added, nodding towards Sue, whom I promptly introduced. From his cheerful and chirpy manner, I knew straight away that everything was all right, and sure enough he confirmed that we had both tested seronegative. We thanked him for his kindness in dropping by, and invited him to join us for a celebratory drink, which he declined, explaining that he was urgently required at home for some zero grazing. We wished him green pastures.

Sig Hansen, an American with striking ash-blond hair, was the East African representative for the voluntary agency known as the Experiment in International Living. For more than two years, he and I had been bumping into each other in places like Addis Ababa and Khartoum, and usually we would end up spending a memorable evening on the town. He was excellent company: a kindly man, intelligent, with an unexpectedly anarchic sense of humour.

Now that we were both resident in Kampala, we saw each other more often, and when Sig invited me to join him on a two-day trip down to Kyotera, I jumped at the chance. He himself wanted to monitor progress at the Kiteredde Construction Institute, an EIL-backed project where people were being taught new methods of building houses from locally-available materials. This sounded interesting, but I was also attracted by the fact that I could do some further research on Slim. And I was downright excited when I learnt that we would be staying with the Banakaroli Brothers, who claimed to be the first and the largest indigenous Christian order in Africa. The reason for my eagerness was that I had been hearing that one of their number, Brother Anatoli Wasswa, was an expert in the field of herbal medicine, and in the treatment of *endwadde enganda*, which roughly translates as 'complicated diseases which people had previously thought to be incurable'. One example of *endwadde enganda* was, of course, Slim.

'You'll like him,' said Sig. 'I suppose you've heard that he casts out witches as well?'

But when I asked what he meant, he went quiet on me. 'You'll find out soon enough. I'm not going to spoil your fun.'

When I met him next morning, Brother Anatoli, the chaplain of the Banakaroli Brothers congregation, did not impress me very much, at least not to begin with. He had been with the order for forty years, and was now presumably in his sixties; he spoke the sort of English that sounded as if it was being translated, word by painstaking word, from the Luganda. The interview that I recorded with him is slow and monotonous – which is a shame, because the work that he was doing was a fascinating blend of the traditional and the innovative.

'I am a herbalist, and I have done this for the last five years,' said Anatoli, as if reading from a prepared script; in fact, his style reminded me of my own performances in the recording studio. I got the impression that he had briefed a lot of *mazungu* about his craft in the preceding months. 'My intention or objective? Well, before the Europeans came, our ancestors used to treat themselves or their people; they had a lot of herbs that helped them. But after a time, when the European type of medicine was introduced, this medicine of ours was forgotten, and many of the special trees disappeared. And I feared that in the future we would lose them. That's why I now collect all kinds of trees and plants, to develop them and get good medicine.'

Anatoli proceeded to show me round his clinic, where he tended to an average of fifty patients a day; he explained that he charged people between 5 and 100 shillings, depending on their income and their course of treatment. There were only two small windows, one of which had been blocked by a cupboard, and after the bright sunlight outside, it was difficult to see for a while in the gloom. When my eyes adjusted, I realised that there were wooden shelves running from floor to ceiling along two of the walls, and that these were stacked with neat piles of labelled plastic packets. Anatoli explained that these were herbal preparations for different complaints and conditions: asthma, stomach problems, high blood pressure, pregnancy, infertility and so forth. There were also some heavy oblong objects, shaped like fat salamis, which he said were clays, containing as many as twelve different types of medicine.

The clay preserved the herbs within for twenty years or more; all one had to do when one fell ill was shave a little off the end, mix with water, and drink.

I picked up a packet and asked him what ingredients were inside, but he admitted that he couldn't remember all the names, since some of the medicines contained as many as five different constituents. Then I asked how he knew that his medicines worked, and he replied proudly that he had already cured more than twenty women who had previously been infertile. Finally, I enquired whether he could help people with Slim. Anatoli answered that his herbs were able to treat many of the symptoms of AIDS successfully, including diarrhoea, skin rashes and sores, lack of blood (presumably anaemia), and 'too much water' in the body. 'We have many kinds of medicine we can use so that a person feels better,' he assured me.

But he was also very careful not to make any exaggerated claims. He kept repeating that he wanted 'some expert doctors' to be appointed to assess the efficacy of his medicines in the laboratory. 'Because if we are really curing our patients, then we can start on the others.' He showed me a letter written by a visiting Swedish doctor from the Traditional Medicine Programme, based at WHO in Geneva, relating Anatoli's claim that 'a certain herbal concoction used in the treatment of AIDS patients with well-defined clinical symptoms has led to a drastic improvement in the patients and, in a few cases, to a total remission of all symptoms over a twelve-month observation period.' The Swedish doctor further suggested that help be offered Brother Anatoli in terms of botanical identification of his plants, and examination of their chemical constituents. But, as I discovered later, no further action was taken by Geneva, where the TMP people were complaining that their budget had been cut, and that all WHO's money was now being spent on the Special Programme on AIDS.

Ugandan Ministry of Health officials had also called on Brother Anatoli on several occasions, often to show foreign visitors his work, and there was talk of possible funding for a thirty-bed hospital in the mission grounds, so that Anatoli and his team could tend to people on the premises. There were also plans for a collaborative programme with the NCPA, and in fact Anatoli went up to Masaka that very afternoon for discussions with Dr Lwegaba. Unfortunately the doctor failed to keep the appointment, and Anatoli returned to the mission disappointed. But that is how things go in a society that is recovering from chaos. Somebody's cousin dies, a funeral has to be attended a hundred miles away, phone lines are down, letters take a month to arrive, people turn up for appointments that are broken, time is wasted, the injured party shrugs, and the matter is put off to another day.

Later, Brother Anatoli told me how the local diocese had originally given him the mission of studying the traditions and culture of Uganda. 'But mainly the culture was based on medicine and healing, because when a person is suffering, he can do whatever he is told, and many were being misled.' He paused, and I started to ask a question, but then realised that he was just turning an internal page.

'In Africa – I don't know if it is the same in other parts of the world – those people who knew the medicine or the herbs, called the native healers, took advantage of the people, and told them that their diseases were caused by the spirits of their ancestors, because someone had had twin children and so on. And these witch-doctors, as we call them, claimed to have supernatural powers, so they could practise their wicked tricks to deceive the people, and take all their money or cows from them. And this was really a great danger to the sick person. That is why I now try not just to cure the sick, but to tell them where their disease comes from.'

Anatoli spoke to a young novice in Luganda, and the man hurried away, to return shortly afterwards with an enormous sack. He emptied the sack on to a bark-cloth mat which Anatoli had laid out on the balcony.

'These are some of the things which the witch-doctors use to deceive people during the night, to pretend that the spirits of their ancestors are speaking to them,' said Anatoli.

The charms and magic tokens were piled high on top of each other: here a wooden spear, or a miniature fishing boat, there a piece of cowhide with cowrie shells sewn into it, or the neck of a local guitar entwined with plastic beads. There were bells, gourds, drums, canes, cow-horns: it appeared that almost any object could be 'witch-doctored' for the purposes of magic and superstition.

I asked how much such people charged for their services. Anatoli replied, 'I found an AIDS victim last week, and they had taken twenty cows from him. They told him, "The spirits are sucking blood from you." The patient has nothing to decide, he gives away whatever he has, until he is left empty. Even the clothes, the cows, hens, money, all is taken from him.'

But Anatoli was growing visibly more weary with the effort of speaking English, and my own momentum was winding down as well. So I was grateful when we returned to his clinic, and he gave me a copy of an article which had appeared three months before in *Exposure* magazine. Written by one Henry F. Mirima, the piece concentrates on Anatoli's confrontations with local witch-doctors, and however idealised the account may be, it is frank and revealing to a degree that no interview between Anatoli and myself could ever have achieved. I am therefore indebted to Mirima for the information that follows.

To be successful, witch-doctors apparently needed to be able to keep secrets, imitate people, and be well versed in natural psychology, Mirima wrote. They operated always in the dark and in secrecy – normally in their own locked houses, late at night. Many of these houses were fitted with bark-cloth screens and false ceilings to conceal the witch-doctor's assistants, who would make sounds, or appear in different guises, at appropriate moments in the consultation. From the start, supplicants were told that if they didn't co-operate, the spirits would shy away, and an atmosphere of fear would sometimes be created by an assistant beating the floor, or the supplicant himself, with a cane, or by another positioned outside who would throw stones on to the roof.

The witch-doctor and the supporting cast, who were often sons or other relatives, made sure they were up-to-date with local gossip, and also adept at assuming the voices of local inhabitants, past and present. Thus, they found it easy to answer the supplicant's questions, or to convince him or her that their ancestors were communicating from the ether. Once the session was in progress, the 'spirit' would demand a goat, a chicken, or money, before he was willing to continue. Again, local knowledge came in useful: if it was known that the supplicant had a cock with a red crown, then that was the gift that would be requested. If, on the other hand, the witch-doctor's wife wanted a new dress, and her favourite colour was purple, then the spirits would explain that suitable medicine could only be prepared by someone sitting on purple cloth.

Later in the consultation, the supplicant would be told the cause of his problem; very often it would be revealed that one of his known enemies in the village was to blame. Perhaps a magic charm would be prescribed, such as an amulet of wood which had to be worn at all times, and the magic might well have to be 'recharged' at intervals, which would involve more cocks and purple dresses. Sometimes genuine herbal remedies were provided, for many witch-doctors had also become expert herbalists. If, however, the problem was ascribed to something as serious as a curse, then the spirits might even demand a new house for the witch-doctor, and a goat for him to slaughter there every new moon. The final clincher in terms of the witch-doctor's inviolability was, of course, that any who revealed the secrets of his house would themselves be cursed, in one of a variety of unspeakably nasty ways. All in all, I thought, it was hardly surprising that when Slim first appeared in the area, half the local population immediately put it down to the witches.

When I'd finished reading Mirima's article, I realised what a courageous service Anatoli had been doing for the community by exposing so many of these charlatans. Apparently over a hundred witch-doctors had already surrendered their magic paraphernalia to him, and confessed their deceptions to packed churches in the district; some of the more prominent had even been taken to address the congregation at Kitovu Cathedral in Masaka. This quiet, hesitant old man had actually been waging Old Testament battles with the forces of evil. But wisely, Anatoli, or his superiors, had realised that some of the witch-doctor's powers could be put to positive use, and hence the witchfinder-general was also the herbalist. 'Our traditional medicines are good, and in many cases better than modern medicine. Come and practise openly,' Anatoli was quoted as saying, at the end of the article. And such skills, of course, were now being used to combat the effects of that most Old Testament of all the diseases.

Soon after leaving Anatoli in his clinic, I came across Brother David, who was looking after Sig and myself during our stay, and who had returned from town with some important news. Apparently the local police and army were mounting a manhunt for someone driving a white Mercedes. They had followed him from Kampala to Masaka, where he was believed to have spent three days, and he was now thought to be trying to escape through Kyotera to Tanzania. Two roadblocks had been set up on the main road south.

'And what has he done, this man?' I asked.

'Well, this was a rich man who became a victim of Slim. And they suspected that he might have been buying women at very high costs, fornicating with them, and then telling them that he had given them Slim. This man didn't want to die alone,' said the brother, with a huge smile. He clearly felt it was a marvellous story.

Not only the story, but even the words had a rather familiar ring, for this same anecdote, of 'the man who didn't want to die alone', had appeared in a Kampala newspaper some days before, and had then been recounted by the waitress at Kasangati. I proposed to David that someone must have just arrived in Kyotera with the paper, and that rumour had done the rest. He was not convinced.

'It was not rumour, because I got the information from the policemen themselves who put the roadblocks around our place. My thought is that one of the women he met before may have reported him to some

authorities who ordered soldiers to come and look for him. I suspect
they may have arrested him around Kyotera.'

'Are you sure about that?' I asked.

'No, I am not very sure,' replied David, still grinning like a Cheshire
cat. I realised he was laughing at himself, at me, at the story, at the
morning. He was sixty years old, and he was still as free as a teenager.

I met Sig for lunch at the Kiteredde Construction Institute, and
afterwards recorded a running interview with four of the trainee
teachers, as they escorted me around the demonstration site. It was a
fascinating project: twenty-five new trainees were taken on every year,
and taught how to build sound, attractive houses exclusively from local
materials. The walls were made from eucalyptus poles and mud, and
were finished off beautifully with a plaster of pure liquid cow-dung and
pulverised ant-hill. The roofs, made to last five years, were of grass and
banana fibres, or else papyrus tied with sisal. And the houses really were
cheap. Even the two-storey version, designed for local yuppies, cost only
20,000 Ugandan shillings, or 330 US dollars at official rates; it took ten
people three months to build. Clearly much of the construction involved
techniques which had been employed in Africa for centuries, but the
refinements produced a stronger, better finished end product, and KCI
houses were now appearing all over Rakai district, as graduates from the
institute disseminated their knowledge to the villages. 'KCI teaches skills
– and skills can't be stolen at a roadblock,' commented Sig.

Christine Walusimbi, a prominent district official, had called in for
some discussions with Sig, and afterwards I got talking to her about
recent developments in Rakai. I asked about Bob Kagoro, the former
DA whom I had interviewed at the Colombo just over a year earlier,
and who had since tragically died of his mysterious illness. 'It wasn't
AIDS, anyway,' said Christine. 'He didn't get slimmer at all – in fact,
he was swollen like a balloon!' I noted that opinions were divided fairly
equally about the cause of Bob's death: those in the civil service or
the NRM all insisted that it had not been Slim, while all the other
local people I spoke to took the opposite view. It was only later that
I discovered that a local newspaper report at the time of his death
identified his fatal illness as herpes zoster which, I am told, is over 90
per cent predictive of AIDS in an African man of his age and level of
fitness. But whatever the cause, it is sad that such a fine and motivated
man died so young.

To begin with, Christine Walusimbi took the 'correct' line on every
issue: there had been many AIDS fatalities in Rakai during 1984 and

1985 because the regimes of Obote and Okello had brushed the epidemic under the carpet, but since the new government took over, there seemed to be 'less death', she assured me. There was now a high level of awareness about AIDS in the villages, she claimed; many people were aware that the disease was fatal, and were observing zero grazing. There were two health educators operating out of Kalisizo Health Centre, and riding around the villages on an old motor-bike; health education pamphlets and posters were being widely distributed; and officials like herself, in the course of their normal travels around the district, were explaining to people how to combat Slim, and selling them boxes of USAID condoms at highly-subsidised rates.

'Do you really think sexual habits have changed, in the hotels of Kyotera, for instance?' I pressed her.

'This can be very well seen. The girls, who were so many in town before, have already left for other towns, because they found out that they had lost their market. And this has left the boys who want to roam about without any girls to move with.'

'That's also sad, though, because some of the girls were undoubtedly infected, and have now spread the disease to other parts of Uganda.'

'That is very true. Some of them have already been seen in places like Kampala and Jinja.'

I turned off the recorder for a while, because I felt that Christine was beginning to talk more openly, and I wanted to encourage her. By the time that I resumed taping (with her consent), she was telling me about the popularity of women from the north-western part of Tanzania.

'They are so dynamic; they can never refuse any man who approaches them; they can go with him just like that. Particularly those that come from Bukoba.'

'What is so special about them, do you think?'

'They are very beautiful, very attractive. In the way they talk and the way they look, a man can just be taken. And they are also very brown, and most men of our place here prefer brown ladies. Also, the young men do say that there is something special about them, but nobody has ever told me what it is!'

This seemed to be a good point at which to broach the delicate subject of how much formal prostitution there was in Uganda. Fortunately by this stage Christine had grown used to the microphone, and was relishing her role as an authority on Ugandan sexuality.

'Well, I would think it is maybe about five per cent, that is where a girl would go and sit in a hotel, or wait on the road, for someone to pick her up. But otherwise, this formal prostitution is not very pronounced in this country.'

So how would you describe the relationships that take place between men and women?'

'It's more of a sort of secretive exercise between the two concerned at that particular moment. But there is very little faithfulness. Once it is finished, the two can definitely go and have other partners, and again it is very secretive, and so on and so forth.'

'And is there some financial involvement at some level?'

Christine roared a deep laugh, from the belly. 'Yes, very much so. Especially the women do expect a lot from the men if they are involved in a sexual relationship. A man is likely to give a woman something in terms of money, a dress, a pair of shoes, or something like that. And this is apart from those who actually earn their living from selling their body to the men.'

'If a woman doesn't get some material token of the man's affection, what does she think?'

'It depends how many times she will be with this particular man. But if she is to be with him several times, she knows that at one time in the future she will be getting something. Not every time, but at some point in the lifetime of their relationship.'

'Christine, which sex do you think is more responsible for spreading diseases like Slim?'

The answer came quick as a flash. 'The men, because the men move more than the women. A man can have four or five women in a day, whereas very few women can have such a ratio of men.'

I began laughing as well. 'And how many men do you know down here who have four or five different women in a day?'

But Christine was indignant at my scepticism. 'About ten,' she said.

'Really? Is that before drinking or after?'

'Some of them don't even take a drop of beer. They just concentrate on women. We say that's their business.'

I am indebted to Christine Walusimbi for both her official and her unofficial versions of the 'state of the district'. My own admittedly sporadic observations in the villages at around that time did not really bear out her optimism about the health education campaign, which I felt to be only just easing into first gear. But I must say that I agreed wholeheartedly with her Ugandan Kinsey report, except perhaps that her 5 per cent figure for formal prostitution, even if taken as a percentage of sexually active females, was probably too high. Such a percentage would, I think, apply only to places like Kyotera which were centres of commercial dealing, together with truck-stop towns like Lyantonde and Lukaya, and certain suburbs of the big cities.

*

It was now late afternoon, the light was clear and the shadows sharp, and I asked one of the drivers if he would ferry me around Kyotera so that I could take some background photographs. It was clearly something of a wild west town, a beehive of huts, shacks, shops and small businesses, the whole dominated by the petrol station on one street, the Milano and the Colombo hotels on the other, and a few slightly more down-market lodges along the roads in between. Kyotera had been virtually destroyed by the Tanzanians during the 1979 war, and hence almost every building was new. This lack of architectural heritage only added to the town's irresistibly tacky character.

A dozen or so barrow-boys were ferrying bunches of *matooke* to and from the market area; there was a line of six or seven lorries, some of them revving their engines in readiness for an evening run up to Kampala; spare parts and jerricans of fuel were laid out on sacks a few feet back from the road. Maribou storks hopped about among the rubbish, while small naked boys – *totos* – scuttled around in the dirt, chasing chickens or, as is the way of African *totos*, screaming when they saw the *muzungu*. Everywhere there was energy: music, drunkenness, laughter, shouting. Two teenaged girls sitting back to back on a tailor's bench posed instantaneously, smiling and smoothing down dresses, as they spotted my camera peering out of the open car window.

Some ten of us had arranged to meet up at the Las Vegas bar, a smaller establishment which had opened in early 1985, on the coat-tails of the two big hotels, and at the wrong end of the boom. Sig was there with his driver, as were a couple of the Banakaroli Brothers (who sounded more and more like a team of acrobats), the four trainee teachers from KCI, and Christine Walusimbi. Lingala music played softly, though the volume was turned up as the night drew in and the place filled up. Overhead, a brass fan swung ineffectually; a single green light bulb lent the room a rather bizarre atmosphere.

The evening wore on, Nile Specials were consumed, and conversations became franker. I was told, almost wistfully, about the scene in Kyotera during 1984 and 1985: how many of the rich men 'who could afford to buy their sex and pleasure' used to come down from Kampala to spend their weekends at the Milano and Colombo; how 'girls of loose morals were drawn there like a magnet'. Now, I was told, the hotels were merely assets on a balance sheet; if they could be picked up and moved lock, stock and barrel to Kampala, then the owners would be very happy men.

I asked about death rates for the district, with its population of just over a quarter of a million people, and most of those around the table agreed that the figures of two or three AIDS-related deaths each

day, and a total number of 2,000 to 3,000 AIDS fatalities since the start
of the epidemic, were reasonable. But one person insisted that just at
Kalisizo Health Centre, which I had visited with Wright and Rukeba a
year before, it was now commonplace for two, three, or even more
cases of AIDS to be clinically diagnosed every day. Meanwhile, nobody
had heard the story I had come across in February, of the boastful
witch-doctor who himself succumbed to Slim, though everyone knew
of a local healer living some 2 miles away, whose sign claiming that
he could cure the disease had been torn down by a posse of indignant
neighbours. I wondered if these were not merely different versions of
the same story. There was, however, another herbalist from Lyantonde,
one Lukwago, who was spoken of with greater respect. The Catholic
newspaper *Munno*, which had the biggest circulation in Uganda, had
apparently printed an article claiming that he had developed a cure for
the disease.

Finally, late on in the evening, I asked one of the KCI lads if
there was, as Christine suspected, some special attraction about the
girls from Bukoba.

'Oh, you mean the BK girls,' he said immediately. (They were
apparently so called because of the car number plate from Bukoba, but
also because of the Kiswahili phrase *'biashara ya kuma'*, which roughly
translates as 'those who sell their vaginas'.)

'There is nothing that we do not already know about over here,' he
said, with obvious pride. When I asked him to elaborate, he mentioned
kachabale, a practice which is commonly thought to have originated
among the Batoro, a people from western Uganda whose women are
famed throughout this part of Africa for their beauty. They are also
famed for their particular lubricity, something which they are wont
to exploit in bed by straddling the man, grasping hold of his erect
penis, and flicking it to and fro between their labia, an activity which
produces both the sound, and the sensation, of an omelette being
beaten. A skilful practitioner can not only bring herself to orgasm
with minimal participation from the man, but can control his orgasm
also, through a sequence of squeezing him tightly, and determining the
point at which he is allowed to revert to normal intercourse. *Kachabale*
had now become highly popular throughout Uganda, Rwanda, Burundi
and northern Tanzania, and we debated as to whether it was contributing
to the establishment of a matriarchal society in those places, such was
the unusual degree of control which it afforded women in the bedroom.
I also wondered whether bruises or lesions sustained during particularly
energetic bouts of *kachabale* might not contribute to a society's sexual
wounds, and hence its vulnerability to STDs such as Slim.

We left the pub at about nine o'clock, and back at the mission the brothers were in the middle of Vespers. I sat down on a patch of grass with the crickets chirping all around, and the strong, clear voices ringing out from the chapel. And then I leant backwards, and the stars were shining above me like crystals on black velvet. As the service drew to a close, I got up and walked across to my room, thinking how fortunate I was to be able to live and work in such a wonderful place.

In the morning, Sig had to hurry back to Kampala, so there was no time for me to see Rakai's new DA, or to call in at Kalisizo to talk with the DMO, or the health education team. It hardly mattered: I'd already decided that I would have to come back to Kyotera again. But back in Kampala, at the Imperial, I had a shock in store. Although it was now noon, the door to my room was bolted from the inside, and there was water seeping out from underneath, and along the parquet flooring of the corridor. It was two or three minutes before Sue heard my frenzied knocking on the outer door, and emerged, grumpily, to let me in. It turned out that she, Barbara and another girl had also had a night of it, as the NRA commander who was my next-door neighbour lost no time in telling me. Apparently their shouting and laughter had kept him awake until four in the morning. In addition Sue had forgotten that the only regular water supply at the hotel was due to arrive at eight o'clock; she had left both of the bath taps turned on, with the plug inserted. The resulting deluge flooded not just the hallway and the corridor outside, but a fair portion of the bedroom as well. Among the casualties were several items of clothing, most of the pillows, and various of my books and notes which had been left at the bottom of a cupboard. It took two days for everything to dry out, and I was not well pleased.

21 · THE AIDS CONTROL PROGRAMME

It was probably the scandal about the article in the *Sunday Sport* which sealed my fate with Dr Samuel Ikwaras Okware, director of Uganda's AIDS Control Programme – if it needed sealing that is. For in the end, it didn't really matter whether he truly believed that I was the author, or if it was simply convenient for him to do so. The net result was exactly the same.

I had made an appointment with him, to ask formally if I could interview certain prominent figures involved with the ACP, and he was on the defensive from the time I entered his office. He said he was too busy to speak to me, that he couldn't provide me with letters of permission to all and sundry right now, it would have to wait till next week, and so forth.

'But you've been saying that for two months now, Doctor.' At least this had the effect of goading him into a more candid response.

'We want to carry on without the press interfering in our programme,' he told me. 'They can even destroy it. Look at Carswell, how the press destroyed him. I was appointed spokesman to shield the other people on the programme from the press, and that's what I'm going to do.'

As I left Okware's office, I bumped into Jim Holt, one of the WHO officials who had been seconded to the ACP.

'What's up with your boss?' I asked him. 'He's not exactly being very co-operative.'

'No, he's not in a very good mood, is he? It seems there's some article in a British newspaper that's caused a bit of a flap: all about Uganda wanting to hang its AIDS patients, or something of the sort. Perhaps he thinks you wrote it,' said Jim.

It was another few months before I got to see the article, but it was no less sensational than I had been led to believe.

It was an incredible piece, even for the *Sunday Sport* – situated on

the front page of the 28 June issue, right below the picture of topless
Zeta. The headline, in letters 2 inches high, proclaimed: 'AIDS VIC-
TIMS TO BE EXECUTED', and a smaller headline reinforced this
with the news that 'Shock final solution is planned in plague areas.'
In the few column inches which remained, it was alleged that Uganda
had 70,000 known 'AIDS victims', that the figure was doubling every six
months, and that the country's entire population of 15 million – men,
women and children – would all die by the turn of the century unless
a ruthless execution programme was implemented. A Dr Walton Sempata
was said to have pleaded, almost in tears, to be allowed to kill his AIDS
patients 'to save our country from extinction'.

The unfortunate thing from my point of view was that 'Dr Walton
Sempata' was uncomfortably close to Dr Sempala of the VRI, whom
I had interviewed some weeks before. Another source quoted in the
article as Dr Randolph Ndumu bore a distinct resemblance to Mr J.
R. Ndumu, a research officer also working at the institute. It hardly
mattered that my two visits to the VRI had occurred after the piece
had already been printed – or that the *Sport*'s 'journalism' regularly
featured such gems as: 'Killer Plants Stalk Queen Mum', and 'Space
Aliens Turned Our Son Into An Olive'. It hardly mattered that, as I
later discovered, the article had been based on a news agency report,
which had been '*Sport*ed up' by the subs in London. For it looked as
if Dr Okware had already made up his mind which Uganda-based
journalist was to blame.

I missed the important AIDS control seminar for DMOs and hospital
superintendents which took place at Makerere University at the end
of August, and so missed hearing Ros Widy-Wirski of the WHO tell
of a sero-survey conducted on all out-patients and in-patients who
had attended Uganda's nine major hospitals during a seven-day
period in June and July. His conclusion was shocking: fully 46
per cent of the 1,109 patients involved had been found to be
HIV-positive on two separate tests. Nearly half of Uganda's hospital patients were infected; HIV was spreading fast through the
land.

The next important meeting with regard to AIDS took place the following week, at the start of September. It was the inaugural conference
of the Uganda National Association of Community and Occupational
Health Workers, and Dr Okware was due to give an address. As I walked
in, I received an unsmiling nod from the minister, Dr Rugunda, up on
the podium. I realised that this was the first time I had seen him since

our Gulu discussion of a year earlier, and it appeared that his mood had not improved in the interim.

Dr Okware's overview of Uganda's AIDS situation was, predictably, defensive. He noted that the worst-affected districts were Rakai, Masaka, Mpigi, Luwero and Kampala, in fact the whole of south-western Uganda, and that the disease seemed to be spreading along the trans-African highway towards the Kenyan border. There also, he said, appeared to be a focus around Gulu and Kitgum districts 'especially among ex-UNLA soldiers', but he hadn't seen any cases from Karamoja or West Nile. The impression he appeared to be giving was that the rest of the country was virtually AIDS-free. This reflected his speech at the Sydney conference, in which he had claimed that AIDS was 'non-existent' in rural Uganda.

He stressed the critical transmission role played by heterosexual contact in Uganda, but although he quoted the Namaara/Carswell figures for high incidence of HIV among prostitutes and truckers, and its virtual absence among the five to fourteen age group and the elderly, he neglected to quote any figures for groups more repre-sentative of the general population, such as pregnant women and blood donors. How softly Dr Okware treads, I thought, how deferential he is to politically-sensitive toes. Next he spent quite some time dismissing the myth that mosquitoes could pass on the virus, finally commenting, 'So please do not rush to buy mosquito nets, it is what goes on under them that is critical.'

Whatever else, Dr Okware could still crack a good joke.

At this point, however, Okware found that he was running short of time, and so had to rush through the activities of the AIDS Control Programme in the space of half a minute, which was a pity, in that this was the part of his speech most relevant to his audience. He turned briefly to controversial issues such as whether or not a seropositive person should be allowed to marry, or a female carrier who was pregnant be allowed to proceed to full term; whether a seropositive should even be told the diagnosis if that knowledge might prompt him or her to commit suicide, or serious crimes; or whether instead one should concentrate on sensitising the whole community to the risks. He ended, however, with an important message: 'In the absence of any vaccine, the consensus of the entire medical and scientific community is that the immediate answer lies in education, education, education, education.'

There was a smattering of applause, but in truth the delivery of the speech had suffered greatly from the time constraints. A few questions from the floor followed, of which the most interesting involved homo-sexuality (rare in Uganda, said Okware, though the situation might be different in the prisons); the safety of breast milk (no evidence to prove transmission, but best to avoid pooling it); and whether men were more susceptible to AIDS than women (apparently not, for in Rakai at least more women were dying, by a ratio of 55:45). Then the conference chairman Dr Eriki, the tuberculosis expert on the NCPA, invited one final enquiry; I held up my hand and he gave me the nod.

'When is the ACP going to make a decision on whether or not to inform HIV carriers of their status?' I called out.

'Well, we have already been examining the question, but each time we have not managed an answer,' said Dr Okware. 'In fact, it's on our next agenda. Hopefully by the next meeting, we should at least be able to give some very general guidelines about what should be done.'

He began to pack up his papers, but Dr Eriki added a comment of his own.

'We've been thinking that the community workers should put out questionnaires, and then we could let the public decide. If you are HIV-positive, would you want to know? Let the people give us the answers. If over ninety per cent say we should tell them' – and here he turned pointedly to Dr Okware – 'then we should go by that.'

I realised that by sheer chance, I had hit on an issue that aroused heated debate within the NCPA. Dr Eriki clearly favoured a policy of openness, and I began to wonder if this apparently random figure of 90 per cent was not in fact the percentage from the Kasangati KAP study who had opted for being told their results (Dr Konde-Lule had already told me that most of the respondents wanted to be informed, and it later transpired that the precise figure was 85 per cent). Dr Okware, meanwhile, stopped what he was doing, and turned to answer the older man in the chair. He looked a little miffed, perhaps at the small challenge to his authority.

'Yes yes. But I have got my own personal view. My own personal view is that there is no point telling anybody the results. Because even if you told him, what are you going to do with him anyway? And if you are dealing with not just hundreds, but maybe thousands of people, what are you going to do with them? On top of that, you are not absolutely sure that all of them will die with the disease: only a little fraction will die. Now why should you inconvenience their mental status? They have children, they have to live. And they are the most active people in society.' (And possibly the most active sexually as well, I thought to myself.) 'On top of that,' he added, 'there is a small percentage that is false positive. Is it really fair to put a man in a cage because he had a false positive test?'

'But you have the Western blot for checking results,' I shouted up from the floor.

'Even with the Western blot, there are human errors. And there's yet another danger: that if you tell him, he will say let me not die alone, let me use up all my money, and then he will run around spreading the disease. We've had four such instances here already. So it's a delicate problem.'

Again, Dr Okware was set to rise from his seat on the podium. But Dr Eriki stopped him.

'Before you go, Dr Okware. There is one gentleman who lost his wife in 1985. Then he was told that he had AIDS. And he's very grateful because he had a chance to organise his child in school, and he now has no more contact with women, because he doesn't want to kill anybody. And most of the people I've talked to feel they should be told: then they can plan their future. And besides, if a doctor knows his patient will go and hang himself, then of course he should hide the information from him.'

Dr Okware made a few more rather disjointed comments, including his most valid point thus far: that people should not be told their results unless they also received counselling. Then he got up and left the stage. As he did so, a doctor in the row in front of me, who I later discovered to be a senior member of the health ministry, turned around and said: 'Your question was very good. It is a pity that Dr Okware dismisses it like that.' But at least by waylaying him in public, I had finally persuaded the chairman of the NCPA to answer one of my enquiries about AIDS. It was the first time this had happened, and as it turned out, it was also to be the last.

Later that same day Sue and I climbed on to the bike, and rolled down the road to Entebbe in the golden glow of late afternoon. It was half-past five by the time we arrived at the Lake Victoria Hotel, and there was just one room left, and that only procurable after a lengthy session of haggling. It boasted a single bed, some running cold water, and not very much else. I left Sue with some magazines, and set off to the bar to meet Jim Holt from WHO. At this stage, the AIDS Control Programme had been in operation for a little over three months, and Jim had agreed to give me a briefing on how things were going. He arrived on time, and we retired to an upstairs bar where we could talk more freely.

First of all, I asked Jim whether the millions of dollars pledged in May had been disbursed, and if the ACP was now fully operational. He let slip that there had been a difference of opinion about the UNICEF pledge of 8 million dollars over five years, most of it earmarked for health education in schools. (As it turned out, UNICEF had merely decided to implement the HE programme through the Ministry of Education, rather than through the ACP, but health ministry officials were clearly upset.) Jim added that there had also been 'administrative obstacles', and that some of the other agencies and bilateral partners who had promised money had been 'rather slow'. I pursued the line of enquiry, to discover that so far only the WHO input of 200,000 dollars had actually been transferred; another 500,000 dollars from the US was on its way. When I asked Jim if this slow disbursement was affecting the ACP's progress, he replied rather tetchily that it was not.

'It's a new programme, Ed; it's the first AIDS Control Programme in Africa, probably the first in the whole world. It's not fully operational yet, but we couldn't be doing more even if all the money was here in the bank.'

Before Jim got offended right at the start of our talk, I asked him what he thought about the Church's 'Love Faithfully' campaign.

'We are trying to compromise, not argue, with the Church,' he added. 'All the churches are getting very involved with the campaign. And their message of "Love Faithfully" will work for the adult believer in the rural population. On the other hand, we know that soldiers, for instance, can't implement this message. Most of them have no family, they move around the country, and they have to try a little bit when they get to a new place. Similarly, civil servants are also transferred to different regions, and businessmen are moving up and down, and they find new girlfriends. We know that young adults will always make love, and not just to one person. So those are the people we're trying to reach with our "Love Carefully" message.'

But to my surprise, I found that he was far from convinced about the efficacy of health education. He told me that he couldn't think of a single successful HE intervention against STDs anywhere in the world, except perhaps for Sweden.

'Health education is complicated, because it has to be adjusted according to the target group. I certainly hope it works in AIDS control, because it's the only hope we've got,' he said gloomily. I was rather shocked to find that a WHO official seconded to help Uganda combat the epidemic could be so pessimistic about the main tenet of the control programme. When I pressed him he mentioned condoms as an alternative approach, but it was clear that he was not even very enthusiastic about them. He suggested that the splitting-condom syndrome that I and others had encountered could possibly have resulted from a consignment getting stranded in the humid heat of Mombasa during one of the periodic closures of the Kenya/Uganda border.

Jim proved very reluctant to give any information about serological data. He insisted that no random surveys had been undertaken for Uganda, only surveys of 'at risk' groups; he included blood donors and pregnant women in this category. Even the Kasangati sero-survey had been only a training exercise, he told me; the fact that the villagers themselves had decided whether or not to participate, and certain other inconsistencies, meant that it would provide only very limited information. The first really representative study would be the national sero-survey, which was due to begin shortly.

'And another thing,' he added. 'At present there is no reporting system for diseases here: nothing is yet working. We are using AIDS in order to establish an effective surveillance system for Uganda, and one that will operate for measles, cholera and other such diseases as well. We now have sentinel observation posts at twelve different hospitals around the country, which are reporting all their AIDS cases, with full information on the patients. We hope that the other hospitals will soon begin to do the same, though at present they don't seem to be managing it.'

I asked Jim the same question that I'd put earlier that day to Dr Okware: why was it not policy for AIDS patients and HIV-positives to be informed of their condition? He told me that the NCPA had decided 'temporarily' not to tell, primarily because of a lack of counselling facilities in Uganda. I thought once again about how devastating the knowledge of having AIDS, or being an HIV carrier, must be; I remembered how nervous I had been while waiting for some of my test results. But I could not escape the feeling that the present policy was a cop-out for a country where seroprevalence was already so high, and that it could only lead to further transmission of the virus. It seemed that if the problem here really was the lack of counselling facilities, then the ACP proposals should surely have included a substantial component for the training of counsellors.

By this stage, several bottles of beer had been downed, and talk was flowing more freely. Jim started telling me about the work of Frank Plummer, the Canadian doctor resident at Kenyatta Hospital in Nairobi, who seemed to have demonstrated that having sexually transmitted diseases, especially those involving ulceration, placed a person at much greater risk of getting or transmitting HIV infection. And then, out of the blue, he said:

'As you know, many African women say that they prefer the way that the *wazungu* make love; they say that African men think that only prostitutes are active in bed, so they just expect a woman to lie still and keep quiet. A lot of the women complain that their men only want penetration, without any kissing or foreplay. And of course, when there's not enough lubrication, and penetration is forced, there's soreness, and abrasions, and more chance of infection.'

It would be easy to dismiss such a claim as racism, except that many young Africans (both male and female) have, while stressing their own considerateness as lovers, told me much the same thing about, for instance, their parents' generation, or people from other tribes. But perhaps that's the same for people the world over – 'nobody's as good in bed as I am'. Once again, only an African Kinsey report could confirm or dispel such claims.

Later I asked Jim about the director of the ACP, Samuel Okware, and explained that, at least in my case, he seemed to be blocking rather than disseminating information.

'I can understand him. Because of the openness of Uganda, most of the press reports from Africa are from this country. Maybe you and your colleagues could get the same material from Rwanda or Tanzania, but you haven't. And so Uganda grows in the international understanding as the most AIDS-infected country in Africa. Basically, we want to avoid the situation where a commander or a senior politician suddenly decides he's pissed off about Uganda being blamed, and tells us, for purely political reasons, to take a low profile from now on.'

'And just how good do you think the ACP is in Uganda?' I asked him finally, as we were finishing off our beers.

'I wouldn't want to comment on the quality of this particular programme, but the point is that it is the first such programme. We've got a kind of show on here in Uganda, and we hope to persuade other countries that AIDS is just another disease, albeit more drastic, and a bigger challenge. We hope that those other countries will open their doors to their own AIDS control programmes.'

'Are they showing signs of doing so?'

'If you compare the situation today with that of eight months ago, at the start of the year, it's an absolutely dramatic change. Now everybody's open about AIDS, you can discuss it in every African country. And even those like Kenya, where people are a bit shy, are doing a lot, but on a low-profile basis. That's the basic achievement of WHO over here: now every country in sub-Saharan Africa has a short-term plan, for three to eleven months, and many already have their medium-term five-year plan underway as well. That's a very substantial achievement in my opinion, to formalise the fight against AIDS.'

And on that optimistic note, Jim downed the last of his drink and headed off homewards. I, meanwhile, threaded my way through a maze of corridors to find Sue fast asleep on the bed, with a magazine still under her arm.

The following morning, when I arrived at the ACP building, I was still feeling slightly the worse for wear from the night before. But although it was only half-past eight, the place was already a hive of activity, and as I walked in through the door, I bumped into someone I'd been wanting to meet for some time – Dr Anthony Lwegaba, the NCPA official in charge of the worst-affected districts of Masaka and Rakai and, more famously, the 'discoverer of Slim'. I liked Lwegaba immediately. He was friendly, precise and quite intense: yes, he had a few minutes to spare, he told me, and yes, he could be interviewed. He started off by recounting the story of how, in mid-1984, when he was the DMO of Rakai, he had heard of a peculiar wasting disease called Slim which was affecting several of the traders and smugglers down at Kasensero and Lukunyu. By November he had submitted a report to the health ministry in which he raised the possibility that Slim might actually be a manifestation of AIDS.

'In my study, I compared all the symptoms and signs, but very many scientists in Kampala took long to believe what I had written, and it was not until January 1985 that blood was taken off, and I was proven right.'

One of Lwegaba's current preoccupations in the south-west was with the problem of young children who had been orphaned by AIDS. President Museveni had himself taken an interest, I was told, and had asked the NCPA to make a survey, and to submit recommendations to the government; Dr Lwegaba was duly compiling a list of the children affected. He could not give me a figure, but he explained that AIDS orphans did represent a special case, in that once they lost one parent, they usually lost the other soon afterwards, and that many of them were also very young. He added that the NCPA would probably recommend that the government take care of the school fees, but that the children should continue to stay at home with their extended families.

Many of these orphans, of course, would themselves be stricken with AIDS, and I discussed with Dr Lwegaba the particular support mechanisms that existed in Africa, for family networks to take care of their own.

'Yes. In Uganda, you find that 90 per cent of the AIDS patients are in their homes, and they will remain there till they die. They may seek medical attention, but only once in a while, and then they go back. I think in a way this is an advantage, because I don't believe our hospital resources could take care of this enormous problem. Anyway, it means that the relatives take care of their immediate needs, and that we have to go to the villages, and teach the communities around these patients how to take decent care of them, so that they are not in danger. And we support the service by providing drugs to alleviate some of the symptoms. At present we have got a man – Robert Sango at Kalisizo – who drives out to the villages on an old motor-cycle, and who does house-to-house counselling. And we hope that sooner or later we shall have more motor-cycles, and can extend the service to the rest of Uganda.'

As I left, Dr Lwegaba told me that he and Robert Sango would be attending a WHO conference on counselling people with AIDS and HIV, to be held in Nairobi in early October. I entered the date in my diary, and told him that I might well see them there.

I next went to the office of Dr Ros Widy-Wirski, the Pole who was both chief epidemiologist for the ACP, and head of the WHO contingent in Entebbe. He sat me down and started telling me about the recent upsurge in discriminatory measures against HIV carriers. Not only were the new US immigration restrictions due to come into force at the start of December, but Cuba was now testing all new arrivals from Africa and the US, and expelling the seropositives; any of its own nationals who bore the virus were apparently being detained. Some African students, Widy-Wirski added, were resorting to paying large bribes to doctors or clinics for false certificates stating that they had been tested and found free of the virus, in the vain hope that these would allow them to continue their studies abroad.

'In my opinion, more and more governments will be pushed towards very discriminatory measures,' he told me. 'And in Africa, we'll begin to see some retaliation.'

It seemed that everyone in the ACP building that day was rushed off their feet. Dr Okware invited me into his office to give me a copy of his speech of the previous day, and when Chris Ndugwa, a professor specialising in paediatric AIDS, walked in, Okware suddenly gave me permission to interview him. I was happy to accept, and took the professor's number, but this was the only time that Dr Okware was ever to exercise his authority so helpfully. Meanwhile, Louis Ochero was preoccupied with devising a programme for a Commonwealth Conference on AIDS, which the NCPA was apparently trying to organise for the beginning of October, just five weeks later (it eventually took place in December). Since he was so busy, I merely confirmed the date of Masaka district's health education workshop that was scheduled for later in September, and left him to it.

In another room, the director of a research programme from Columbia University briefed me on the 600,000-dollar study which was about to begin in Rakai district. HIV-positives and AIDS cases were to be recorded over a four-year period in serial surveys, in addition to which there were to be KAP surveys, a health education component, and an assessment of condom usage, which at present, I was informed, extended to just 3 per cent of the district's population. I remember wondering whether the condom survey was going to run into problems. Apart from the President's attitude, more than one Ugandan at the ACP had observed that many of the US programmes on AIDS seemed to be tied up with family planning, condom usage or similar population-control measures. In addition, there was some opposition to the USAID technique of 'social marketing': charging a small fee to help finance the next condom shipment. 'Typically American!' one non-Ugandan had commented. 'They deliver the first batch free, get the country hooked, and then offer discount rates thereafter.'

Lastly, I visited Dr Chisale Mhango, a WHO Maternal-Child Health planning adviser. As soon as I sat down, he began telling me how worried he was about the lack of protective clothing for village midwives. 'Seventy per cent of our deliveries are done by midwives who also do normal chores like working in the garden, and who often have cuts on their hands, cracks around the fingernails and so forth. Most of them have not even heard of surgical gloves, so they're handling the placenta and all that blood with their bare hands. I don't know how many village women are carrying the virus, but we're now hearing figures of over 20 per cent of pregnant women in Kampala.' Dr Mhango told me that they were seeking 3 million dollars over five years to conduct a survey of the country's midwives, to give all of them some basic training in hygiene and sterilisation techniques, and to supply them with proper delivery kits. But perhaps the crucial point was that nurses at local health centres were being encouraged to transfer problem pregnancies to hospital at an earlier stage, so that there was less likelihood of a possibly HIV-contaminated blood transfusion being required. I had never imagined that HIV would have such far-reaching repercussions for almost every sector of the medical profession.

Poor Sue was still waiting for me at the Lake Victoria Hotel, bored and hungry, for it was now nearly afternoon, and I was some hours later than intended. We took a late lunch, and then headed back up the road to Kampala. Half-way there, just after the small town of Kajansi, we came to the spot where an enormous plaster man, 10 feet tall, stood incongruously on top of a pedestal. He was clad only in a rather conservative pair of black swimming trunks, and his biceps were raised aloft in celebration of his mighty strength. Miraculously, no soldier had ever been tempted to take a pot-shot at this irresistible plaster titan; incredibly the Kajansi Turkish Baths were still open seven days a week for sauna, weight training and massage.

Men and women were not normally allowed in the sauna together, but since there were no other customers, they decided to waive the rule. I threw a cup of water on the coals, and climbed to the upper step, letting the sudden blast of heat take me over, letting my mind go numb.

'Is everything OK?' asked Sue, after a while.

'Yes, I'm fine, thanks.'

But I had drifted miles away, 15 miles to be precise, back to Entebbe and the ACP. I was enormously impressed by the fact that, at a time when the rest of Africa was still tending to deny the terrible impact, or even the existence, of the AIDS epidemic, Uganda had had the courage to confront the problem head-on. Also commendable was the headway that the ACP had made in a relatively short time-span, and the energy and apparent sincerity of many of those working on the programme. But I had some real reservations too. On a personal level, there was the growing obstructiveness of the chairman, Dr Okware, which did not reflect well on the underlying spirit of the programme; I wondered whether he was merely a natural bureaucrat, or if he had actually been directed, perhaps by Dr Rugunda, not to co-operate. Then there was the fact that he was forever flying off to attend AIDS conferences in Australia, Ecuador, and the like, and was still spending many of the afternoons at his practice in the Pilkington Medical Centre. On one level this was entirely understandable: Ugandan salaries are lamentable, even for those on internationally-funded programmes, and who in his right mind would turn down the prospect of a foreign travel allowance in dollars, and payments from well-to-do private patients? Nevertheless, on another level, it said something about Dr Okware's level of commitment.

As for Ochero, I had reservations about him too. He was known to be strongly opposed to the use of condoms, largely, it seemed, on tradition-alist grounds. Also, it was said that much of his commendably ambitious district health education programme had not gone ahead as scheduled because of administrative problems. Yet instead of concentrating on these important workshops, where the AIDS control message was meant to be relayed to each part of Uganda, Ochero was even now preparing for a nebulous Commonwealth Conference on AIDS which had clearly been planned at far too little notice. In addition, there was a lot of criticism abroad at the apparent nepotism of Ochero's section, with all the artwork for the poster and leaflet campaigns being commissioned from his own daughter, Grace. Many felt that, though the technical execution was good, and the ideas inventive, the messages were far too high-brow for the general populace; that they lacked the simple, visual impact of the Kenyan fist, and Rwanda's snorting buffalo. Many doctors were bemoaning the fact that the WHO health education expert, who was supposed to give Ochero advice and backing, had not yet been appointed.

I wiped the sweat from my brow. 'Not bad, but could try harder,' was my considered report on the ACP's first term.

22 · CONFRONTATIONS

I had become very attached to the seedy, ramshackle charm of the Imperial Hotel in the year since my departure from the Speke, and it was undoubtedly bad news when the announcement came, at the beginning of September, that in seven days it was to close indefinitely for maintenance and repair work. Never mind that the only cold water was that which rolled from the taps for an hour or less each morning; the only hot water that which one paid the room attendant to carry up in a jerrican. Never mind that my permanent next-door neighbour was an NRA commander who was apparently involved in intelligence work, and whose presence necessitated a reversion to sign language whenever any conversation became too sensitive. Never mind also that a member of the PLO's diplomatic mission occupied the room directly below mine, and that the musical and amorous processes whereby he entertained his lady guests sometimes involved a certain lack of sleep on the part of others in the vicinity.

Staying there felt like being part of an enormous family. I had got to know most of those on the staff, from the nightwatchman who got so drunk after payday that he tried to fight anyone entering or leaving his car park, to the floor supervisor who brought a pot of flowers for your room because of something nice you'd said that morning. There was James, the cleaner who was so honest that he placed lost bank-notes inside your glasses case for safekeeping. And there was Fred, the barman at the Baraza, who could always find me a bottle of Nile Special, or Sue a pack of Sportsman, even when the rest of Kampala had long sold out.

The really bad thing was that not just the Imperial, but all the government hotels in the capital were to close, to allow for a facelift before a big international conference that was scheduled for December. This impending dearth of accommodation lent a certain urgency to my various lines of journalistic enquiry. I was collecting material for an article on the Ugandan economy, for which I had already interviewed the Minister of Planning (another former cell-mate), and compiling some radio pieces on the Oxfam-sponsored orthopaedic workshop at Mulago, and the construction institute at Kiteredde. At the same time I was putting together an entry entitled 'Fighting AIDS in Uganda' for the WHO photo competition, and attempting to follow as much as possible of the testimony given to the quite splendid 'Commission of Enquiry into Human Rights Violations Between 1962 and 1986', which performed a valuable therapeutic role for those who had suffered at the hands of previous regimes.

After one of these hearings the witness, a former police inspector called Charles Tindyebwa, was arrested and charged with the murders of four European journalists who, back in 1979, had crossed Lake Victoria by boat in order to record the death-throes of Amin's regime. I was asked to cover the story by *Stern* magazine, and by the Swedish daily, *Dagens Nyheter*. It turned out that Tindyebwa was yet another alumnus of the Luzira class of '83, so when his case came up for mention, I turned up at the cells at the back of the magistrates' court. Tindyebwa recognised me, and readily agreed to my taking a few photos, and asking him some questions. Afterwards I was just packing up when a drunken intelligence officer arrived on the scene, demanding to know what I was up to. My protestations that I had full permission from the police superintendent in charge cut no ice at all with this gentleman, presumably because of our lack of a shared prison history, and he was on the point of dispatching me, also, to the cells. Eventually I managed to sneak away as he got embroiled in another dispute with one of the warders.

I also spent rather a lot of time trying to follow up army commander Elly Tumwiine's public declaration that journalists could visit Luzira Prison to inspect the prevailing conditions. After my own experiences at Luzira, I felt a special kinship with those imprisoned there, and since I had been hearing repeated rumours of overcrowding, lack of medical care, and the presence of some 700 illegal NRA 'lodgers', I thought I should go to see for myself. I wasted three mornings trying to arrange this while the Minister of Internal Affairs and the Commissioner of Prisons dreamt up ever more convoluted excuses for denying permission.

Meanwhile, I went back to the army HQ at Republic House to apply, once again, to be allowed to visit the war-zone in the north. As on my previous visits there, I found that neither the army commander nor the two deputy ministers in the Ministry of Defence could see me, so I had, as usual, to leave my request in writing. As I left Republic House, I walked round the side of the main gate to the quarterguard, where miscreant soldiers were supposed to be held in custody. I had heard from a relief worker that civilians, including some schoolboys, were also being held there. Standing below the high window of the quarterguard I could see several faces pressed close to the iron grille, and after checking that the coast was clear, I held up a pack of cigarettes which I'd bought for the purpose. They were quickly grabbed.

'Thank you very much sir.'

'Why are you locked up in there? What did you do?' I asked as casually as possible. There was some talk in Luganda, and then one of the men at the window replied, in little more than a whisper, 'We did nothing.'

'Are some of you in there schoolchildren?' I asked, as quietly as I could. At that moment, a soldier appeared round the corner, less than 5 yards away.

'Well?' I asked again, looking straight at the soldier.

'Yes sir, some of us are,' said a voice from above my head.

'What are you doing over there?' asked the soldier. 'You're not supposed to be there.'

'I'm sorry. I was just offering these lads some cigarettes. They looked like they needed a smoke.' And I shook his hand, and moved off round the corner as casually and quickly as I could manage, to where I had left the taxi parked some way away from the main gate: on this occasion, a taxi had seemed preferable to using the bike.

As we drove back to Kampala, I was thinking that the term 'schoolboy', in Uganda, could include young men of eighteen, or even twenty, who could quite conceivably be involved in such activities as theft, violence, or anti-government activities. Also, because of the urgency, I had asked a leading question: it was quite possible that someone had merely given me the answer which they thought I wished to hear – and which would be of most use to them. But for all that, my gut feeling was that some of those locked up in the quarterguard had been civilians, and quite young ones too. If I was right, it was yet another small example of how this regime was beginning to bend the rules, and move along the same extrajudicial path as its predecessors.

Looking back on this period now, it is clear that my existence in Uganda was beginning to get extremely confrontational. But at the time, I don't think I saw it like that at all. Perhaps I couldn't afford to examine too closely the way things were going. And the fact that I was forever running into army men and plain-clothes intelligence officers, and having problems with them, actually encouraged a feeling of relaxation rather than paranoia. There is a level on which things become much easier once one assumes that every stranger is a spy, that one's entire surroundings have turned into an enormous eavesdropping ear.

Three weeks had passed since I had submitted my questions to the President, and I had not so far received any summons to State House. I thought back to the first press conference that Museveni had given as President, at the end of January 1986, just after the capture of Kampala. I had spent most of the previous two days sitting on a sofa in the Office of the President, hoping to get a radio interview with the new leader for CBC, the Canadian Broadcasting Corporation. I hadn't been lucky, and the fact that a BBC reporter from London had been did not make me feel any better. The press conference was convened at short notice, and attended by a couple of dozen members of the local press, together with the fifteen or so foreign reporters remaining in Uganda, and for two hours Museveni – resplendent in battle fatigues, with the glow of victory still on his face – simply shone. He was in turn serious, compassionate, dynamic and witty: the press audience, by and large, was dazzled.

At the end of the conference Benny Kanyanjeyo, who was revelling in the title of 'Personal Private Secretary to the President', stood up, thanked his boss for answering our questions, and asked if it might be possible for him to grant me a ten-minute interview in private, since I'd been sitting so diligently on his sofa for the past two days. But Museveni was unmoved: what was the point of having a press conference, he asked reasonably enough, if you embarked on a series of interviews afterwards? But he did allow me to ask one final question. I glanced down at my list, and decided to plump for one which would give him ample room for comment.

'Mr President, the last fifteen years of Uganda's history have been characterised by an endless cycle of violence and abuse of the law. How do you, and the NRM, plan to break that cycle?'

Perhaps I should have chosen something more specific; perhaps he was just tired, and impatient to get home. Whatever, he was not very generous.

'What cycle of violence . . .?' he began, and spent the next half-minute decrying my question before getting up, thanking us all for coming, and walking out. I felt my cheeks flush with embarrassment. In Nairobi, during the peace talks just two months before, he had given me an interview lasting well over an hour, during which he answered my every question courteously and thoroughly. He had appeared to approve, both of what I had written about Uganda in the past, and of my understanding of the issues. I could hardly believe that suddenly he could be so dismissive. What had happened in the interim, of course, was that he had become Uganda's President, and despite his avowed dislike for the trappings of high office, despite his expressed intention of remaining one of the people, he had already become too important, and too busy, to be doing any favours for a foreign journalist.

At around this time, Sue and I went out one evening to join some friends at Half London. This splendidly-named establishment is one of the most popular of the many small eating and drinking places which have sprung up in Kampala's richer suburbs over the last few years, and which cater for those who like to sit out in the open, eat some home-cooked food, drink some beers, and watch the world go by. Half London's particular forte is spit-roasted chicken, but it is also famous as a watering-hole, and much care needs to be taken by those driving past between eleven and midnight, when Half London's patrons lurch into their cars, and begin their tortuous journeys homeward.

Towards the end of this particular evening, I noticed a woman two tables away who was gesticulating in our direction. Her face was so contorted with drink that I didn't recognise her: I even looked around to see if she was trying to catch someone else behind me. Eventually, her gestures made it certain that it was me she wanted, and I went over. It was only as I was taking her hand that I realised who she was: a woman working with the Presidential Press Unit at State House, and whom I had known years ago, in her previous job. But even though I had got her name and number, I was still having some difficulty making out what she was saying. She was totally pie-eyed. Presently I asked her about my questions to the President: was he going to give me an interview? She muttered something into her glass, of which all I could make out was: 'You should come closer to us. Why don't you come closer to us, Eddie?'

I replied that sure, I wanted to be friends, but I was a journalist, not a public relations man. I had to do my job as I saw fit. In her previous work she had always come across as a woman of dignity, and I was sorry now to see her in this state. I told her something about how my life was going, though she was really too far gone to hear; then, after a decent interval, I got up and took my leave. Now I knew for sure that I wasn't going to get a call from the President.

There were two foreign journalists visiting the country at the time, both working on the AIDS story, and they were as chalk and cheese. One was Randy Shilts, the genial, curly-haired reporter from San

Francisco whose massive tome 'And the Band Played On', about the scandalous sequence of denial and indifference that had characterised the American AIDS epidemic, was due to be published a few weeks later. He had flown across to get an update on the AIDS situation in Africa before his long series of promotional appearances began.

The other was Teresa Guerreiro from the BBC World Service in London: tough, lean, serious, and politically committed. She and Shilts had spent a day together down in Rakai district with Dr Lwegaba, on what had by now become the standard ACP trip for journalists: Kalisizo Health Centre, the singing of the AIDS song in a local school, and a visit to a nearby village to see some of the home care being provided by Robert Sango's team and to meet, though not to interview, some of those affected by AIDS. The two journalists had not, it seemed, got on terribly well.

I myself only spoke with Randy for thirty minutes or so, at the BHC Club the night before he left, but I was interested by his theories. He believed that HIV had been exported from Zaire in the 1970s, when the Haitian civil servants and managers who had been training their Zairean counterparts returned home; and then onwardly transmitted from Haiti to America by homosexuals holidaying in the 'gay haven' of the Caribbean. He talked of Gaetan Dugas, the Canadian airline steward whom he had dubbed 'Patient Zero', because of his carnal knowledge of so many of the first Americans to fall sick with AIDS. Before he left, I gave him some dollars, and he promised to send me a copy of the book.

But I spent several hours talking with Teresa. She was admirably energetic, and in the course of her ten days in the country had gathered a tremendous amount of material; when we compared notes, she often gave me more tips than I did her. But there was one significant point on which she and I had to differ. She was, I felt, far more gung-ho about the progress of the Ugandan AIDS Control Programme than was warranted. She said that everywhere she went she saw AIDS posters, leaflets and badges; she was impressed with the plays on TV and radio, the songs sung by the schoolchildren in class, the help given to PWAs in their homes. By contrast, my own impression was that the ACP's health education and home care programmes, however admirable on paper, had barely got off the ground except in places like Kalisizo, which were being shown off to the press.

When Teresa's well-compiled documentary came out on World Service the following month, she used extensive quotes from Dr Okware, who trumpeted Uganda's candour about the epidemic and blamed both the local and the Western media for exaggerating the problem. He claimed that AIDS was 'not the most serious problem we have . . . not one of the top ten killer diseases in this country . . . in traditional rural areas, the incidence [of HIV] is almost nil.' He provided the only lop-sided note in an otherwise balanced programme. I suspected that Teresa's reaction to Uganda had been coloured by her experiences in the two other African states she had hoped to visit: Rwanda, where she was told that no official was available to speak with her, and Zambia, where she was allowed to interview only the Director of Medical Services. I was happy to agree that Uganda was probably more forthright about AIDS than any other seriously-affected African country, but I also felt that it still had a long way to go.

One evening at around this time the phone rang in my room, and there was Dora at the other end, asking for Sue. Since my interview with her in 1986, Dora had become as bold as brass, always asking for drinks, or a ticket to the disco, or sitting down at my table and introducing herself to my friends or colleagues. All of which was understandable (I had, after all, made the first move towards her, and had also made money from the resulting interview), but still, I have to confess, sometimes very irritating. I explained that Sue was busy in the bathroom, and asked if I could pass on a message.

'You bring her for me,' she insisted.

'I told you Dora, she's washing. Now is there a message or not?'

'Ooh, Eddie, you are very tough,' she squealed down the line. 'You tell her that a friend of hers is waiting in the bar downstairs.'

We went down together, to find Dora with two men, one of whom seemed to know Sue. Dora immediately grabbed hold of me, and started trying to tell me something, but I was watching Sue, who had walked over to the man and kissed him on the mouth. As soon as I could detach myself from Dora, I went over and stood beside her. She did the introductions, but in an unusually quiet voice.

'Eddie, meet Patrick. Patrick – Eddie.'

'Ah yes, of course,' I said. 'From the French embassy, I think,' as I shook his hand. I offered him and his friend a drink, but they refused, they already had some beer; Dora would take one though. I ordered for her, and then turned back towards Patrick, and asked what his job was at the embassy. He pretended not to understand, even when I repeated the question more slowly.

'Ah . . . excuse . . . my English is not good.'

Is it hell, I thought. It's good enough for you to speak to Sue, though, isn't it? And I noticed that from his bar-stool, his foot was

brushing lightly against her leg; she was swaying slightly, as if trying
to keep her balance. I decided that I didn't like this man, and that I
wasn't going to let him take any liberties. So I put my arm round Sue's
waist, and for the next twenty minutes comprehensively took over the
conversation. I explained to Patrick at some length about what I did,
and about the trip out west that Sue and I were planning, I enquired
if he had met Roland Neveu, asked him why Michel Platini had played
so badly in the World Cup; there were lots of things, I discovered, that
I wanted to talk about with Patrick. I don't know if he understood me
or not, but that was hardly the issue. In the end he conceded defeat,
though none too graciously I thought, and explained that they had to
be somewhere for dinner. He almost barked at his friend, who tipped
back his drink and followed him out, with Dora shouting goodbye over
her shoulder, and bringing up the rear. I asked Sue if she'd like another
bottle.

'No thanks. Not right now.'

'Are you sorry to see him go?' I asked, not looking at her.

'No, I'm not. I was liking him sometimes, but not now. I'm with
you now.'

I gave her arm a squeeze. 'Your past tense is getting much better,
you know.'

'What's that?'

'I'll explain later over dinner. Come on, I'm taking you out to
the Palace.'

The other important interview I had at around this time was with
'Fred Bishop'. I'm not quite sure how to describe Fred without identifying him, except to say that he was a well-informed, rather intense
muzungu involved in the mobilisation against the threat of AIDS, but in
a less formal role than Jim Holt.

First, I asked him about seropositivity levels, and he told me that
there were still only a few data points available. I asked which, and he
said that there were indications of very high levels among the soldiers
of the NRA, though he declined to elaborate. There were also rumours
of infection levels of over 10 per cent in the Sese Islands which, he
commented, was not entirely surprising for an island population, even
a purely rural one. Also, a very limited sample taken from households
in rural Kyebe had displayed between 10 and 15 per cent seropositivity.

I said that my own observations in Kyebe would have led me to
expect even higher levels of infection, to which Fred replied that the
sample had been small, and that 10–15 per cent positivity among entire

households was equivalent to 20–30 per cent infection rates among the sexually active, which was very high for a rural area. He added that without proper testing mechanisms, it was difficult to determine whether those people that I had seen in Kyebe were actually dying from AIDS, or from any of a number of other diseases common to the area. I described the symptoms of two or three of those I had met: the wasting, unrelenting fever, diarrhoea and cough, and he had to concede that they sounded very much like 'end-stage' AIDS patients – and that some of the others, like Dick Ssentamu with his four-year illness, could possibly have been cases of prodromal AIDS, or AIDS-Related Complex, ARC. He added a warning, however. 'It's very important that we're strict about who is and who isn't an AIDS patient; if we're sloppy, we'll get sloppy results.' I agreed with him, and said that I hoped that the results of reliable tests, like the Columbia University study in Rakai and the national sero-survey, would not end up being filed away as 'confidential'.

It turned out that Fred was depressed about the methodology employed in the Kasangati survey, particularly that respondents had volunteered, instead of being selected by random sampling techniques. This, he said, had rendered the study less epidemiologically significant than it might otherwise have been. But he also added, as an aside, that over 40 per cent of those tested in the preliminary survey, at the actual trading centre in Kasangati, had been carriers. I expressed astonishment. 'It's a very focal point,' he explained, 'with men and women hanging around the bars, just like at a truck-stop.'

He pointed out that it was only through KAP surveys like the one mounted at Kasangati that effective HE programmes could be devised. The Kasangati results, for instance, would be useful as a guide to the Kiganda culture, but other studies were needed of the many other cultures in Uganda. I asked him for his response to the HE programmes that had been staged so far. He stressed that the education effort had only just started, but added that from the little bit of travelling he'd done, he'd not been impressed with the distribution of pamphlets and posters. Neither had he seen any evidence of direct co-operation between the NCPA and the NRM, about implementing health education through the local resistance committees. Finally, at a particularly candid moment, he added: 'They're all acting as if it's not important. Everyone is saying the right things, but translating that into action is something else again.'

What would he do to limit the spread of AIDS in Uganda if he were in charge, I asked. He became diffident, but I was really eager to know what approach he favoured. 'Uganda is such a complex muddle of politics, economics, different cultures, leftover colonialism, and now an incredibly difficult and puzzling killer virus,' he began. 'I personally think that a much more massive public education campaign could be marshalled here. Much of that twenty million dollars from the donors' conference could be made available for health education programmes, particularly those which rely on the spoken word, which I think is still the most common means of conveying information in the rural areas. The trick really is to translate those dollars into action.'

Fred was not alone in mentioning that very high levels of HIV-positivity were being encountered in the ranks of the national army. An article which had appeared in *The Economist* back in March had asserted that NRA soldiers had been tested by a team of Cuban doctors, and that the preliminary results indicated that a third were infected. At around the same time Dr Corti, in Gulu, was telling a visiting reporter that thirty-five out of every forty soldiers that he saw were now suffering from one or more venereal diseases. Opinions differed as to whether condoms were actually being issued free to all troops, as the NRA newspaper claimed. Meanwhile the commendable policies of ethnically balanced recruitment, and of inducting former soldiers from other armies and guerilla forces, had led to the NRA's exponential growth by a rumoured factor of five, to over 70,000 men. I began to wonder whether the NRA High Command realised that every time it redeployed these soldiers around Uganda, it also redeployed the human immunodeficiency virus.

It was now the second week of September, and the Imperial had officially closed, although Sue, myself, and some few others had been allowed to stay on for a while, until the builders actually needed to move into our wing. I had promised Sue that we would go out to western Uganda for a few days to stay with her mother, and that I would then travel back through Masaka, for the district HE workshop, and onwards to Nairobi, for the WHO conference on AIDS counselling. Altogether, I had about a fortnight's worth of AIDS-related research to do in Nairobi, so the plan was for Sue to stay on in the village with her mother, and for us to meet up again in Kampala in early October. The only problem was that first I had to complete my outstanding work in Kampala, particularly the two sets of articles and photos for the Tindyebwa story.

Work on the Tindyebwa piece was taking longer than planned, but it did give me a chance, in the evenings, to sift through my pile of back issues of the local papers. There had been a lot of AIDS stories of late. An extraordinary article by Vincent E. Bua of the *Topic* criticised 'that lonesome and miserable cow' in the 'Zero Grazing' advert, and Okware for his further obfuscation of the chalice issue, before describing, in purple prose, how 'gumbooted paramedics' at Mulago Hospital had thrown the corpses of three 'AIDS victims' on to a narrow trolley, for all the world as if they were about to shout, 'Bring out your dead.' The *Topic* had also run a timely front-page lead about the common practice at Mulago of reusing unsterilised needles and syringes. A lengthy article in *New Vision* joked about 'Acquired Income Deficiency Syndrome', and the strip cartoon 'Ekanya', in the same paper, featured the fat, balding, eponymous hero being asked by his wife: 'Ekky, darling, do you still love me?' to which he replies, 'Of course I still do . . . Only now, I love you carefully!' On the letters pages there were angry attacks on the banning of the communion cup (which was condemned as 'changing God's word'), and the promoting of the 'Love Carefully' message ('which will encourage the perverts and the sexually loose'). There was a more serious article detailing the smuggling of chimpanzees out of Tanzania, at 5,000 dollars a time, for use in AIDS research; and another which maintained that most seropositives were actually false diagnoses, and that the AIDS scare would soon pass, just like such frightening events in the past as 'firing squads, the talking tortoise, child abductions, exported skulls and genitals, trees rising from the dead . . .' The talking tortoise? Sometimes I was impressed all over again by what a strange and wonderful place Uganda was.

We also found time to track down the two of Sue's sisters who were still residing in the suburbs of Kampala, rather than scattered to the four corners of the continent, like her other siblings. The first sister we met was a *mulokoli*, or born-again Christian, who was so delighted by the reunion with Sue that she wanted her to stay for some days; I managed to effect a rescue by claiming prior obligations elsewhere. But the second, Harriet, proved harder to find; she had left her old residence some years before, and her new place was apparently too difficult for us to locate, even by following directions. Instead, her former neighbour promised that if we returned for lunch the following Sunday, she would arrange for Harriet to be there to meet us.

We went along the next Sunday as directed, and sure enough, there was Harriet. The two sisters had not seen each other for eight years, and it was an emotional reunion. But also present were a number of off-duty soldiers, who were apparently in the habit of using this place as a sort of informal bar at weekends. I got a strong feeling that one or two of them were from Military Intelligence; and I felt that I had no option but to tell them from the outset that I was a journalist, so as to avoid potential misunderstandings later on. But my honesty led to a very stressful afternoon for both myself and Sue. One of the soldiers, already well drunk, came over and clasped my hand for some ten minutes, and insisted on explaining to me, at laborious length, what a good job the NRA was doing, how they were liberating the country for all Ugandans, and so forth. Then, like a schoolteacher testing his star pupil, he wanted me to tell him what I thought about the army.

'Be honest, you must be honest. Are we good people? Are we a lot better than those Acholis?'

This is the point, of course, at which one must never ever be honest. Several beers have already gone down, and anything less than soaring praise will just not suffice. I had seen it all before, with drunken soldiers of the UNLA who would corner you in bar or disco, watch you with beady red eyes, and hold your hand tightly: half brother, half prisoner. I would have liked to tell this man whose rather sweaty palm was clasping mine how much I admired the high-minded seriousness of the NRM, which Museveni, his deputy Kategaya, Rugunda and some others had managed to retain from the bush: no smoking or drinking, a clear head, and almost puritanical zeal. I wanted to tell him how disappointed I was when I saw NRA soldiers breaking their own code of conduct by getting drunk, by forcing their way into discos with rifles on their shoulders, by arresting people for purposes of extortion or revenge. I wanted to tell him how sad it was that ministers and senior officers were once again becoming '*waBenzi*', and were to be seen riding round town in their big limousines, sometimes with jeep-mounted machine-guns and motor-cycle outriders fore and aft – not as bad, to be sure, as the ten-vehicle, high-speed, middle-of-the-road motorcades once favoured by Obote and his cronies, where if you, the citizen, failed to hit the kerb in time, a nasty fate awaited – but an unmistakable step down the same potholed road.

Eventually we exchanged brotherly switched-grip handshakes, and I managed to detach myself for long enough to ask Sue, on the other side of the room, how she was doing. She seemed to be fairly well occupied with a sixteen-year-old *kadogo*, one of the famous boy-soldiers who had helped the NRA topple the Obotes and Okellos, and who were more than a little frightening because of their youth, and their apparent need to prove themselves. He had one hand planted, rather self-consciously, on Sue's upper thigh. She caught my eye and smiled, and said everything was fine, but there was a definite message in her voice for me to keep cool.

And keep cool we did, for the next two hours. Sue kept cool as the *kadogo* brushed his hands against her, and explained in Kiswahili that he could have me arrested any time. I kept cool when a couple of the lads, who had retired to the yard outside, did a pointed, if drunken, chorus or two of Jimmy Cliff's 'Africa for Africans'. We waited for the meal that the neighbour had cooked for us, and then, as soon as we could, took our leave of a rather chastened Harriet, and the remaining soldiers. Then I rode off fast down the alley and out to the fresh air of the public highway.

I never knew to what degree that afternoon had been a chance encounter, or a set-up job. I only knew that for several days afterwards I was angry about the soldiers' arrogance and casual brutality. More than any other experience in Museveni's Uganda, it made me feel that not enough had changed, that too much power still resided with the bully-boys.

We packed all our cases, took them to a friend's house, and then went down to Clouds, the best disco in town, for our last night out in Kampala before we set off west. It ws a strange evening, for most of Sue's old friends had arrived from Nairobi during the previous week, and of course they were all there, dressed to kill: Barbara, Joyce, Anna, Catherine, and cousin Maria. It was a bit like a reprise of that night in the Carnivore, back in March, the night before Sue and I split up. Except that this time, Sue kept very close to me all night, and squeezed my hand a lot, while her girlfriends stood in a group to one side of us, as if keeping their distance. Only Maria came and sat down with us for any time, and she was drunk. After half an hour, there was a row about a bottle of beer, and she stormed off.

We only got up to dance once, and as I was following Sue from the brilliance of the dance-floor into the surrounding darkness, a hand was pushed up towards me in greeting. I couldn't see who it was to begin with, but took the hand anyway, and peered down as the spinning coloured lights slowly picked out its owner. But even when I could see him clearly, I still couldn't recall who he was. In the end, he had to help.

'Come on, Eddie,' he shouted up at me. 'Patrick. Patrick Karegeya.'

'My God, you bastard, Patrick.' I was so surprised that I didn't know myself if I was speaking in anger or jest. 'So you couldn't trust me, eh? You had to send someone to arrest me the very next morning.'

'What are you talking about, Eddie? I didn't know you'd been arrested. When was that?'

I looked at him for a moment; could feel the others at his table, men and women, tuning in to the conversation.

'Never mind, Patrick. It doesn't matter. I'll see you around, OK?'

I felt sure that he was lying. Or, if he wasn't, that for an intelligence officer he had very bad intelligence.

23 · A HOSPITAL IN THE HILLS

Sue's mother lived in a village in the shadow of the Ruwenzoris, otherwise known, rather more picturesquely, as 'The Mountains of the Moon'. In ancient Egypt they drew these mountains on their maps, and ascribed to them mythical properties, for they apparently believed them to be the source of the River Nile, and thus the spiritual womb of their own civilisation. In fact they are not – that honour belongs to the hills around Rutana, in Burundi, where the Kagera River springs from the ground, but the Egyptians were not far out, for the Ruwenzoris actually comprise a watershed between the basins of the Nile and the Zaire, two of the greatest river systems in the world. Each morning when I got up from my bed, I would go outside and watch the cluster of snow-capped peaks as they slowly, almost shyly, emerged from the cloud cover to dominate the landscape. On the Lands and Survey Department maps that I always took with me on safari, they still bore the names of old colonial explorers such as Stanley, Speke, Baker and Gessi, but it was quite possible that they had since been rechristened in honour of more contemporary African luminaries. During the 1970s, for instance, the nearby lakes Albert and Edward had been renamed Mobutu Sese Seko and Idi Amin Dada, but since then the practice seemed to have gone out of fashion, and I was fairly sure that there was as yet no Mount Museveni or Tumwiine Peak.

Despite the several streams that tumbled off the mountain face, down here on the plain the nearest river – which since the breakdown of the village hand-pump was also the nearest water source – was 3 miles distant. Sue and I walked there one day with her youngest sister, and some other children from nearby houses; we filled the jerrican, and then continued round to the sandy-bedded reach which villagers used as a wash-place for themselves and their clothes. We observed local custom, and bathed separately, in the proper places for women and men. And after our plodding return, when we took it in turns to carry the full jerrican – I on my shoulder, and they on their heads, using an *enkata*, or cushion of knotted grass – I felt less hard done by the following morning when Sue gave me a single cupful of the slightly coloured liquid in which to wash and brush my teeth. I even managed to limit my intake of drinking water, which I craved more than anything in the steady equatorial heat.

But for all the hardships of living in the village (which is, after all, how nine-tenths of all Africans live, many of them in places far less hospitable than this), I felt happier and more relaxed here than I had for months in the hustle and bustle of Kampala and Nairobi. Against all tradition, I would sit with the women in the cooking-hut, and get Sue to act as translator between her mother and me. The old lady and I got on well, with her forever telling me how naughty Sue had been as a child, always forgetting to keep the chickens out of the garden, or dropping the water, or stealing the sugar.

'Ah mama,' I would say, 'she hasn't changed one bit.' And Sue would say it again in Kinyarwanda, and the old women would slap their sides and cackle. They killed a chicken for us, of course; actually rather a tough old bird, but so much care went into its preparation that when it finally arrived, surrounded by groundnut sauce, and jostling for space on the plate with the sweet potatoes and spinach and *matooke*, and cassava chips roasted on the fire, it was truly a meal fit for a prince. Afterwards, some of the local elders came to the hut, and *waragi* was sent for, so that we menfolk could drink and discuss issues of importance, which we did until late into the night.

And in the morning, early, the children took me to the cattle-pastures, where the long-horned cows would graze away their day; and later they sang songs for me, some of them just children's songs, others praise-songs for Museveni and the NRA, who had delivered them, the westerners, from their Nilotic oppressors in the previous army. I taped them secretly, hiding the recorder in a bag, and then put the headphones on each in turn, and let them listen to their own voices. Their wonder and joy was huge, in the way of children everywhere when they discover something unexpected and new.

At night, before retiring, I with the men, Sue with the women, the two of us would walk out a short way under the stars, and she would take my face in her hands and kiss me deeply and silently, so that nobody from the family could hear, though all knew where we were. Then we would stay outside for a while, under the brilliant night-sky that in Africa is so unforgettable. And I would tell her under my breath how happy I was when I was with her, how good the safari had been, and then she would kiss me again, say she had to go, and without another word turn towards her hut.

And in truth, the safari had been good. From the first ride to Mubende, in the back of a speeding army truck, where it was all we could do to hang on and keep our bags from bouncing out the back; to the endless bus journey the next day to Fort Portal, or Kabarole as it was now known. And then our detour across the northern end of the Ruwenzori range, via a tropical rainforest which lived up to its name, to Ntandi, where we dried out for a day with the Batwa, the pygmies, and Sue learnt the Katoni-toni dance, with its funny steps and nonsense chant, taught her by an old, toothless granny who stood on a level with her bosom.

We were also introduced to the assistant chief. 'I am smoking *bhangi*,' he announced to us, as he gave another long, bubbling pull to the bamboo stem of his pipe (a pointed kalabash, decorated with burn-marks, and fitted with a smooth stone bowl packed full of marijuana leaves); 'I am smoking *bhangi* . . . because I am Mutwa.' And he roared out the final syllable, and rolled his eyes, while all the kids around us giggled and screamed. But he also told us more serious things, like how the Batwa hunted pythons, baboons and other monkeys with their arrows, which they tipped with a lethal poison made from pulverised roots and berries: how sometimes they even captured such animals with their bare hands.

In fact, the pygmies' hunting activities had already resulted in their participation in an important scientific experiment which had served to weaken the simian theory of HIV transmission. At one stage, many Western scientists had hypothesised that pygmies might well represent a reservoir of HIV infection, because they lived in close proximity to monkeys, they hunted them and ate their meat – either raw or cooked – and they seemed to come close to that anthropological fantasy, a 'pristine community', largely unsullied by the ways of other tribes. In the event, the blood samples taken from a pygmy community in the Central African Republic were found to be quite free of HIV infection, save for a few that were taken from individuals who had had sexual contact with 'outsiders'; neither was any natural immunity to either the human or simian version of the virus detected. I was reassured when I learnt about this, for I myself had frequently eaten monkey meat, grilled rare, during a trip I had made to Zaire in late 1982. Until informed otherwise, I had thought it was beef, marinaded to the point of extreme and succulent tenderness.

The pygmies were the happiest, most amusing people I had met for a long time, and I was sorry to have to leave Ntandi so soon, but the district workshop in Masaka beckoned. On the way back to Kabarole we stopped to see the hot sulphur springs of Mongiro, and we then got drenched all over again, drenched to the skin, and to the innermost recesses of our luggage, by another tropical storm which had been hovering above the jungle canopy, waiting for our truck to pass. Never mind: the next day we collected together the mats, the clothes, and food, and cooking oil which we had purchased, and caught a Peugeot taxi southwards towards Kasese and the village where Sue's mother was living. And it didn't even matter when the taxi, in attempting to take us down the side-road to the village, got stuck in the mud and had to turn around, and we in turn had to take off our shoes and carry the eight or nine baskets which we had accumulated through 300 yards of sludge to the hillock on the other side. Sue went off to fetch some help, and returned an hour later with a *mzee*, three young boys, and a bicycle with rubber straps tied to its luggage rack. In the village, there's always a way.

But even here in the village, the long arm of Slim had reached out. The son of one of our close neighbours had died of it just a couple of months before, Sue told me, but I was not to let on to anyone that I knew. In a small community like this one, such events bring great shame to the family concerned; everybody knew of the tragedy in their midst, but was too polite to mention it. Later, when I met the father of the dead man, he told me that his boy was staying away from home.

After three days in the village, it was time for me to take my leave. I felt quite emotional as the family lined up to shake hands and say goodbye; I found it hard to convey just how much I had enjoyed my stay. It had been decided that Sue, together with her kid sister and one of her friends, would accompany me as far as the district headquarters at Kasese; and the four of us ambled off along a dusty footpath that, after an hour or so, emerged on to the main road. A *matatu* soon picked us up, and by mid-morning we were ensconced in a comfortable hotel, and tucking into enormous breakfasts in the restaurant below. It took five or six glasses of fruit juice before I felt that my body fluids had returned to normal.

We had arrived in Kasese a day earlier than was necessary for my trip to Masaka, because I wanted the opportunity to assess how another up-country district was coping with the AIDS situation. For the rest of the day I duly moved around town interviewing whomsoever I could find to interview. Opinions varied as to whether Slim disease had yet arrived in the district. A senior official from the local department of the Ugandan Red Cross, for instance, actually told me that the VRI had chosen Kasese as one of the areas for its base-line survey (which presumably meant the pilot study for the national sero-survey) for the very reason that it had no known cases. And he was not alone in his beliefs, for half an hour later, they were echoed by the Kasese District Administrator, Jonam Kabachelor. 'We have not had a problem here: we have buried no people,' he told me. 'Both our hospitals here – Kilembe and Kagando – are open to you, and you will see that we have not had any cases.'

It was late on in the afternoon when I finally managed to track down the man I most wanted to see, who was a senior district official from the Ministry of Health. His observations about AIDS directly conflicted with the other information I had been given. He told me, for instance, that they had seen an estimated fifty AIDS cases in the district, five of them children, in the eleven months between August 1986 and June 1987. He added that there were some 350,000 people living in the district, but that there was 'a lot of population dynamics', and that people from elsewhere tended to come to Kasese to get treated. The district had air and rail transport, a major highway running through from Kenya to Zaire, cement and salt factories, and bountiful agricultural produce, all of which attracted people from as far as fifty miles away.

But for all that, he was worried. 'We run the risk of having a certain age-group wiped out. People with big jobs, who have gone to school, who have important positions in society – those are the type of people we are losing. We will find ourselves as old men, with no one to follow us,' he told me. And the doctor had an interesting theory as to why there were no specific risk-groups for Slim in Uganda: the democratic, classless nature of local society. 'In Uganda, a man who sells charcoal can put on a suit in the evening, hire a taxi, and go to a pub and drink with a minister. A permanent secretary can pick up a prostitute from a local bar – he doesn't get sacked.' The doctor emphasised that at present, AIDS seemed to be an urban rather than a rural problem, that the villages were still fairly safe 'because a man will maybe only come into town once in six months, and then, hopefully, he won't get exposed.' He admitted, however, to being concerned because he didn't know the true incidence of AIDS, or the prevalence of the virus, in the area. I mentioned to him that in Kampala, they were finding that roughly one in seven pregnant women and blood donors were carriers of the virus. He was clearly shocked. 'Well, that one is quite terrible. Here, I suppose we might have one in twenty or one in fifty, but I suppose we might rise to that Kampala level in ten, or even five years', time. That means that we will start losing relatives,' he concluded, his voice now rising in panic.

I asked him which health education measures had already been implemented in the district. 'Well, we can't be proud that we have reached the rural population. But we have got posters saying "Love Carefully", which we hang on the wall, and we have got a mobile health team which goes out quite often to immunise children, and they talk about AIDS to mothers. Also our hospitals and health centres have been authorised to tell people about AIDS. But our target has been mainly the schools, from Primary Four, the ten-year-olds, up to secondary school. We think that young children are quite an important group because, even if they don't know exactly what we are talking about, even if they themselves are safe at that age, once they are convinced that there is a very terrible problem, they will be able to warn the rest of the population. We thought that if it came from a son, or a grandson, or a brother, the news might be easier to take than from some doctor with a microphone in a market-place.'

The doctor went on to tell me that they were also distributing condoms, but had only received a total of about 6,000 in the nine months since the start of the year. They had concentrated on supplying them to sexually active people in the urban centres, where they were needed immediately; and where people were more likely to be familiar with their use, either as a contraceptive, or as a barrier against venereal disease.

I thanked the doctor for his candour and his help. But as I walked back towards the hotel, I couldn't help feeling that my fears were grounded in fact: that despite the intelligent responses of men such as this particular official, there was as yet almost no formal governmental or ACP policy on AIDS being implemented in many of the up-country districts. And Kasese was not even particularly remote or inaccessible from Kampala. In addition, from what I had heard from one aid agency source, the district might in fact already be having a considerable AIDS problem: Kagando Hospital, near the Zairean border, was said to be receiving one or two new AIDS cases every day. I was glad that the DA had told me that I was free to see for myself, for that was exactly what I intended to do.

It was a good tarmac road southwards from Kasese. On the left, Lake George, a grubby-looking expanse, with low banks of partly-submerged vegetation close to the shoreline. To the right, two huge elephant tusks standing erect, their tips almost touching, announcing the beginning of the Queen Elizabeth National Park. Soon afterwards, a junction where the road veered away to the Zairean border. There we stopped to pick up more passengers.

Meanwhile Franco, 'Le Grand Maître', came on the radio, with his backing band, Le Tout Puissant OK Jazz, and their musical warning for 'les citoyennes', entitled 'Attention na SIDA'. SIDA was the Francophone name for Slim, and the fact that the greatest living exponent of Lingala music had recorded a fifteen-minute epic song warning of its dangers was an important development. 'Oh AIDS, a terrible disease; AIDS, an unforgiving evil; AIDS, an illness that spares no one. Oh that plague: AIDS, which leaves medicine powerless; Aah ...' declaimed Franco, to a background of tinkling guitars. There followed a typical Lingala refrain, with the TPOK contributing close harmony, as Franco drifted into a series of spoken monologues, containing advice for different groups like the young, the sexually active, the churchmen and the politicians. Franco would be responsible for the saving of many lives, I thought. Not his own, however, for two years later Franco himself succumbed to a wasting disease believed by many to have been the 'unforgiving evil', and Zaire went into four days of national mourning.

Soon we turned off on to a bumpy track leading up into the mountains. This was fertile land, and the small plots of coffee, *matooke*, maize and beans had clusters of palm trees standing incongruously in their midst. Away on the horizon, a procession of taller trees traced the line of the opposite ridge. Then, suddenly, we rounded a corner, and there was Kagando; the mini-bus stopped, and as I jumped down from the step I felt the freshness of the air, even though we were only a thousand feet above the burning heat of Kasese. The setting was breathtakingly beautiful. The hospital grounds were liberally sprinkled with trees: cypress, *mvule*, eucalyptus and wild olive, and the Ruwenzori foothills stretched away in all directions, row upon row of wooded ridges, with valleys slicing down between. Higher still, just palely visible through the morning heat-haze, were those snow-tipped peaks.

Dr Helen Hughes, a shy woman, apparently in her late twenties, had only taken over as medical superintendent of Kagando Hospital four days before, and she seemed a little taken aback at being approached by the press so soon after assuming her new post. Nevertheless, when I explained my interest in AIDS, she agreed to talk with me, though she watched carefully from the other side of her desk whenever I noted anything down.

Dr Hughes told me that they had first seen an AIDS case in the wards just over a year before, in August 1986, and that since then there had been many more who conformed to the WHO clinical case definition. I asked how many more, and she pulled out a register from her desk. Altogether, she concluded, there had been 102 suspected cases in the previous thirteen months, with thirty-eight cases having being seen in June and July alone, when she and her predecessor were specifically checking among the out-patients. Although she could not be certain that all 102 were suffering from AIDS, she added that when they had sent blood from eleven suspected adult cases to Mulago for checking, nine had been confirmed as HIV-positive, and the other two cases could possibly have been so well advanced that their antibodies had disappeared.

Although the recent incidence rate was nearer one case every two days than the 'one or two a day' which I had been told, this was still an alarming number of cases for a supposedly AIDS-free region. I asked her where the AIDS patients had come from, and she mentioned places as far afield as Mbarara, Kamwenge on the railway line to Kampala, Ntoroko on Lake Albert, and even Mutwanga in Zaire. Some of these towns were 80 miles distant. The majority of patients, however, were from Kasese district, and were either businessmen, prostitutes, or young professionals with a history of many sexual contacts. There were also a number of monogamous wives of infected husbands.

Did they inform their patients? 'Usually people have been very sick for some time, and they've already heard of Slim. So if we think they definitely have it, we sort of tell them,' Dr Hughes explained, with commendable candour. She went on to say that patients were referred to the chaplain, who offered spiritual guidance to both them and their families. Then, unless they had an infection that would benefit from in-patient treatment, they were given a small supply of therapeutic drugs, such as anti-diarrhoeal tablets or aspirins (which were all the hospital could afford), and sent back home to be cared for by relatives.

She added that, following consultations with the district medical and education officers in Kasese, senior staff from the hospital were visiting secondary schools and teacher training colleges, to inform students about the dangers of AIDS. When she showed me the teaching programme, it turned out that it was based on the 'Answers' leaflet pioneered by Rick Goodgame and the Baptists. The mission hospital was also trying to encourage the pastors in nearby churches to discuss the problems of AIDS with their congregations, and not to keep it as a taboo subject 'like cancer was in Britain in the past'. I remembered my first visit to Kyebe, and Nazareth mission, and could only agree with the wisdom of this approach.

There was only one patient with Slim in the hospital at that time: Maria, a young woman of twenty-six who had been sick for four months, and who had no relatives or family; finally, she had become unable to look after herself, and had been admitted a couple of days earlier. I had been told that I could interview her, and went looking for her in her ward. She was not there, but eventually a nurse led me outside, to where she was lying resting in the shade of a tree. She had covered her head with a rather dirty white cotton sheet, and she was wearing what must once have been a very pretty blue polka-dot dress. I talked with her for a few minutes, while the other patients who were enjoying the sun smiled at us, and moved slowly closer, so that they could listen in to the conversation. At the end, there were people all around us, but observing an invisible 'cordon sanitaire', seemingly with a radius of about 6 feet. Nobody was willing to venture any further past that invisible line.

After an afternoon spent looking round the hospital, talking with some of the doctors and nurses, and photographing the queues of a hundred or more waiting to be seen at the out-patients clinic, I finally managed to locate the chaplain, Reverend William Ndishabandi. William was apparently an ebullient man under normal circumstances, but now he was a veritable powerhouse, for his wife had just given birth to a son the previous night.

The chaplain related to me the behaviour pattern to which, he claimed, almost every Slim patient at Kagando conformed. First of all, most had not been told that they had the disease, but the very fact that they had been referred to him made them realise the gravity of their situation. To those who enquired what was wrong with them, William would explain that there was no absolute proof, but that the doctors suspected that it might be a case of Slim. Almost invariably, there followed a period of denial, when the patients often quarrelled with the doctors, claiming that they had made the wrong diagnosis, and after this they often tried to blame the person they thought must have given them the disease. Then, finally, they all – even those who did not already profess themselves Christians – accepted Jesus Christ before they died.

I was a little cynical about this, and said so; surely such patients were on a hiding to nothing once they knew they were dying of AIDS? But William was undeterred, and showed me the diary he kept of his conversations with different patients: in every case, it seemed, the words 'accepted Jesus Christ as saviour' featured at some stage before the end. Even those most loose-living of women who had had countless sexual partners, he told me proudly, had finally discovered the path to redemption.

Later, another British doctor called Richard was giving me a lift back to Kasese through the centre of a fantastical, God-given sunset, and I raised the subject again. Were conversions which occurred in such circumstances truly meaningful?

'I think they are. The way that God acts in someone's life is something we can't understand,' said Richard. 'And I think a conversion, or a religious experience, although it has some psychological elements, is also something deeper. I think I'd have to say that it's supernatural. As a Christian, I believe in supernatural experience. It may have the effect of comforting or calming in people, which is more than can be explained by mere psychology. We talk about God's permissive and his directive will. God may permit AIDS, but a person is still free to accept or reject the Christian message. He's not forced by the fact that he's got the disease to accept Christ.' We drove onwards into the supernatural blaze of light.

Richard told me how impressed he was with Dr Goodgame's 'Answers' initiative, saying that it offered some hope, in particular for those dying of AIDS, for whom none of the secular bodies had anything to offer. 'If those people are all just written off, it will be very sad indeed. I think counselling is going to be very important in the future; many AIDS patients are actually relieved when they're told they have the disease, because then it's out in the open. If they're told, and then treated in a caring way, it can be of great help to them.'

He confirmed that he had not yet seen much evidence of the government's health education campaign in Kasese district. 'The important thing,' he went on, 'is that the government has sanctioned other health education campaigns, like Goodgame's. The fact that they're allowing, even encouraging, any group to use any educational means at its disposal is commendable.'

It was dark by the time we approached Kasese, and we could see the lights of the town twinkling away to our left. I had been leaving one important question to last, because of its potential sensitivity, but now it was time to ask. Earlier in the day, the matron in the maternity ward had mentioned to me that two British students from Cambridge University had come to Kagando in 1986, and had taken blood samples from a number of people, both inside and outside the hospital. Was this true, I asked Richard; and if so, had any results been released?

'Yes, I thought you might have heard about that,' he laughed. 'Well, primarily, they were here to do some trial runs on a new method of assessing HIV-positivity, known as the Karpas test. It's been developed by a Cambridge professor, Professor Abraham Karpas I think his name is, and its main advantages are that it's supposed to be cheaper, and easier to use in rural hospitals. All you need is slides and reagents, because there's an easily visible colour change; there's no need for an expensive reader.'

'So which people did they test?'

'They tested men, women and children from the hospital, together with everyone from the TB ward. And they also tested a number of unmarried women from the trading centre at Kisinga, just two miles away from Kagando – the implication being that most single girls living on their own in trading centres are likely to be prostitutes, at least on an occasional basis.'

'And what results did they come up with?'

'Well, there were some positives in every group. But of course they were just preliminary results, they had to confirm them back home on ELISA and so forth. Anyway, since then, we seem to have lost contact a bit. They had asked us to do some follow-up tests, but our lab technicians had some problems with reagents spilling out of their wells. So we didn't do any follow-up, and we haven't heard from them since.'

Richard had already been so helpful that I didn't want to press him further; he clearly wasn't happy to relate dim recollections of preliminary findings. But, before he drove off again, he gave me the name of the student who had been in charge of the research, one Chris Hudson, from Corpus Christi College. About a year later, I came across the relevant medical paper. The study had actually been carried out in August 1986, at two mission hospitals in rural south-west Uganda: Kagando, together with Kisiizi in Kabale district, near the Rwandese border. Roughly equal numbers of out-patients at each hospital 'reflecting the age and sex composition of the general population' had been sero-tested and questioned about sexual activity and other factors. Three per cent of those tested (in fact, an equal number at each hospital) had proved to be seropositive, this breaking down into none of the patients aged under twenty, but 7 per cent of the twenty to forty-nine age group. However, 25 per cent of the thirty-six suspected prostitutes from Kisinga trading centre had proved to be HIV carriers (and fully 46 per cent of them proved antibody-positive on the TPHA test for syphilis).

The paper concluded by suggesting that AIDS in Uganda was spreading rapidly into the rural areas, although the epidemic was still at an early stage compared to that in Kampala; that the risk factors for HIV exposure were the same as for a history of STD; that the major risk activity involved in this spread was male sexual contact with prostitutes, which 61 per cent of all men tested in the study reported having had during the previous five years; and that having had two or more sexual partners, or a sexual partner who had lived in or travelled to a major town, also placed someone at significantly higher risk of getting the virus.

In terms of control, the paper suggested that health education must start at primary school level, since some of the ten-year-olds questioned in the study were already sexually active; that short-term control using condoms would be cost-effective only if they were distributed to prostitutes; and that 'an improved status of women in the community' might prove beneficial in terms of reducing prostitution. The authors also commented that, although AIDS awareness was 'disturbingly low in all age groups', it was best among school-age children, and worst among those adults who were most at risk.

That night I took Sue and the kids out for a farewell meal, an enormous pizza that we had ordered the previous evening, and which someone had baked with more enthusiasm than intimate knowledge of Italian cuisine. But for all that it was delicious, and all the more so because it was hot inside the restaurant and we ended up moving our table outside on to the pavement, to enjoy the feast there, like Roman senators. And the following morning, at half-past four, I pulled on my clothes, kissed Sue goodbye, shouted for the nightwatchman to come and unlock the gate, and sprinted through the darkness and the back streets of Kasese, arriving just in time to catch the bus to Kampala.

It was one of those journeys that, try as one might to enjoy them, are in the end not quirky, colourful, or character-building, but merely an enormous bore. First of all, as we barrelled southwards along the tarmac road, it proved entirely impossible to find a comfortable place to sleep. The seats were just too short and narrow, and there was a permanent draught of cold air coming through the window. We stopped for what seemed an age at Katunguru, the truck-stop beside the Kizinga Channel which links lakes George and Edward, but there were no interesting high-risk activities to be spotted, merely a terrible clanking and shouting as the conductor, aided by various local fishermen, loaded bundles of dried fish, bicycles and God knows what else on to the roof-rack. We rolled onwards, into a greyish dawn, and struggled up the Kichwamba escarpment (crashing gear-changes; copious exhaust fumes) past the picture-postcard lakes around Rubirizi, and onwards into the fertile heartland of Ankole. It was still freezing cold.

By the time we reached Bushenyi, the first major town *en route*, the sun had risen just high enough to have made a dent in the temperature graph, but my fitful slumbers were disturbed by a swarm of young boys bearing hard-boiled eggs, dripping skewers of roasted meat and chicken, biscuits and bunches of bananas. The window beside me had a half-inch gap between glass and frame, which had defied all my attempts to bridge it, and the boys headed unerringly for this slit, thrusting grubby fingers inside, trying to slide back the glass and sell their complete range of foodstuffs at a stroke.

Later on there was a rainstorm, during which I discovered that I was seated directly beneath a gap in the false ceiling; presently, when the bus swerved to avoid an oncoming army lorry, a long stream of oily grey fluid sluiced downwards, all over myself and the woman beside me. After the initial shock, I had to join the rest of the bus in seeing the humorous side, but when it happened for the third or fourth time, the joke began to wear decidedly thin. At Mbarara there was another lengthy delay in the bus-park, when the driver disappeared somewhere for half an hour, and after we resumed our journey, we began bouncing a lot more than before. This particular stretch of road is notorious throughout Uganda, largely because it has been breaking up for the last twenty-five years under the incessant pounding of heavy lorries bound for the heart of the continent; at this stage, in late 1987, there was about as much pothole as road. We frequently slowed to walking pace to lumber over the more corrupted sections, and I remembered once again why it was a bad idea to sit near the back of a Ugandan bus.

Just as we entered the famous truck-stop of Lyantonde, there was another downpour. Through the rain-splashed windows, all I could make out was a long street of single-storey shanty dwellings, and a lot of lorries drawn up by the side of the road. This was the place, just inside the boundary of Rakai district, where one year before Warren Namaara had tested the blood of 186 barmaids, and subsequently found that two out of three were carriers of HIV.

We arrived in Masaka at half-past two, after a ten-hour journey, and I was only glad to be avoiding the final leg to Kampala; I hired a taxi to take me to the District Medical Headquarters. There I met the DMO, Dr Buluka, who told me that the district health education workshop had been cancelled. He had arranged the venue, he told me, and notified the appropriate officials, only to be informed from Entebbe a few days before that the three-day workshop would have to be postponed *sine die*. Louis Ochero was apparently supposed to drop by on his way to Mbarara to explain, but had still not turned up. Rather ruefully, I said that I expected that everyone was busy preparing for the Commonwealth AIDS Conference scheduled for two weeks later. Dr Buluka snorted and said:

'That all sounds like castles in the air to me. I've been doing this job for three months, and so far I've received no directives from the ministry.'

A little later, I asked him if AIDS had made people change their behaviour at all in Masaka.

'Well, most people are zero grazing nowadays, except of course after a drink,' he replied.

I mentioned that I'd heard that 50 per cent of the out-patients at Kitovu Hospital in the town had tested seropositive.

'So what? What good does testing do?' he demanded. 'How does it help you if you know?'

'I would have thought most people would have tried to change their behaviour, not to spread it to others,' I said, feeling suddenly on the defensive.

'Ah, the moral argument. That one requires very high discipline, and the majority don't have that. Weak minds would just commit suicide, as so many already have.' According to one newspaper report, one of his predecessors as DMO of Masaka was among them.

I sat down on the wall outside the DMO's office, feeling fed up and exhausted, and trying to decide whether to visit the Masaka hospitals, or return to Kyotera and Kalisizo, or perhaps go back to Lyantonde and spend the night there. But my mind was made up for me a few minutes later, when Seth Berkley and his wife rolled into the compound in their Suzuki jeep, and told me they were leaving in ten minutes for Kampala, and could give me a lift if I wanted. I did. Seth, an erudite and energetic American whom I had first met in Darfur two years before at the height of the Sudanese famine, was now heading the Entebbe office of the Task Force for Child Survival, and helping to re-establish a disease surveillance system at Uganda's hospitals. The size of the task, he told me as we boarded the Suzuki and drove off, was indicated by the situation at Kitovu Hospital, which he had just been visiting. Apparently they had seen a total of 34,000 out-patients since the start of the year, and no records whatsoever had been kept. And at Masaka Hospital, the official government hospital in the centre of town, the AIDS questionnaire forms which he'd handed out some time before were being torn in half, and used by the medical staff for notepaper. He was still fuming by the time we left Masaka and hit the open road heading for Katonga bridge and the capital.

The conversation we had during that journey went through a wide range of AIDS-related subjects, until our throats went hoarse from shouting above the noise of the motor. Do AIDS control programmes really work? Why does transmission apparently occur that much more easily in Africa: is there some co-factor which has not yet been discovered? How long would it be before the seroprevalence curve levelled off? Would the adult curve just keep going upwards, like that of the San Francisco homosexual cohort of 1978, about 80 per cent of whom were now seropositive? We talked about the

multi-million-dollar USAID family-planning survey being implemented by Westinghouse, which would include questions on AIDS, condoms,
and suchlike. Finally, as we approached Kampala, Seth observed that
the Uganda situation in 1987 closely resembled that of Sudan two
years earlier: war-torn, trying to get back on its feet, 'everyone's
favourite baby', the aid agencies asking how many noughts to put
on the cheque. It was a rough vision, but there was some truth in
it.

We only stopped once on the way, and that was when, as we rounded
a long curve, we came up behind a man wheeling a push-bike. Laid
across the luggage rack was a long, stiff bundle, wrapped in bark-cloth.
We halted the car some 50 yards away, and Seth and I got out and, having
asked the man's permission, took photographs. It was his wife, he told
us, and no – she had died of typhoid.

A couple of days later, on my way to the airport to catch the plane down
to Nairobi, I called in at the Central Medical Stores in Entebbe, where
the latest material for the ACP had just arrived: rubber boots, plastic
gloves, aprons, more ELISA machines, 400,000 needles and syringes.
And in the course of my visit, I did manage to solve one mystery. I
went into the tablet stores, where the last of the 2 million USAID
condoms were being kept, and took a look at the roof, which was
painted to reflect the light, and insulated with asbestos. It seemed
very unlikely that the temperature inside the store could – even at the
height of the hot season – get close to the crucial mark of 40°C, above
which the thin rubber of a condom was liable to perish. And indeed,
it turned out that the condoms which Dr Carswell had given me were
part of a previous consignment, sent to the Family Planning Association
of Uganda in the days before Slim was widespread. But for all that,
the date marked on the packet – Aug '84 – indicated that they were
just three years old, and well within their supposed five-year life-span.
All this suggested that the shelf-life of condoms might be significantly
shorter than normal in equatorial conditions.

'There definitely should be care about the quality of the condoms
distributed,' commented the chief storeman. 'Because if the quality is
poor, and the condom is something new for local people, and it doesn't
work properly, then it is obvious what their reaction is going to be.'

At the airport, the same security officer was there, still smugness
incarnate, and still looking vaguely familiar, though I couldn't quite

place him. And I did a very stupid thing: I tried to make a little joke. When he asked me why I was travelling to Nairobi again, I answered lightly: 'Oh, you know, I just thought I'd pop down to tell the Kenyans a few of your secrets.'

When I looked up at him, he was staring at me very hard, without a glimmer of a smile of complicity or understanding. Uganda and Kenya were just then going through one of their bad periods, with massed troops and occasional shooting incidents along the common border, and angry, accusing articles in both sets of newspapers. We stood for some seconds like that, he and I, neither of us backing down, before he stamped my departure card and waved me through.

24 · IN CONFERENCE

I spent my first couple of nights in Nairobi with Steve, a European in his mid-thirties, and on this particular morning he had gone to work early. I slept through until eight o'clock, and then had to cross his bedroom to reach the bathroom; I crept through quietly because his girlfriend – a small, vivacious twenty-year-old – was still asleep. As I reached the door, she suddenly sat up in bed, allowing the sheets to fall from her breasts. She was smiling at me.

'Hello,' she said. 'I thought it must be you.'

'Yes, it's me all right.' I carried on into the bathroom, not unaware of the sexual *frisson*, but trying hard to resist.

But not trying hard enough. During supper the previous night, she and I had chatted for some time, and her foot had begun stroking mine under the table; and now, when I made some coffee, I decided to take her a cup. She was still in bed, and patted the mattress beside her for me to sit down. I did so, and placed the cups carefully on the bedside table, whereupon she promptly rolled out naked from under the covers, and grabbed me round the waist.

'Now hang on, Wanjiko,' I said, using the Kikuyu family name by which she was normally known. 'Joseph's just outside, and he'll be coming in any minute to clean up.'

'No he won't,' she said.

'And you know I've got a girlfriend up in Uganda,' I tried again. But we both knew that I wouldn't have been sat on the bed at all without wanting to be there, and presently her smooth skin and warm body got the better of me, and I lay down on the bed beside her. She rolled over on top of me, and wiggled her bottom in a victory salute. It was nice to have a cuddle, I told myself; that was OK. Wanjiko started licking my neck.

'What's wrong then? Don't you like me?' she asked.

'Of course I like you. You're a very attractive woman, and under other circumstances, I'd love to. But I've got Sue, and you've got Steve, and he's my friend for God's sake . . .'

'That's all right. We can meet somewhere else if you like. There's a party I'm going to tomorrow night; you can meet me there.'

But by now, loyalty to Sue and Steve had belatedly overcome the attractions of Wanjiko's small, firm body. I eased myself out from underneath, scribbled down her phone number, and then took my leave, promising to get in touch. On the way to the bus-stop I threw away the scrap of paper, knowing that Wanjiko would not mind losing one European from her several options, but as I did so I detected a definite spring in my step.

The Training Workshop on Counselling for Persons with HIV Infection and Other Related Diseases had already been in progress two days, and as soon as I arrived I was told that the discussion sessions had been declared off-limits to the press. But the workshop co-ordinator, Dr Manuel Carballo, director of research and development at the WHO's Special Programme on AIDS, did agree to talk to me. He and I ventured out on to a landscaped grassy mound behind the prefabricated wooden office buildings; we sat down side by side in the sunshine with a polite space between us, and I quickly discovered that his meticulous appearance, his empathetic manner and his fluent stream of words actually concealed some very firmly held views. Some of them, however, seemed better suited to Geneva than to Rakai.

He told me that the delegates included clinicians, nurses, medical social workers and health administrators from Kenya, Uganda, Tanzania, Malawi, Zimbabwe and Ethiopia. Such people, he said, were not normally trained in the relatively new subject of counselling, but they were now needed, in increasing numbers, to provide such services to HIV-positives, to those who suspected they were HIV-positive, to people with AIDS, and to the families of those with AIDS.

'It's important that people don't feel that being HIV-positive necessarily means that one is going to die. Scientists might come up with an effective therapy tomorrow; we just don't know. But we do know that the greater the stress that the individual is under, the more likely it is that progression from HIV infection to AIDS will be accelerated. We also know that individuals who are HIV-positive may have five to seven, if not more, productive life years ahead of them: economically, socially, intellectually, and most important of all, in terms of keeping the family together and child-rearing. The last thing we want to do is to have people who are diagnosed as HIV-positive assuming that this is the end of the story. They still have many opportunities and possibilities, and that's what we want to encourage.'

But it was only after I resorted to a little role-play, with myself cast as the libertine who was belatedly realising the risks, that I realised that Dr Carballo, like Dr Okware, had great reservations about the benefits of informing HIV carriers.

'Bear in mind one thing,' he said, 'this is the first disease that mankind has dealt with, where very specific and sensitive screening can be undertaken, and yet there is very little to offer the infected person. Right now all we have to offer is counselling, health education, and social support, all of which can be offered whether or not someone knows that they're infected. But once a person does know their status, then that person has very, very unique and special needs, and unless we can be sure that we can respond to those needs, we're better off at this juncture making sure that everyone has the same information, support and education. That's what the NCPA in Uganda has attempted: to develop a broad-ranging health education programme that will benefit everyone, whether positive or negative.'

Dr Carballo added that he was confident of a positive response to the HE campaigns that were being mounted in different countries. 'This is not like an anti-smoking campaign; this is not like promoting oral hygiene. Here, we're talking about taking action quickly and effectively to save the lives of everyone in society, because everyone, one way or another, is at risk. We're monitoring blood transfusions, and screening donations; we're counselling mothers and couples about the risks of mother-child transmission; we have programmes to educate about the risks of skin-piercing, and of needle-sharing in intravenous drug use. That leaves the most important route of transmission, the sexual route, which is the route least amenable to any kind of intervention. You can't legislate about sexual contact, or introduce screening for it. It's not going to be easy. But we're trying to encourage safer sex, and we're very optimistic about the changes in behaviour.' I headed off to the dining-room wishing that I felt as hopeful as Dr Carballo.

Lunch had a definite end-of-term atmosphere, with one of the Ugandans attempting to chat up an attractive Ethiopian delegate and getting a frosty response, and another Ethiopian then informing me that AIDS was almost certainly present in her country 'because of the number of foreign relief workers in our cities'. Then, after the obligatory group photograph, we all trooped inside again for the closing plenary session, and one of the speeches did indeed give some grounds for optimism.

Mrs Elizabeth Ngugi, former chairwoman of Kenya's National AIDS Committee, was speaking on 'The Outcome of Counselling'. Mrs Ngugi was a member of the University of Nairobi team which had been working with female prostitutes in the Nairobi suburb of Pumwani, and she was at that time Kenya's only counsellor on HIV infection. She turned out to be a nervous woman with a rather poor speaking voice, but I got the feeling that she was probably much more at home when dealing with the Pumwani prostitutes than when addressing a roomful of doctors, health workers and reporters. Yet from her opening statement, on the topic of whether or not to inform, it was clear that she had forthright views, and that these did not always correspond with those of Dr Carballo.

'It is only logical to assume,' she said, 'that unless both the people with AIDS and HIV are made aware of the facts, there is no way the health care worker and others can begin to facilitate a sexual behaviour change. The infected persons will continue with their sex lives, unaware that they are spreading infection to their partners.'

She proceeded to tell the story of how, between May and November 1986, the prostitutes attending Pumwani clinic had been individually counselled about AIDS. The process, as recounted by Mrs Ngugi, had been to see each woman in private, to invite her to sit and talk about children and family, and only when she was clearly at ease and ready to listen to introduce the subject of AIDS, and explain about the three major methods of transmission. The fact that there was no known cure or vaccine was underscored, as was the importance of not getting infected, or passing on infection to others. Then a threefold strategy was outlined. First, the woman was encouraged to stop prostitution. If this was not possible, she was then encouraged to enforce condom use among her clients, and lastly urged to reduce her number of sexual partners.

The prostitutes were then tested and informed of their results (apparently not one of the women had preferred not to know). Of a total of 169 prostitutes tested, 74 per cent were found to be seropositive. Over half the prostitutes (including a higher proportion of the seropositives) subsequently expressed a desire to stop prostitution, the upkeep of children being cited as the main reason by those who said they would continue. In addition, over two-thirds of both categories said they intended to enforce condom usage in the future, either to protect the clients from infection, or themselves from infection or reinfection, as appropriate.

It was apparent that this approach of counselling subjects both before and after the HIV test had been highly successful in terms of encouraging the type of sexually responsible behaviour that would benefit both prostitute and client. Mrs Ngugi finished by saying that her team was now in the process of following up, to establish to what degree intentions had translated into actuality. And, at a conference in London, three months later, she announced an astonishing success story. The policy of individual counselling, combined with open-air *baraza*s on the subject of AIDS, and such educational methods as written tests, role-plays and the singing of 'The AIDS Song' (composed by Ngugi herself) had apparently resulted in half of Pumwani's prostitutes enforcing condom usage all the time, and a further 40 per cent enforcing condom usage occasionally. By contrast, one year earlier, only 8 per cent of the cohort had been using condoms, and then intermittently. Mrs Ngugi also reported that there had been a threefold reduction in the rate of seroconversion among women insisting on condom use.

The workshop was meant to be formally closed by Professor Thomas Ogada, the Director of Medical Services, but he failed to turn up, so finally the participants disbanded themselves. But as it happened, I was to meet Professor Ogada the very next morning in Afia House, the headquarters of the Ministry of Health, where I was trying to arrange an appointment with the minister. I was just giving my name to the secretary when the professor walked in and demanded to know my business. I told him.

'In your own country do you just go and see the minister for nothing?' he demanded. 'You have to show him proper respect. We are not just here to be treated like boys. Go away, you are not going to see the minister.' As he turned to go, all three-piece-suit and bombast, he relented slightly, and told me to go and see his deputy, Dr Mueke, if I had any questions about AIDS.

In the end I did so. Dr Mueke turned out to be a small, harassed-looking man, whose words had a habit of running away with him. After five minutes' worth of confusing verbiage, he finally told me:

'If you want information for publication, write to the Permanent Secretary, or to the DMS, with a list of your questions. Your letter will then be forwarded to me. That is my cover. In case anything is distorted, I shall be in the clear.'

'But I'm in the business of reporting, not distorting, Dr Mueke.'

'It's all the same thing. Some people say we are trying to cover things up, but we are not. I assure you my friend, this would be just the same if you were enquiring about malaria. You understand, I think.'

But to be fair, not all Kenyan officials were as rude as Professor Ogada, or as evasive as Dr Mueke. The following week, I paid two visits to the impressive red-brick campus of KEMRI, the Kenyan Medical Research Institute, and eventually managed to get through to see the director, Professor Mugambi, who was also the chairman of Kenya's National AIDS Committee. He told me that he had time to answer perhaps two or three quick questions. Ah well, I thought, that's one or two more than I've ever got around to asking Dr Okware.

Professor Mugambi told me that Kenya's five-year AIDS Control Programme had been approved at the end of July, and funded to the tune of 2.94 million dollars for its first year of operation. 'That was exactly the amount we asked for – no more, no less – so I guess we will be satisfied with that,' he added. It struck me, not for the first time, that a lot of Kenyan officials must have been fairly peeved to have received so much less funding than Uganda; and this impression was only reinforced by the professor's subsequent references to 'realistic budgeting' and 'limited resources'. But before he left, and to my relative amazement, Professor Mugambi jotted quick notes to three other doctors with whom I had requested interviews. One of these was the Canadian doctor, Frank Plummer, who was the *de facto*, if not the official, leader of the Pumwani team. Another was Dr Ben Were, the director of clinical research at KEMRI itself, and I got to see him that same afternoon.

The main study that Dr Were had to tell me about involved the clinical trials of the therapeutic drug AZT, which were due to start later in the year. The UK branch of Wellcome was sponsoring this research, which was designed to test the drug's efficacy and toxicity on African, as distinct from Caucasian, patients. Wellcome would provide a year's free treatment for those volunteers who were accepted on to the scheme, and would continue to supply those patients who were still alive at the end of that period. I commented that surely AZT was prohibitively expensive for general use in the African setting, and Dr Were agreed, eventually acknowledging that the actual cost of a year's treatment would amount to 160,000 Kenyan shillings, or roughly 10,000 dollars. I asked what clinical improvements were anticipated for that sort of money, and he told me weight gain, some improvement in the immunological system, and a consequent reduction in opportunistic infections. It seemed clear, however, that while the trials might temporarily improve the lot of the African volunteers (at least those who did not suffer from unpleasant side-effects such as bone-marrow deficiency and chronic anaemia), the research findings would be of far greater value to the Wellcome corporation than to the

Kenyan Ministry of Health, at least while Wellcome continued to charge such very high prices.

Before leaving, I asked Dr Were what he thought was the best hope for those already suffering from AIDS.

'The best thing of all would be if we could kill off the virus, and deal with the primary problem like that. But even if there was a cure, I'm sure that it wouldn't arrive in Africa until a few years after it arrived in the developed world. So, in the mean time, we'll have to limit our activity to giving the most efficient care and the best counselling to our patients, so that we improve the time that they have left.'

But other doctors I spoke with were less hopeful than Dr Were. They worried that unless an AIDS cure as quick and cheap as a smallpox jab was discovered, then neither government nor pharmaceutical company would be willing to finance the curing of Africa, even if that curing were to take place 'a few years' after that of the West.

I had an eleven o'clock appointment with Dr Frank Plummer, the renowned Canadian infectious disease physician based at Kenyatta Hospital. Plummer's work with prostitutes, and his copious output of medical papers, was prompting an increasing amount of attention from his medical colleagues. I had noticed how his name normally appeared in second or third position in the list of co-authors at the head of these papers, and suspected this to be prompted by caution as much as modesty, given the dramatic nature of their findings. I had twenty minutes to spare before our meeting, so I went to the hospital cafeteria, purchased a cup of tea, and sat down to leaf through the seminal Plummer article on HIV, entitled, 'AIDS Virus Infection in Nairobi Prostitutes'.

In early 1985, Plummer and his team had tested two groups of Nairobi prostitutes – sixty-four from an economically depressed neighbourhood (Pumwani), and twenty-six who were recruited from the bar of a tourist hotel (which turned out to be Buffalo Bill's). The prostitutes had an annual average of 963 and 125 sex partners respectively, reflecting the fact that the Pumwani prostitutes (who charged an average of 50 cents) needed to have sex with more men than their sisters from Buffalo Bill's (who charged an average of 10 dollars), in order to procure a living wage. Sixty-six per cent of the Pumwani group, and 31 per cent of those from BB's, had proved to be HIV carriers, as confirmed by two different ELISA tests and a Western blot. Two other sample Nairobi populations were also tested, namely a group of male attenders at a STD clinic, and a control group of medical personnel: 8 per cent and 2 per cent respectively were found to be infected. Despite the small numbers of the samples, the findings were clearly both alarming and significant, as were the secondary findings that although there was no detectable correlation between HIV-positivity and sexual exposure to men from Europe or North America (indeed, not one of the Pumwani prostitutes had had sex with a non-African), there was a significant correlation with sexual exposure to Rwandese men, and a similar trend with men from Burundi and Uganda.

I finished my tea and headed down to Dr Plummer's office. He turned out to be a genial, bearded Canadian, much younger than I'd imagined, who was eager to get down to business straight away. I was immediately impressed with his straightforwardness and lack of guile: his belief in the importance of his team's findings clearly outweighed any natural reticence he may have felt about speaking to the press. He told me that they had begun working with a group of about 600 of the Pumwani prostitutes in January 1985, and that the project currently catered for roughly 900 such women. The majority, he said, were Tanzanian, and from one particular tribe, the Bahaya, who seemed to have a tradition of travelling all over East and Central Africa as prostitutes; a smaller number were Ugandan, and an even smaller proportion were from Kenya itself. The average age was just under thirty; the average time spent in prostitution three years. The mean number of partners was roughly four a day, or well over a thousand a year. They exhibited very high levels of both STDs and HIV.

'And how many of the women have so far seroconverted?' I asked.

'Well, the first tests in 1985 showed over sixty per cent to be seropositive, and since then there's been a tremendous rate of new HIV infection. About forty per cent of the HIV-negative women have become HIV-positive each year.'

'So what is the current level of seropositivity?'

'It's close to ninety per cent.' His reply was almost offhand, but its content was quite dreadful: 90 per cent was a higher level of seropositivity than that for any other cohort of which I'd heard. I did not press for a more precise figure.

'Have many of the original group already died of AIDS?'

'We know of only about six deaths among the first 600 women, but many go back to their home districts to die. The frequency of progression to some sort of illness is about six per cent per annum, which is similar to other studies.'

'And what form is your study currently taking?'

'The most important part is the attempt to intervene, using education about STDs, HIV and condom use. Then there's the study of the frequency of progression from one stage of HIV infection to another. And lastly, we're trying to determine why some women get HIV infection while others don't.'

'Don't you find that the first study rather conflicts with the third?'

'Of course, but there's nothing you can do. That's probably the most important work you can do in Africa: to try to persuade people to limit their risk.'

'And how do you seek to do that?'

'I think that once a person has even minimal information about AIDS and HIV, you can show them how to use condoms, and give them the opportunity to have them. Over ninety per cent of our women now have their partners use condoms at least some of the time, and that's irrespective of the HIV status of the woman. It's related to the level of education: the more intensively educated they are about condoms, the more likely they are to use them.'

We went on to discuss factors which tend to encourage prostitution in Africa, such as the taboos against premarital sex in rural areas, the taboos against married women having sexual activity for a lengthy period after the birth of a child, the common practice of husbands abandoning wives who prove to be barren, the relatively late age at which African men (as compared to women) tend to marry, and the migration of young men to towns to look for paid employment.

I asked him about the other medical research which he had been involved with since his arrival in Nairobi at the start of the 1980s. Dr Plummer explained that he had been carrying out STD studies for the last seven years, and consequently had a lot of stored sera from prostitutes, men with STDs, and pregnant women. Retrospective sero-analysis had allowed him to chart the inroads made by HIV in the capital between the years 1981 and 1985. During that time, HIV-positivity among all prostitutes tested had risen from 4 per cent to 61 per cent; for men attending an STD clinic, it had gone up from 3 per cent to 15 per cent, and for pregnant women from zero to 2 per cent. He described the figures as the documentary proof of 'a rather explosive epidemic of HIV infection in Nairobi'.

The second important piece of research work concerned the incidence of genital ulcer disease, as a result of such infections as syphilis, chancroid and herpes. Basically, African men and women with GUD had a far higher incidence of HIV than those without, Plummer explained, adding that this was important biologically, but also from the point of view of prevention, since the type of genital ulcers common in Africa were susceptible to antibiotics.

'That's probably part of the answer as to why HIV spreads more easily heterosexually in Africa,' he went on. 'And in America, in places where there is a lot of heterosexual transmission – like parts of Florida, New York and Los Angeles – there have also been epidemics of chancroid, one of the major forms of GUD.'

I suggested that this might indicate that, in sexual transmission, it is the virus in the bloodstream, rather than that in the semen or the vaginal secretions, which is dangerous to the other party.

'It's not absolute,' Plummer replied, his scientific interest apparently aroused. 'I believe that you can get HIV transmission from man to woman and woman to man in the absence of any apparent lesions or breaks in the skin. But it probably happens much more frequently when genital ulcers are present.'

Next, I asked him about the study which had fascinated me ever since I first heard of it from Wilson Carswell several months before: the results of sexual encounters between a group of seronegative men and seropositive women. How could he possibly know that each man had had just the one sexual encounter with an HIV carrier? Were men being grabbed hot from the mattress?

Plummer explained that his team had recruited men who visited the Nairobi STD clinic after having had sex with one of the Pumwani prostitutes – and whose chance of having had sex with an HIV carrier was therefore roughly 90 per cent – and that those men who had had other encounters with prostitutes in the months preceding were then eliminated from the study. He admitted that a major weakness of the research was that the entire group had already been presenting with STDs like gonorrhoea, chancroid, or syphilis from the outset. But, of those men who had been followed up over a period of six months, fully 13 per cent had seroconverted. In addition, those with GUD had seroconverted at a much faster rate than those with other STDs. Plummer added that the rate of onward transmission could be even higher, because not all the Pumwani prostitutes were seropositive, and because even those who were would not necessarily all have HIV in their genital tracts at the time that intercourse took place. In summary, he said that he believed that in Nairobi, 5 to 20 per cent of those men who had a single act of sex with an HIV-infected woman would themselves become infected. Even though I had been getting increasingly blasé about HIV statistics, I felt quite horrified.

It struck me that many Kenyan officials must have felt the same way, and I asked Plummer what sort of response he was getting to his studies. Surely some of his work was highly controversial?

'I think the prostitute studies have been controversial. But we haven't extrapolated our figures to other groups of prostitutes in Nairobi, as some have accused us of doing. Anyway, it doesn't really matter if seropositivity is thirty per cent, forty per cent or sixty per cent with prostitutes; if it's thirty per cent today, it's going to be ninety per cent in three or four years' time. Even five per cent is dangerous: it's all just a factor of time.' He added that although sometimes his team had had to step carefully, the Kenyan government had never actually stopped them from performing a study, or from presenting a medical paper.

Plummer confirmed what Mrs Ngugi had said – that all seropositives on the study were both informed and counselled. I pointed out that some other African countries, perhaps because of a lack of counselling facilities, were only informing patients at the individual doctor's discretion.

'I don't like that approach. First, because I think the patient is the person responsible for his or her health; the job shouldn't be delegated to the Ministry of Health, or to a doctor. It's only fair to give people the fullest information. Secondly, if someone doesn't know, how can they protect their spouse, their girlfriend or boyfriend? They have to know. Even though it's very unpleasant for everybody.'

Lastly, I asked Plummer what he felt the main significance of his research work to be.

'The most important thing we've shown is that behaviour modification does work in the African setting; that you can persuade people to use condoms to prevent transmission of HIV. Worldwide, there's a sort of a collective search for a cure or a vaccine – a quick solution. But we can't look at that as a saviour. We've got to work towards a change of behaviour right now, or else it's going to be too late for so many people. And the second significant finding is that genital ulcers are an important factor in HIV transmission, which has given us a concrete point of intervention against the virus.'

It was now lunch-time, and Dr Plummer offered me a lift back into the centre of Nairobi. As we walked to his car, he offered a slightly more informal view.

'Actually,' he said, 'we're dong the best work in Africa, bar none. And we've probably prevented thousands of HIV infections by our work with prostitutes.'

'How many thousands, do you think?' I asked.

'Think about the number of Pumwani prostitutes, and their regular number of partners. My guess is that we've halved the number of transmissions.'

It was a proud boast, but it seemed to be well justified.

The place was one of Nairobi's inner suburbs, and there were five of us around the table – four doctors and myself. Three of the doctors were expatriate, the other was Kenyan, and the ground rules for the meeting were that I could make notes, but not record; all comments were to be unattributable. Perhaps because of the clandestine set-up, a lot of grouses and dissatisfactions with the status quo were aired, but also a great deal of fascinating information came to light. Much of it, I felt, tended to be confirmed by the very numbers present.

First of all, I asked about the progress of the health education campaign, and the response was predominantly negative. Comments were made about the banning of Ng'weno's sex education series 'Usiniharakishe', the lack of public safety films on TV, the poor distribution of the Red Cross posters outside the main towns. The Kenyan doctor claimed that virtually no information about AIDS was filtering through to rural communities.

'Nobody wants to be quoted,' he told me. 'There's a lot of fear. You are conscious of the political implications all the time. You are not given a free hand to go on a platform and pass on the message the way you would like to; it all has to be cleared first, then censored. You might not even be able to pass across a medical fact.'

'This is a Christian country,' said one of the others. 'They don't, of course, have STDs. AIDS is regarded as a disease of foreigners.'

The criticisms extended to most of the structures which were meant to be involved in the fight against AIDS. The standard of work at KEMRI was said to be poor – despite its substantial resources, there were at present only four research programmes, including that of Plummer's team, underway. The National AIDS Committee was accused of being strangled by its own bureaucracy, as was the ministerial committee on AIDS, which was supposed to liaise between such departments as health, tourism and education. My own research confirmed that voluntary agencies were waiting many months for their AIDS projects to be approved; that several important initiatives had been stifled by official inertia.

We turned to the history of the Kenyan AIDS epidemic. The first confirmed case had apparently occurred in 1983, but it was not until 1984 that a case of Slim came to the notice of the press, and then mainly because the deceased, one Don Kabeba, was himself a journalist from

Uganda. Three of Kabeba's girlfriends also died the following year, by the end of which the Kenyan government was acknowledging the presence of ten AIDS cases, thus becoming the first African country to do so. But 1985 was also the year that Biggar's infamous seroprevalence study was published; and the consequent furore in Kenyan medical circles caused research work to fall behind. In fact, the repercussions were still being felt, being at least partially responsible for the current atmosphere of mistrust and secrecy.

There were many examples of this. At around the time of the squaddies saga, some medical personnel had been phoned up in the middle of the night by a mystery caller demanding to know who had 'supplied the figures'. And although ELISA machines had begun arriving in Kenya in 1986, many of the up-country hospitals were no longer sending in results from the testing carried out on the premises. In recent months no data had been submitted from Kisumu or Nyanza province in western Kenya, an area which was normally responsible for 60 to 70 per cent of Kenya's AIDS cases. It was almost certain, therefore, that the current official total of 625 cases was a considerable underestimate.

Regarding current seropositivity, there was general agreement that in Nairobi the figures for HIV prevalence were relatively low among the general population: still running at about 2 per cent, even at the maternity hospital in Pumwani itself. The figures for Nyanza province were thought to be much higher: almost 6 per cent of all adults at the start of 1987. Specific groups, however, were far worse off: over 10 per cent of prisoners, waiters, hotel and bar staff in western Kenya had tested HIV-positive, as had 25 per cent of a group of prostitutes from Kisumu. Mombasa was also reporting levels higher than Nairobi, with over 4 per cent of the general population seropositive. Although the town was further down the trucking route, Mombasa was a terminus, where the lorry crews inevitably spent more time. There was also the fact that the tourists and foreign sailors on R and R tended to attract more prostitutes.

Someone added that seropositivity levels in East and Central Africa seemed to be much higher again: some 40 per cent of a group of ante- or postnatal women in Kigali, Rwanda; 25 per cent of young adults in Bukoba, Tanzania; and 17 per cent of young mothers at Lyantonde had proved seropositive in recent tests, as had 47 per cent of a group from the Zambian army, and 30 per cent of one from the NRA. Nobody had any idea of seropositivity in the Kenyan army, though it was also felt likely to be high, compared to the general population. Epidemiologically, all this data, together with the fact that so many of the prostitutes enrolled in Plummer's studies were from Tanzania and Uganda, substantially reinforced the picture of an epidemic that was spreading outwards from the African heartland.

One doctor observed that were it not for the fact that the land border with Tanzania had been closed for several years following a political dispute, and that with Uganda periodically, then Kenya's levels of HIV infection might well have been even higher. As it was, although Kenya was probably two or three years behind Uganda, its HIV-infected population was doubling roughly every six months.

Someone else commented that, in respect of sero-surveys, Africa was much better off than Europe and North America, where most of the available data concerned not seroprevalence, but actual cases of AIDS, and thus reflected not the current epidemiological picture, but that of five or more years ago. What limited serological data there was suggested that HIV levels in parts of New York City, among pregnant women for instance, were currently about the same as those in Nairobi.

I left the meeting with the dire prognoses of my hosts still ringing in my ears. 'There's no cure for a retrovirus like HIV,' said one doctor. 'Once it's entered the body of a host, it's there to stay.' 'It's going to be a disaster for Africa,' said someone else. 'The epidemiological curve is exactly the same as for homosexuals in the United States.' And a few doors down from where we had met, I came across a Mini van parked beside the road. On its back window, three stickers. 'Do It In A Van', said one; 'If It Feels Good, Do It', enjoined another. The third featured a romanticised version of a speeding articulated lorry, drawn from a submissive position, down at ground level. The slogan read simply: 'Truckers Do It Best'.

25 · ANNA

That Sunday the Zambian President, Kenneth Kaunda, declared publicly that his thirty-two-year-old son, Masuzyo, who had died the previous December, had been suffering from AIDS. 'How he got AIDS I do not know,' he told a news conference in Lusaka. 'But it does not need my son's death for me to appeal to the international community to treat the problem as a world problem.' It was a remarkably courageous statement by Kaunda – the first time in Africa that the death of an individual from AIDS had been treated as newsworthy, in the way that the deaths of Rock Hudson and Liberace had been in the West. And the President's motives were clearly similar: by publicising one death, others might be prevented. As much as any other single event, Kaunda's speech helped change the perceptions of African leaders, and some of the stigma surrounding AIDS seemed to disappear overnight.

Pumwani is more commonly known as *Majengo*, a name widely used by East African Moslems for a slum district. And while it is not as run down as Mathare Valley, with its houses built of flattened tin cans, Majengo is indeed a place of poverty, with open sewers, communal toilets, and rough single-storey dwellings of mud, sticks and corrugated iron. The male inhabitants are mostly unemployed, and living on the fringes of the criminal community; the young women – apart from the relatively small number who are married and living with their husbands – are mostly surviving by prostitution. Near by is Nairobi's main lorry park, which gave Pumwani its immortal pseudonym of 'Trucktown' in the first Panos report.

Since it was still early in October, I had expected that the Pumwani clinic might be almost empty; I had been warned that in the week or so following payday at the end of the month, most of the prostitutes were busy working, and did not have time to come in for check-ups, even if they were necessary. But I arrived to find that there were over thirty women sitting on the wooden benches waiting their turn. For some reason, I had expected a place of gloom and solemnity, heavy with the communal expectation of impending sickness and death, but the clinic was actually a happy place, filled with the noises of conversation, laughter, and babies.

I introduced myself to the doctor-in-charge who, far from having any objections to my remaining, even offered to answer a few questions before the clinic started. He told me that apart from the basic health care provided by the clinic, which mainly involved the treatment of gonorrhoea and chancroid, there were a number of scientific studies underway. Apart from those which Dr Plummer had already mentioned, there was another study investigating the effectiveness of spermicidally impregnated pessaries as inhibitors of HIV, and another, more controversial project to assess the risk factors of oral contraceptives.

I left the doctor to proceed with his clinic, and instead started talking to one of the nurses who was filling in the personal history questionnaires that each patient had to complete before an examination. She told me that only about one in twenty of the women at the clinic spoke English, but she offered to help me find one who was willing to be interviewed. Then she returned to her forms, while I sat down on one of the lateral benches to survey the scene. Several of the women glanced up and smiled at me in a friendly way. Many of them were much more attractive and well groomed than I had expected; there were expensive perms and swinging braids on view, and some smart, functional, non-seductive dresses. Some wore *khangas* wound round their heads, or draped across their shoulders, which added to the impression I had that a large proportion were Tanzanian.

More women were coming in all the time, while others, their examinations complete, were heading off home with cardboard boxes in their hands. I went across to the nurse to ask about these, and it turned out that they were condoms of the same type which I had received in Uganda, though these were newer, having been manufactured only three months before. And, I was told, the local authorities were beginning to complain about the number of used condoms being picked up in the streets by local kids, some of whom were blowing them up like balloons. I could imagine the sort of emotions which that little controversy must have aroused.

Later the nurse returned to tell me that one of the women had agreed to talk to me after her examination. She nodded towards a well-built woman who was just disappearing behind the curtain of one of the examining rooms. 'It seems that she's been seronegative for the last year,' she added quietly.

When the examination was finished, the woman came out and introduced herself to me as Anna. She was smartly dressed, in a silver-coloured blouse and a blue and white striped skirt; she had an expensive wet-look hair-do, but there was an ugly burn on her hand that looked as if it might have been done deliberately with a cigarette. Her breath smelt very slightly of *waragi*. I told her my name, and she promptly asked me:

'And what is your work going to do for us, Eddie?' It was a good question, and demonstrated that Anna was not in the habit of putting up with any nonsense. I told her about the book, how I hoped that what I wrote might increase people's understanding about the AIDS problem in Africa, and even, in time, perhaps mean more money coming in to help with projects like the one at Pumwani. Then I added that it might also help my own people, *wazungu* people, realise that AIDS was not solely a homosexual disease, but one that could affect everyone, in every walk of life. And she nodded to me, seemingly satisfied. We walked outside, and took a taxi to a friend's office in town, where I knew that we could talk in private.

We chatted for a while surrounded by the typewriters and files, and again I was impressed by how direct she was, and how well she spoke English. After some few minutes I switched on the recorder, and we began the interview. Anna told me her full name, her age – twenty-eight – and that she came from the town of Nyeri.

'So are you Kikuyu?'

'Yes, I am Kuke by tribe.' Her voice was small, a little husky.

'And what is your profession, Anna?'

'Prostitution,' she answered quickly, and then laughed, as she began to lose some of her nervousness.

'When did you start working as a prostitute?'

'Nine months ago, in January this year.'

'How many men do you usually have in one day?'

'It depends on the boom. Maybe eight, maybe more than eight. But it is all controlled by the boom days at the end of the month, and on the fifteenth, when the men get their pay. Other days there is sometimes only little business.'

'And how much do you charge a man for having sex with you?'

'It's only ten bob for a short time.' This was about 60 US cents.

'How many minutes does that take?'

'It's very few minutes, two or three. He doesn't take his clothes off; the only thing he does is remove his shoes. He just puts it in, comes to his climax, and then he leaves.'

'Do you ever charge more than ten shillings?'

'It depends. If he's a regular customer, he can add on some more.'

'Because he's a friend?'

'Because he's a friend, or maybe because you give him good service.'

'Good service?'

'You hold him nicely, you give him sweet words. Then he becomes a regular customer. But the rest, you just tell them "Do what you want", and then you move.'

'Do you have kids?' I asked.

'No ... no kids at all.' Her voice quavered; then she reasserted herself. 'I was married five years, and I disagreed with my husband because I couldn't get very much kids. So ...' and here she sighed, '... I had no alternative. I decided to do what I had to do to earn my living, because I had no one to assist me any more.'

'And do you earn enough to live on?'

'Most days I get more than eighty bob a day, because some of my regular customers can even give me a pound. It's not that much, but you can live on it.' But I was looking at her clothes and hair style, and feeling a little sceptical.

'But Anna, you've got a lovely wet-look perm ... surely that must have cost you four hundred shillings or so?'

She giggled at the compliment. 'If you're nice to people, at least you get a man-friend who can assist somehow. And of course I have to do my best to look good.'

'And why do you attend the clinic out at Pumwani, if you live in the centre of town?'

Anna had relaxed by now, and her reply was unexpectedly candid.

'Some friends in my lodging-house told me that it was a good place, some months ago. I'm a regular patient. Today I was there for a check-up because I had some pains inside the vagina. And they told me it might be because I am wearing nylon knickers, and the climate is now very hot. They took some blood, and I have to go back in a few days to get the results.'

'Have you ever had any sickness diagnosed?'

'I've had some small diseases like gonorrhoea, like that.'

'Have you ever had ulcers?'

'No, never.'

'And have they told you about AIDS, at the clinic?'

'Yes, and I've been checked for that. I'm OK. I'm negative.'

'Are you not afraid that you might get it?'

'Well, I think this is a normal disease. Whether I'm a prostitute or not, I have to get it. If you get a blood transfusion, and maybe he or she has AIDS, then also you have to get it. It is not only through prostitution.'

'That's true. But isn't sex the way that most people get it?'

'What I understand is that most people affected by AIDS are these homosexuals. But we prostitutes, the only way we use is straight sex, and I don't think there is any problem ... yes.' But her voice wobbled as she added that small word of self-assurance at the end of the sentence, and I was sure that she knew better.

'What advice do they give you at the clinic about AIDS?'

'Well, they give us lots of advices to take care of ourselves. They provide us with condoms. If we are sick, they give us injections and some tablets. They help us very much.'

'And do the doctors at the clinic advise you to cut down on the number of sex partners?'

'Yeah, and they always advise us to get married. But where are the men? There are no men around.' She laughed, and I noticed again what a lovely musical voice she had. 'If you are lucky enough, you can get a man who can marry you. If you are unlucky, you just continue the profession.'

'So do you make your partners use condoms?'

'Oh yeah, I do,' she said cheerfully.

'Every time?'

'Not every time, because there are some who say they don't feel anything when they wear the condom. They say they don't feel satisfied, or don't come to their climax.'

'Can't you insist?'

'I can't insist because I need the cash, you see. My problem is the cash. It would have been better only to use condoms. No risks. Because you don't know what the man's carrying; you don't know if he's got the disease or not. But just because my problem is the cash, I agree. There are men who are reasonable enough, who can demand the condom, and if you haven't got one, they can't screw you.' (It was the first time in our talk that she had used the language of the street.) 'Most of such people are these married men. They like to protect themselves because of the family ... the wives and the children. Yeah.' Her voice had gone husky again.

'So how many of the men you screw use condoms, and how many don't?'

'The majority are the ones who don't. In the day, perhaps four can demand the condom ...'

'Out of how many?'

She laughed. 'Out of eight, or nine, maybe. It depends, anyway.'

By this stage, we were both laughing again. When we stopped, I found that I was still smiling at her, but inside I was feeling angry and sad as well.

'Anna, do you really believe what you told me before, that you're bound to get AIDS?'

'No, I don't believe that. I always go to church and pray God not to be affected by such diseases; I'm only doing it because of problems ...' She stopped, because she was almost crying, and I stopped my questions as well. When she had composed herself, I asked if she wanted to continue, and she agreed to do so.

'Have any of your women friends got sick with AIDS?'

'No, none.' Her strong voice was back.

'Do you think that any might be infected with the virus?'

'Well, I don't know, because everyone takes the results their own way. One person can't tell another what result she had, or what the doctors told her.'

Later, I asked Anna where she lived and worked. I detected a moment of shyness, but then she told me it was in a lodge only a few streets away, and that she shared a room with two other women. Each woman paid 40 shillings a night or, to put it another way, four acts of intercourse.

'And what is the best time to do business?' I asked, adopting her own argot.

'The best time is very early in the morning, that's the time some customers pop in before they go to their offices. They come, they have a screw, at least one, they feel they're OK, and they've got the energy to go to their offices. That is from six to seven-thirty. And after that, the best time is around lunch. They come for a bit of lunch – *nyama muchomo*, roasted meat – and they have a screw. Or usually they have a screw first, and then take lunch. Then, after two, we have a rest. If we want to go out, we can go out and do something else. If we're not busy, we have a sleep. We wait for the time again, for five o'clock, when people come out from work. And that's it, up to eleven o'clock.'

'And what sort of jobs do the men do?'

'So many. I can get a customer from the office, the market, clerks and so forth. You know this is nature, and everybody, if he feels like screwing, then he comes for a screw. Even if he is a professional, he has to come for a screw.'

'And how do the men meet you?'

'They come up from the first floor to the third floor, and we line up – we women, we line up – and then he selects any woman that he wants. We can even pull him, and take him inside the room. Sometimes, when it is busy, we three women in the room can all have customers at the same time. It is no problem; each woman has covered her bed with curtains, so there's no embarrassment. And then the one who shoots quickly, off he goes, and then you wash with water and soap, and you go out and look for another customer. Just like that.'

I had to leave, but then Anna offered to show me where she worked, so that I could see how things went on there. First, however, I had to promise that I would not do any interviews while I was there, nor reveal that I was a journalist. In the end, we decided that I would pretend to be an English teacher who had been working in Kenya for a year. We would meet again three days later, by which time the boom should have eased up a bit.

It was nearly five o'clock, and I was hurrying across a stretch of waste ground to get to the Press Centre at Chester House before everybody went home. I believe I was fairly preoccupied, for I hardly noticed the two girls until I had almost walked into them. Then I realised that this was exactly their intention.

'Hello darling I love you,' said one, putting her hand on my arm. Her friend burst into a high-pitched giggle, and then, when I turned to look at her, she suddenly moved her face closer and popped out her fat tongue, to wiggle it slowly to and fro between her teeth. My thoughts had still been with Anna, and I found the gesture rather off-putting.

'Yes, hello,' I said, and pulling my arm away, moved round them and back on to the path. But they were already walking on in the opposite direction, and I could hear them laughing at their own bravado as they disappeared into the distance. And then I recalled being told that Buffalo Bill's had closed down for good a few days before: it was apparently destined for reincarnation as a Chinese restaurant. I wondered if some of its regulars were now finding it harder to meet *wazungu*, and if that was why I had just been approached in the middle of town in broad daylight.

It was a small room, maybe 12 foot by 15, situated on the first floor of Anna's back-street lodging-house; it had just enough space for the six rickety metal tables and twenty-four chairs. There was the standard wire-mesh grille in front of the bar, with a hole where the barman handed out the bottles; there was a juke-box set on 'loud', and already, by half-past three, the place was beginning to fill up with women from the upstairs rooms, and punters. There were four of us sat around the table in the corner: Anna, Eddie the English teacher, the great and beautiful Gertrude, with her pale brown flawless skin, and all-enveloping electric green dress, and the rather gawky Mary, who wore glasses and had a huge inoculation scar on her upper arm.

We had ordered some beers, and some bags of stale home-made potato chips. The room grew more crowded: there was a friendly, easy, end-of-the-day kind of atmosphere. Some of the men coming in from work were undoubtedly surprised to see a *muzungu* in their midst, for this was not a typical tourist haunt. But there was no unpleasantness; indeed, several of them smiled a greeting in my direction. Perhaps because of my presence, the pick-ups were very cool; there would be a glance, a confirmatory nod, and then after a decent interval a girl would get up from her seat, and reappear some few minutes later. Gertrude got up three times in a couple of hours; never was she away longer than the time it takes to smoke a cigarette, and each time she gave me a small, almost apologetic, grin as she returned.

It turned out that Gertrude was a Muhaya, one of the famous BK girls from northern Tanzania about whom I had been hearing so much. And she was certainly good at her profession: her rather splendid green high-heeled shoes, bought to match the dress, had apparently put her back 750 shillings, or almost 50 dollars. She told me that she also made money by bringing clothes from Bukoba to Nairobi, through Uganda. Later, Anna whispered to me that Gertrude was very popular, and could earn as much as 300 shillings on a good day. I managed to refrain from doing the obvious bit of division out loud, and instead asked Gertrude why it was that women from Bukoba were said to be such good lovers. She laughed, and replied: 'What do you think?'

At this point, Anna began egging me on. 'Do you want to try, Eddie? You can have her if you want to.' I detected just a hint of possessiveness here, so I assured Anna that I did not want her. Two minutes later, Gertrude was off again, and a man from Kisii, who was rather more drunk than anyone else, leant backwards to fondle the large globes of her buttocks as she squeezed her way past. She waited a while before slapping his hand away. Soon afterwards, Anna excused herself also, to go for a 'short call', and was back inside a few minutes, though I caught myself wondering if it had been long enough for a 'short time' instead. Then I realised that I was feeling a little possessive myself.

By half-past seven we had finished off the chilli-smothered *nyama muchomo* ordered from the restaurant downstairs, and were on our fifth or sixth bottles of beer. Anna started whispering loudly into my ear about her visit to the clinic that morning, how she had been given an injection and tablets, presumably for 'a small sickness', though thank-fully we didn't go into details. She added that the sister at the clinic had mislaid her blood test results, but had told her that they 'weren't very bad'.

The small bar was now packed; no one had fewer than two bottles of beer lined up on the table in front of them – it seemed to be some sort of local etiquette. A window had been opened to let out the smoke. Mary, who had hardly said a word all evening, was for the first time summoned upstairs; she left promptly. On Anna's other side was Alphonse, a friendly Mukamba, who had earlier told me that this was his first time in the bar. Now he leant across Anna to confide that she was in fact his 'sister'.

'Well, Alphonse, I suppose that means you must be my brother-in-law,' I commented, which went down well, as family jokes nearly always do in Africa.

Anna, whose thigh had stayed glued to mine throughout the quaffing of the last two bottles, suddenly whispered to me that now was a good time. So we eased back the table, and gingerly made it to a standing position. It took us a minute or so to get out past the other custom-ers, and several of the men gave me knowing glances as we passed. Alphonse squeezed my elbow; someone else momentarily clenched fist and forearm in mock-phallic salute. Only the drunken man from Kisii was less than friendly. 'Look at Moneyman, look at Moneyman,' he shouted, waving his fingers above his head. Others hissed at him, in Kiswahili, to shut up.

We went up two flights of green-painted stairs to her room. There was no running water in the place, and I was hit once again by the smell from the toilets. And although Anna had told me previously what to expect, I was still surprised to find the upper corridors and landings almost lined with women and punters. The women were dressed in various fashions, with the emphasis on *déshabillé*. There was much bosom on view, peeping or gaping from the tops of brassières under translucent nylon blouses; there were several lurid, straining pairs of slacks. I noticed two women whose puffy faces testified to their having been beaten up, and not long before. A few gave me the eye, and one brushed her fingers against me as I passed, but most seemed to accept that I was already taken. The men were mostly African, with a few brawny-looking Asians thrown in. Some of them stared at me long and hard; I kept my eyes fixed on Anna's back.

As we turned to enter her room, Anna pointed to another door at the end of the landing.

'That's the owner's place,' she said over her shoulder.

'Does he screw his tenants?' I enquired.

'Yes, of course he does. We all pay our rent that way sometimes.' The answer, a little more abrupt than usual, betrayed Anna's nervousness.

Her room was about 12 feet square, and was painted bright orange, with a design of red spots stencilled on top. It had three beds, each of which was surrounded by a set of cheap cotton curtains. Two other girls nodded nervously in my direction as we entered, and then embarked on a lengthy conversation in Kikuyu: I got the feeling that they were helping me to feel at ease. Anna kicked off her high heels, gave me a slightly awkward smile, and then slipped under the curtain that surrounded her bed. I unlaced my shoes, placed them together with uncharacteristic neatness, and followed suit. She pulled the curtain to, so that we had privacy; then knelt down on the bed, facing me. We both fell silent.

'They think we're screwing,' she whispered presently, with a broad grin. Then she began gently bouncing up and down on her haunches, making the springs squeak, and I began to do the same. We were both a bit drunk. Every time we looked at each other, we started laughing, and eventually Anna had to bury her face in the pillow to muffle her snorts.

Then I remembered why I was there. I got the pencil and paper out of my pocket. To all intents and purposes, we had finished quickly, and were now having a little post-coital chat.

'Where are your things?' I whispered, with exaggerated lip movements. When she understood, she leant down and pulled a large soft bag from under the bed. Very slowly, hamming it up somewhat, she unzipped the bag to reveal a pile of neatly ironed clothes. She smoothed down part of the blanket and began laying them out item by item, almost reverently, on the bed. Blouses, skirts, dresses, underwear, a small vanity bag of her perfumes and creams. This, apparently, was the sum total of her possessions. Seeing my expression, she shrugged pretended indifference.

'It's a difficult life,' she murmured, 'but what to do?'

Then one of the other girls said something loudly in Kikuyu, and the two of them could be heard leaving the room. Now that we were alone, I began for the first time to feel embarrassed. We carried on talking, but in half-whispers, still acting out as if in mime. To break the ice again, Anna showed me the curtained alcove at the end of the bed where there were two plastic bowls, a soap-dish and a jug of water. 'This is where we wash after we finish,' she explained.

'Do you ever finish properly?' I asked, out of the blue. 'You know . . . come . . . have an orgasm?'

'Sometimes. When I'm with a boyfriend. But normally I don't; it's all over so quickly.'

'Would you let a man do whatever he wanted? If he paid you enough, would you let him have you from behind, or in the mouth?' A pause. 'The men round here don't go in for that sort of thing. And anyway, if I did that with my customers, I'd be risking my life.'

'Why is that?' I asked, a little too innocently. But Anna wouldn't answer. Although she was far from embarrassed talking about sex, she quite clearly viewed acts of anal and oral sex as dirty and unnatural. In addition, she had probably realised the dreadful irony of her last comment.

Now it was my turn to try to put her at ease. It was not very difficult. She visibly perked up when I began examining the two film posters which she had stuck up on the wall: 'The Blue Birds' and 'The Gnome Mobile'. And underneath these, near her pillow, was taped a smaller cyclostyled sheet entitled 'The Ten Commandments of Love'. I began scribbling down the text on my sheet of paper:

1. Love me and accept I am your best choice.
2. Learn my weak and strong points; likes and dislikes.
3. Respect me: I will respect you; never neglect me.
4. Problems are part of life. Never yell at me . . .
5. Advise me rather than criticising me.
6. Forgive and forget my past mistakes. Never look for faults.
7. We both contribute to make a quarrel. Don't blame me alone.
8. Let us settle differences before we go to sleep . . .
9. Accept your mistakes and ask for forgiveness.
10. Remember to pray to God. He'll solve all our problems.

I wanted to ask Anna more questions, but she was busy making sure I had written down the 'Ten Commandments' correctly (in fact I missed 5, 6 and 9). And instead of questions, it was Commandments that kept running through my head, like a litany, as we got off the bed, put on our shoes, and ran the gauntlet back down the green stairs. We didn't bother about the beers left on the table, about saying goodbye to Gertrude and Mary. We walked straight out of the hotel, round the corner, and Anna found me a taxi.

And she escorted me to the Norfolk Hotel, where I was due to meet an American journalist for dinner. We sat in the back seat, a foot apart now, and made smalltalk.

'The other girls will compliment me on my customer,' she said. 'Not many of us have ever had a *muzungu!*'

We laughed, and in the dark I put some money in her hand, to compensate for her loss of earnings.

'I'll just have one drink, and then I'll go to bed,' she told me.

'Please use those condoms, Anna,' I said. 'You know it's not too late to start using them all the time, don't you?'

'I will, Eddie, I promise.'

We arrived at the Norfolk, and I got out of the car. I wanted to kiss her, say something more, but in the end I just leant down and whispered, 'Take care.'

'And you,' she said, and squeezed my arm. Then the taxi swung round to take her back to her drink in the bar.

That Saturday's edition of the *Daily Nation* was particularly interesting. A large front-page headline proclaimed 'Stop lying, Moi tells Uganda', and featured the President's denial of Ugandan claims that Kenya was training Ugandan rebels. Instead, Moi said, it was actually Uganda which was sending Kenyan dissidents to train in Libya. There was also a large feature on the previous day's celebrations of twenty-five years of independence in Uganda, which told how many Ugandans were 'unconvinced that the quarter century had brought any benefits to the former British protectorate'. In addition, there was a report from Naples, where a conference on 'AIDS and Associated Cancers in Africa' was being held, and which quoted Jonathan Mann as saying that Africa was now much more open about AIDS, with thirty-six countries reporting a total of 5,826 cases to the WHO, and AIDS control programmes already established in many of them.

But in actual fact, as the last quarter of 1987 progressed, it was clear that in Kenya's case, at least, not enough had been done to combat the spread of the virus. Ten weeks had passed since the Minister of Health's disclosure to a shocked national assembly that Kenya now had 625 cases of AIDS, and the following day's announcement that donors had provided nearly 3 million dollars to fund the national AIDS Control Programme. Yet there were few signs of action; neither were there to be for many months to come. Instead, there was the breast-beating. The Minister of Energy declared in parliament that 'AIDS victims' should be quarantined lest they 'run wild and cause havoc'; and Professor Ogada, the DMS, was quoted as saying that the government was 'strengthening medical teams and facilities in the frontier areas through which the disease [is] expected to come, including Malindi, the popular tourist town, and Western and Nyanza provinces.'

Vox populi seemed to concur: one reader's letter advocated the installation of AIDS screening machines at border posts, and the issuing of certificates to foreigners found free of the disease. Another advocated that nature be allowed to take its course with those undertaking 'anti-social activities' – like drug addicts, homosexuals and prostitutes. Such opinions, of course, were no different from many of those being expressed, and published, in the USA, the Soviet Union, and the rest of Europe.

But not everyone was rendered so panicky by Slim. Later that day I called on David, an artist friend of Sue's; the front door was open, and I found him sitting at his easel, sketching his kids. David was a refugee who had been living in Kenya for some years; he had recently become successful enough to be able to support his Kenyan wife and their two children by the sale of his paintings. I told him about Sue and myself, how we were back together again in Uganda; then I asked him about his work.

David got up, and walked to the back of the room, to show me a painting on the wall. The canvas was quite large, almost 3 feet by 4, and depicted a crowded scene of perhaps fifty people standing around a bar shaped like a horseshoe. Quite unmistakably, it was Buffalo Bill's.

'I finished it a week ago, just before they closed the place down,' he told me proudly.

In the foreground of the painting, an Asian man was being introduced to a statuesque *kitenge*-clad Luo woman, whose hair was piled high into an angry vertical ponytail; performing the introductions was an older woman in a red beret, and the Asian's arm was draped idly round her shoulder. Meanwhile, inside the county gaol, an energetic argument was taking place, with the sheriff nowhere to be seen. Towards the back of the room an elderly *muzungu* in sleeveless safari jacket and shorts, and clearly the worse for drink, was resting his chin on his hand; but his girlfriend, an attractive half-caste, was more interested in the attentions of the African boy to her left. Elsewhere, across the horseshoe-shaped bar, bright eyes were flashing their messages. A woman in a formidable hat was just leaving, clearly displeased about the state of business.

David told me that the picture had been commissioned by an American family-planning organisation for which he did occasional work. It was going to be exhibited in Washington that November, and he'd been asked to fly out to present it in person.

'But why Buffalo Bill's? Why did they want a picture of that?'

'In places like this, it's so easy to get a lady, and ultimately you end up in bed,' David explained. 'And these are exactly the places where people get disease. What is needed is education. Our scientists and doctors haven't got the facilities to protect the people. So they've got to tell them that AIDS is here, that it's dangerous. They've got to educate them to take care of themselves. That's what my painting tries to do, to educate.'

'But for now everyone's carrying on just like before?'

'The women perhaps; they can't survive without. But not the men. Not these days. You see that big box up there on the wardrobe? I give those out to friends, when they're going for a night out on the town. There's a great need for condoms, of course. When people are poor, it's only this' – he put his two palms together, and thrust them forward – 'that gives them pleasure.'

On my last night in Nairobi, I went over to Steve's place, for a farewell drink. Conveniently, Wanjiko was not there. I'd been getting rather concerned about Steve for some time, and I wanted to have a chat with him. Before long, the conversation came around to Slim, and I asked Steve whether, since he was still screwing around with a number of women, he was using condoms.

Steve pondered for a while. 'I know that's the level you're seeing it at, and indeed it's a very important, practical level. Screwing around. The problem with screwing around is that there's not much point in doing it unless it's fun. Once it starts getting to be a problem in one way or another, because you've got to put pieces of rubber on yourself, or because you're terrified of picking up, or passing on, some terrible disease, once those kinds of hazards start looming on the horizon, then a shadow falls across the prospect.'

'But a shadow hasn't exactly fallen across your prospect, has it? What about that Luo woman you picked up last week? Did you use a condom with her? Or did you just think about it?'

'I did think about it. I think I donned one. In fact, I screwed a bit with it on. But a little bit with it off as well.'

'So you're not worried if you get it or not?'

'I may already have it. I've never had a test.' Steve was sticking his neck out now. I decided to do the same.

'How many girls have you slept with since you came to Nairobi?'

'In three years, I suppose I've had about twenty women. Perhaps twenty-five.'

'I was doing that sort of thing back in the early 1980s. But the difference between us is that, since the start of 1986 – when admittedly I had a few lapses – I've basically reformed, whereas I'm not sure that you have. I mean, do you think it's enough to use condoms half the time?'

'Smoking ten cigarettes a day is better than smoking twenty.'

'True, but why not give up altogether?' Not much finesse here, I admit, but I wanted Steve to get serious for a moment; he needed shaking up. I was pretty sure, for instance, that he was not aware that Wanjiko, whom he classed as a girlfriend, was also prepared to play the field when he was not around.

'I suppose it wasn't very clever to pick up the Luo girl the other night, but I was drunk,' he conceded, finally.

'But that's no excuse, is it?'

'It happens, that's all. It was a bit unfortunate for the poor girl, really. I don't like to do it to them. I don't like to make whores of them; there would be no whores without clients. The problem is that, in this environment here, what we are talking about is mass prostitution.'

'But in large areas of Africa – including Uganda for instance – most women would not dream of actually asking for money.'

'Look, even a woman in a nuclear family prostitutes herself to a man; she just hopes to get a good deal. Prostitution is economically so important. There are thousands, if not hundreds of thousands of women in this country and neighbouring countries who hire themselves out to men in order to survive economically. That's the way the school fees are paid, and the maize-meal; it pays for the new dress, and for the rent. The only difference is that in countries like Kenya which are comparatively conservative, and where marriage and chastity are still valued commodities, you get a particular group of women who practise prostitution for money. Whereas in most of Uganda and Zaire, where chastity is not such a big deal, things are a bit more permissive generally. You get very little formal prostitution as such, but many women, whether or not they're working, have a fair number of boyfriends, and the boyfriends are expected to give them presents, and society as a whole doesn't disapprove.'

Steve was right. But it wasn't until much later, while reading a medical paper that discussed many of the same issues, that I realised that this helped explain the great difference between the patterns of HIV prevalence found in Kenya and Uganda. In Nairobi, for instance, prostitutes were displaying particularly high levels of HIV, up to 90 per cent, while only some 2 per cent of women attending an antenatal clinic were infected. By contrast, in Lyantonde, Uganda, 67 per cent of the barmaids who slept around with the lorry crews had HIV, as compared to 17 per cent of pregnant women in the town. At that point in time, in 'conservative' Kenya, prostitutes were forty-five times more likely to get HIV than females in the population at large; in more easy-going Uganda, the differential was four. Clearly the Ugandan situation encouraged a far faster rate of HIV spread into the general population.

The next morning, at the airport, there was a sale on at one of the duty-free shops. For a few dollars, I managed to pick up a bottle of tequila, another of calvados, and a third containing some rather seedy-looking mandarin liqueur. I was looking forward to some celebrations with Sue when I got back to Kampala.

26 · IN LIMBO

These things always start so softly. At Entebbe airport, as I reached the immigration desk, I noticed the official look up and over my shoulder; I followed his gaze, and was just in time to see another man standing behind me give a slight but perceptible nod. But I was stamped into the country as usual, and was in the luggage area, waiting for my bags to come through on the carousel, when the erstwhile nodder suddenly walked up and stood in front of me, his legs slightly astride like a boxer's. He was not very much over 5 feet tall, but he compensated for his lack of inches with a particularly unpleasant expression.

'Is your name Edward Hooper?' Already, from his tone, I knew that this was trouble. I tried to keep as calm as possible.

'Yes, it is.'

'Give me your passport please.' I did so, and began asking what this was all about, but was merely told brusquely to be quiet and follow him. I had very little choice but to comply.

I was brought before the airport's head of immigration, who was also diminutive, and had an unfortunate disfiguration of the mouth which caused him to push it over to one side of his face when speaking. Disconcertingly, it gave him the appearance of a street-corner spiv, touting girlie pictures, or tickets for the big match. But his message was anything but underhand.

'By the powers vested in me by the Ugandan government, I hereby inform you . . .' I can't recall the exact wording, for by now my head was reeling. The essence was that my work and residence permits were revoked, that I was declared a prohibited immigrant, and that I was advised to leave Uganda by the first available means. My attempts to elicit a reason, or to be allowed to contact the British High Commission, were fruitless. But when the others were out of the room for a minute, I pressed him about who was behind all this, and he muttered that 'it might be something to do with the military'. He told me to collect my luggage, which was executing lonely circuits of the conveyor belt, and then he accompanied me upstairs, to see if any of the light aircraft flying down to Kenya could give me a lift. And he stayed with me, to make sure that I didn't phone Kampala from the office of one of the charter companies. But by this stage, I was having uneasy memories of escalating officialdom in 1983, and was as eager to leave as was he to have me leave. Some businessmen in a Fokker Friendship were also apparently having problems, and they said they'd be flying back down to Nairobi as soon as they could get clearance, and yes, certainly, I could have a lift.

The two businessmen, it turned out, were the managing director and East African representative of a large multinational company. They had flown up from Nairobi that morning, and as their plane approached Entebbe, the pilot had been instructed by the control tower to change his normal flight path into the airport, and to approach from the other direction. This he did, and, as the plane taxied to its bay, it was surrounded by airport security, and the occupants placed under arrest. Apparently the revised approach had caused them to overfly the presidential residence at State House, on the edge of Entebbe town. Despite their protestations of innocence, they were refused entry, and told to return to Nairobi.

There was a clue to what lay behind all this in that morning's *Daily Nation*. A Ugandan pilot had just been arrested and gaoled for two months for flying into the Kenyan airport at Kisumu without a passport or proper clearance papers. In his defence, he had reportedly claimed that he regularly flew without papers into Wilson Airport at Nairobi, where he had always been allowed to land for the night, and fly back in the morning.

'Sounds like the Ugandans might be getting their own back,' commented the MD.

'Not at all a good day for flying,' I replied, ruefully.

And not a good day for landing, either. At Wilson, the airport for light planes, I handed over my passport to immigration, and was promptly given a two-week-entry permit. But as I was walking out of the office, the immigration officer called me back.

'Where are you going when you leave here?' he enquired, rather absently.

I felt like I'd already got through this stage. In my mind, I was already on the way to the British High Commission, to ask them to intervene with the Ugandans on my behalf, and I didn't recognise that this was one of those moments in the game when one should stop and take a long, deep breath. And then watch the ball, as it rolls the 3 yards into the back of the net.

'Oh, England, I suppose.'

He was still casual. 'What do you mean, you "suppose"?'

I was still looking towards the centre circle. 'Well, obviously I can't go back to Uganda, so I'll probably go to England. Or perhaps Tanzania . . .', I ended, tailing off, noticing now that there was a linesman waving a flag.

The referee had noticed too. 'Bring me your passport,' he ordered, suddenly alert. Too late now, I kept my mouth shut and handed it over; I was unable to believe what I'd just done. He really hadn't noticed that I'd been thrown out of Uganda; not until I'd explained it to him in capital letters, that is. Meanwhile he was turning over the pages of the passport, more carefully this time, and presently he called to his colleague, who walked across and joined him in a minute examination of the offending document. They started talking softly in Kikuyu. Then he looked up at me. 'Wait outside until we call you, Mr Hooper,' he said.

After this, things went from bad to worse. I waited for ten minutes outside, and then popped my head back through the door to ask what the problem was: I'd come to Kenya as a place of refuge – surely they weren't going to turn me away? I was told, none too kindly, to wait until I was called. Later, one of the officials came out to explain that they were 'doing their best for me'; I suppose that this was the moment when I should have found that I had 20 dollars burning a hole in my pocket. But I really couldn't believe that they were going to carry this through; surely in another five minutes, they'd tell me that everything was all right, it had just been a technical hitch, and I was free to leave. Uganda and Kenya were, after all, hardly on speaking terms at this point in time.

Meanwhile, there was an altercation in the customs office next door; a large American man was being relieved of his radio, on the grounds that he had no papers to prove that it was his personal property, and that it was not liable to duty. He bellowed for some ten minutes, but eventually had to comply. It was only then that I recalled the case of the Ugandan pilot, and the fact that these guys had just got burnt in the pages of the Kenyan papers. Naturally enough, they were feeling pretty keen on flexing their official muscles; were probably, in fact, looking to exact horrible revenge on anything airborne, particularly anything airborne that happened also to be a journalist.

At this point, I decided that I had better wander back into the immigration office, bearing bottles of calvados and tequila.

'I'm sorry, Mr Hooper,' said the man who had originally stamped me in. 'I'm afraid we've had to refer your case to a higher authority.'

'But what's the problem, for goodness' sake? What have I done wrong? It's Uganda that I've got difficulties with, not yourselves. I came here to seek refuge.'

He explained something about a reciprocal understanding existing between the two countries, dating back to 1977 and the days of the East African Community. I realised I'd been called offside.

At around four o'clock, twenty or so journalists arrived on the scene. For a moment I thought that a posse of the Nairobi press corps had hotfooted it up from Chester House to my rescue. But no – some European priests had been released after spending several weeks as hostages of the SPLA, and they were just about to fly in from Juba. Nevertheless, it was a timely coincidence, and various colleagues undertook to pass on messages. One woman in particular put herself at some risk by pressing the immigration people for details of what action they were taking and why, until eventually she was advised, quite brusquely, to mind her own business.The answer was that they themselves didn't know, at least not yet.

The reporters left, it was dark, Wilson Airport was closing for the night, and still nothing had happened. The immigration officers were impatient to get off home. Maybe for the first time, they wished that they hadn't started this particular ball rolling; but there again, I was their token of good intent to their bosses, their hostage to fortune, and they would have stayed with me all night if need be. Eventually the phone rang in their office, and some minutes later I was told that I was to be taken up to Kenyatta, Nairobi's international airport. Unfortunately there was no transport to get me there. One of the immigration officials told me that there was no alternative but for me to hire a taxi, for myself and my guards, and for the first time that day I had a good laugh. Eventually, after further phone calls, a vehicle was found, and seven of us all piled in, together with my luggage. One of the armed guards ended up perched on my lap.

At Kenyatta, the head of immigration was much more amenable, and eventually allowed me to phone the British consular official on night duty. But for all this, by nine o'clock it looked odds-on that I was to be deported on the midnight flight to London. However, some more phone calls by the official to the High Commission, and to Kenya's Principal Immigration Officer, Mr Ole Ncharo, brought about a last-minute compromise. If I could arrange for someone to sign a bond covering the cost of my flight back to London, then I could have a twenty-four-hour stay of execution, and present my case personally to Ole Ncharo in the morning. I phoned a friend and fellow journalist, Michael Anders, and he told me he'd drive out straight away.

An hour later Mike arrived and signed the necessary papers. I had already told the official that, if deported, I would prefer to use my existing Uganda Airlines ticket from Entebbe to London, so he agreed to release me on bond for two nights, until six o'clock on the Wednesday morning, that being two hours before the departure of the next Uganda Airlines flight. As we left, to walk through the deserted airport to the car park, I realised that I was completely bushed. It was now midnight, and I felt as if I'd been involved in a battle of wits and wills ever since the moment, eleven hours before, that I'd been stopped at the door by the immigration officer at Wilson. A shame that I hadn't starting living on my wits five minutes earlier.

'Thanks, Mike. I really can't believe you got me out of there,' I said, as soon as we were in his car.

'You're not out of it yet,' he replied. 'They just did that to make sure they wouldn't have to cover the cost of your repatriation. This way, one of us will have to pay, namely you. And you'd better have a think about what you're going to say to Ole Ncharo. By all accounts, he's a pretty tough character.'

Mike and I stayed up until three, drinking the quite disgusting mandarin liqueur and discussing the best lines of approach for me to take. I realised for the first time why the Ugandans hadn't deported me, but had merely advised me to take the first flight out of the country: nobody wanted to pay for that air ticket back to London. I had a fitful sleep, and at half-past seven in the morning, with a horrible headache, I began phoning the hotel where I had arranged to meet Sue in Kampala. It was almost an hour before I got through, but she answered her extension almost immediately, her voice sounding small and frightened. She already knew that something had happened. I made smalltalk for a little while, asking how was everything at home, how was the journey back to Kampala, and then I told her the bad news. She promised to stay in the hotel, and I to phone her back as soon as I knew how things were going to turn out.

I had a bad feeling as soon as I entered Ole Ncharo's office. He was a short, bull-necked Masai, impeccably dressed in a three-piece suit, and he gave me the tips of his fingers to shake. The Third Secretary of the British High Commission, who had accompanied me, did his very best on my behalf, greeting the man with a courteous diplomatic flourish, and giving a brief background of the case from my point of view. But Ole Ncharo was implacable. Apparently the only relevant factor was the understanding which obtained between Kenya and Uganda which meant that a prohibited immigrant in one country was also prohibited from entering the other. In fact, he added, it was 'an insult' that Uganda had allowed me to board a plane for Kenya in the first place, instead of repatriating me direct to the UK.

In the middle of the interview, one of the four brightly-coloured phones on his side-table began ringing, and with a small gesture of apology, he swivelled backwards gracefully in his leather chair, instantly plucked the correct receiver from its cradle, and then, looking into middle distance and holding the handset fully 2 inches from his face, whispered his instructions on some matter in Kiswahili. It was an impressive performance, and conveyed his enormous power and importance most successfully. Presently, he turned back to us, brushed aside all attempts to discuss the matter further, and explained that the decision had already been taken. I would have to leave the country in the morning. As I got up to go, I commented that, upon my return to London, it would be necessary for me to explain to the press how I had been treated.

'Ah, Mr Hooper,' he sighed. 'I'm sure that you won't be saying anything that would endanger the good relationship between our two countries,' and he glanced at the Third Secretary, who nodded fairly hastily. In actual fact, I knew damn well that I wouldn't be saying anything to anyone that would endanger any relationship, but it was good to see just a ripple pass across Ole Ncharo's lake of studied calm. He escorted us the 30 feet or so across to the door of his office, and before leaving he and I touched fingers once more. Nobody enjoyed any flashes of extraterrestrial enlightenment.

From this point onwards, I knew that I had no option but to go; the only question was how. I wasn't even very bothered about the reasons: whether it was just bureaucratic pettiness, or the desire to bash a journalist, or whether Kenyan security had been monitoring my progress and, having been given the opportunity by the Wilson Airport officials, had now decided to terminate my AIDS researches once and for all. Instead of bothering about post-mortems, I just headed off to Uganda Airlines, where a kindly supervisor listened to my tale of woe, and eventually agreed to break the company rulebook by rewriting my existing ticket. He gave me one that would get me from Nairobi to London via Entebbe; all I had to pay for was the extra leg from Kenya up to Uganda, which saved me from spending several hundred dollars on a full-price flight direct to London. The only trouble was that I would have to return to Uganda, albeit for just the ninety minutes needed to change planes.

'Don't worry,' said the supervisor, when he saw that I was doing so. 'They are good people at the airport; they won't harm you. And anyway, you'll be in transit, not inside Uganda itself.' I knew that what he said was true, but I still felt slightly apprehensive.

I could have started rushing round town, trying to get hold of as much last-minute information as possible for the book, but I didn't have the heart. Instead, I grabbed a quick bite, my first of the day, and then went to meet Mike as he left work.

'Hard luck,' he said, when I told him the result. 'But I warned you he was tough.'

We bought some beer, and went back to his place, to discuss what I could do about Sue. I didn't have to think twice about it: I knew straight away that I wanted her to come with me.

Three hours, much discussion, and half a dozen phone calls later, we had worked out a plan. Jonathan Wright from Reuters was due to drive up to Uganda in a couple of days, but only as far as Tororo, the first town across the Kenyan border. Apparently he had a particularly good lead on Alice Lakwena, whose Holy Spirit Battalion had been working its way down through eastern Uganda for several months, and was now reported to be attacking cars on the road from Tororo to the capital. Jonathan, as helpful as ever, said that if Sue could get herself to Tororo, and meet him at the Rock Hotel, he would give her a lift across the border and down to Nairobi. Meanwhile, some other friends of Sue's said that they would look after her when she arrived, help her get an air ticket to London, and phone me so I could meet her at Heathrow. The only flaw in this marvellous plan was that travelling from Kampala to Tororo had become rather dangerous. I didn't want Sue being hit by one of those 'holy bombs', or 'cut', as the Lakwena followers euphemistically described one of their acts of human-assisted divine retribution. (On the evidence of the end result, 'boned and rolled' might have been more appropriate.) Nevertheless, I was sure that nobody would be better informed of local conditions than the Peugeot drivers in the taxi parks of Kampala and Jinja.

It was almost nine o'clock by the time I phoned Sue in Kampala; fortunately, I had told her to wait in the main part of the hotel, and to make sure that one of the staff was there to answer the call. I got straight through. But it was not an easy conversation to have by phone. I started by explaining how I'd failed to persuade the Kenyans to let me stay.

'I love you. You know that, don't you?' I said.

'I do,' she said, snuffling. 'I love you too, Eddie.'

'Do you trust me, Sue?'

'Yes.'

'Well, if I can arrange it, will you come with me to England, and see how we get along together?'

It was the longest pause. Five seconds went by, even longer, and then she whispered, 'Yes, I would like that. But . . .'

'What?'

'How can I get there? I don't know how to buy a ticket. I never do it before.'

And as slowly and clearly as possible, I told her the plan: where she was to go, who to meet, and on which day. But the fact that she couldn't write the information down made everything particularly vulnerable to mishap. As did the fact that she had left her passport with a friend for safekeeping, and that she wasn't sure quite where the friend was staying.

'What?' I shouted. 'You gave someone your passport?' I managed to calm down about that one, but in the end, as she was trying, for the sixth time, to repeat the name 'Jonathan Wright', I swore in exasperation and she started crying. All this was not the way to do it: knowing local phone links, I was aware that we might be cut off at any time, and I needed to make sure that she had all the information clear before I boarded the plane in the morning. I calmed her, and then told her to bring Margaret, a girlfriend who was going to spend the night with her, to the phone. I repeated everything to Margaret, and she wrote it down.

'Don't worry, Eddie. We'll get her there,' she said. And then she put Sue back on the line. It was a difficult farewell; I knew that if the plan failed, as well it might, then I would probably never see her, or talk to her, again.

But as it turned out, it was not her plan that failed, but mine. After another session of burning the midnight oil with Mike, we were both rather slow getting going in the morning. By the time that he got me up to Kenyatta Airport for the flight, it was a quarter to seven, which under normal circumstances was a little late for checking in for the eight o'clock flight, but not disastrously so. Except that the airport immigration official who had helped me on the Monday night had been referring to an old timetable, and the departure time had been moved forward an hour, to seven o'clock. I had never thought to check the actual ticket.

Even then, all was not necessarily lost, for planes in Africa very often take off later than advertised. Although the flight was officially closed,

I left my bags at the check-in desk and, with an airport security man, sprinted through customs and immigration, and out to the departure lounge. Through the windows, I could see the Ugandan plane down on the tarmac, with the last passengers just boarding. The only problem was that all the departure gates had been locked, and there was nobody around who had the authority to open them. I ran to the enquiries desk, and tried to get a message up to the control tower, but even as I watched the steps were rolled back, and then the engines started up and, a couple of minutes later, the plane moved off towards the taxiing lane. I felt enormously depressed. I'd had enough of this business, and just felt like getting back to the safety of England.

Naturally enough, the immigration people weren't willing to let me loose on Nairobi once more, so I had to spend another forty-eight hours in transit, waiting for the next Uganda Airlines flight to leave for London. But it wasn't long before I realised that there might be some advantages to this latest delay. Not only did I have the chance to call various friends in Kenya and say goodbye, but I also had the opportunity to rearrange plans with Sue; I had been getting increasingly uneasy about the wisdom of her travelling to Tororo. I sat down for an hour or so, to work out the pros and cons, and then phoned Dave, the friend in Kampala who was looking after my luggage, and asked him if he was willing to help Sue get on a plane to London. Realising that this would involve a fair amount of time and energy on his part, Dave was not enthusiastic, but he did agree to see what he could do.

By this point, I had used up more than half of the 150 or so shilling coins that I had coaxed out of the duty-free shops in the departure area, and even further purchases of newspapers and sweets failed to elicit any more. Besides which, keeping the ramp of the payphone filled with coins when it was swallowing them at five-second intervals made it difficult to concentrate on what was being said, let alone jot down any notes. This was apart from the other hazards, such as knocking the piles all over the floor, or a bent coin getting stuck in the works, and cutting off the conversation. What's more, I knew that explaining the change of plans to Sue was going to require many more than the sixty or so coins remaining.

But once again I was lucky. The various immigration officials at Kenyatta covered the full gamut from the frustrated sergeant major to the kindly social worker, and one of the latter variety, an extremely sympathetic *mzee*, allowed me to phone Uganda from his office. In fact, he even left me alone in there so that I could speak in private, and despite my protestations, absolutely refused to accept any payment for his help. When I got through, I called off Tororo – to the relief of both of us –

and told Sue that she had to get hold of her passport straight away and then contact Dave, who would help her get a ticket, inoculations, and clearance to leave the country. If everything went well, she might just be able to get on the same Friday flight as myself. 'And if you see me in the airport, or even on the plane, don't say anything to me, smile at me, come up to me . . . don't do anything until I make a move to you,' I told her just before saying goodbye.

Apart from the frantic making and changing of plans – and of course, every time I put the phone down, I thought of something else I should have told her, or warned her about – the two days dragged by terribly slowly. Also stuck in transit were two born-again Christians, a husband and wife, who'd been refused entry when they flew in from Germany with just 30 dollars, and who were forever waiting for their Kenyan friends to phone and say they'd managed to rustle up some money. We took it in turns to wait by the bank of public phones for return calls. Sadly for them, none came. I stayed up late with them one night, and listened as the man told me about how God always found a way to open doors for them, and wondered if he was thinking that I might be the channel of divine intervention. And indeed, although I only had 400 dollars with me, I came close to lending them the 200 that would have got them into the country. It was only at the last minute that I remembered that I'd been caught by plausible stories before, and I wasn't entirely convinced that these two were on the level. For one thing, it seemed that they were expecting God – and their Kenyan brethren – to pull quite a few strings for them, without doing very much themselves to lend a hand. On the Thursday night they were deported back to Germany; as they left, I did feel a twinge of guilt for my failure to be an angel, but I hoped that, if God was watching, he wouldn't hold it against me and Sue when it came to the final reckoning.

Early on the Friday morning my flight was called, and we took off, right on time, for Entebbe. By this stage, I'd spent four days technically in transit, and I was feeling tired and odoriferous. I was also nervous about how the Ugandan authorities at the airport would react to my return.

In the event, as soon as I walked into the airport building at Entebbe, I was met by the squinty-mouthed chief of immigration, who lost no time in demanding my press card, which he'd obviously forgotten to extract from me four days earlier. I told him that indeed, I still had my press card, but reminded him that I was a passenger in international transit, and that he had no rights to demand anything of me.

'There, he admits it, he's got it here with him,' he shouted over his shoulder to the little security man with nasty eyes, who was hovering in the background. At this point, I decided not to argue; I was after all in a delicate position, and I wouldn't have any more use for the press card anyway; better to keep these guys sweet till I got on that plane. But I made Squinty-Mouth ask for it again in a civil fashion before I agreed to hand it over.

At this point, one of the baggage handlers came over, to say that an official from the British High Commission was outside, trying to gain admission to see me; and I suddenly recalled that the BHC in Nairobi had said they would phone Gordon Brown, and ask him to come down to Entebbe to ensure that everything went smoothly. But the small security man stopped me from walking towards the exit where Gordon was apparently waiting.

'Oh no Mr Hooper, you can't do that, you know.'

'All right then, let Mr Brown in to see me here. He has a right to do so, as my consular official.'

'Nobody has a right to come into the airport, if we don't let them. And we're not admitting your Mr Brown.' He was standing in front of me, blocking my path, much as he had done four days before. I started to walk around him, but he moved, blocking me again. 'If you want to get tough, Mr Hooper, then we can get tough too,' he said.

'Yes, I'll bet you can. I'll just bet you can.' I gave the baggage handler a verbal message for Gordon, thanking him for coming, and then I went upstairs to wait in the transit lounge.

After ten minutes or so, the first passengers for London began filing past the immigration desk, and I took a bottle of beer to a table in the cafeteria, so that I could watch. There was as yet no sign of Sue, and I was feeling increasingly certain that she had not managed to get everything arranged in time. Presently I got chatting to Ann, a young woman from the Save the Children Fund, who was just leaving after a week's flying visit, and her calm presence helped to soothe my nerves. Every few minutes I would glance up casually, to see who was at the front of the queue. And then, suddenly, there was nobody there, and the immigration official had gone as well. Surely this couldn't be everyone who was on the flight? There were only fifteen of us in the transit area. All sorts of horrible scenarios began running through my mind, and eventually I told Ann about my predicament.

Half an hour passed before there was a long note of feedback from the tannoy, followed by the sound of someone clearing their throat. All of us fell quiet, and looked up at the speakers. 'Uganda Airlines regrets to announce the cancellation of flight QU 772 to London, due

to a hurricane that has struck Gatwick Airport. Will passengers in transit
please return to the check-in desk to reclaim their baggage? We apologise
to our passengers for any inconvenience.' Hurricane? Inconvenience?
What was all this? Just who did they think they were fooling? But Ann
confirmed that she had heard the closing headlines on the BBC that
morning, and that there had indeed been something about a hurricane
hitting the south of England.

'They didn't say anything about closing down the airports, though,'
she moaned. 'And I have to be somewhere tomorrow.'

'Well, I'm not too happy about it either,' I said. I knew then that I
was going to have to spend two more days in a plastic transit lounge,
protected from the law enforcement agencies of a country which had
just turfed me out only by the niceties of IATA codes of practice. I
wondered if they'd hold up under the strain, and I began wishing
that I'd given that money to the Christians in Nairobi. Meanwhile,
before setting off for Kampala, Ann promised that she'd phone Dave,
and Gordon Brown at the BHC, to let them know what had happened.

They didn't wait very long. They waited, in fact, some five minutes
after the transit lounge had emptied of passengers, and then they came
for me. There was Squinty-Mouth, of course, and he was flanked
by Bad-Eyes and another security man who was taller than his two
colleagues, but not by very much. Their very tininess made them look
all the more menacing. 'By the powers vested in me by the Ugandan
government . . .' began Squinty-Mouth.   'Oh no,' I groaned, standing
up ready to resist arrest, my chances not improved by the fact that I'd
just removed a shoe to straighten an errant sock.

'I hereby inform you that you are to be taken to a place of
safekeeping until such time as your onward flight is ready to depart
for London.' He sounded as if he should have been wearing a black
cap.

It was the moment for which four years spent in Uganda had
prepared me: what they were trying to do was illegal, and if they got
me as far as a 'place of safekeeping', I knew full well that it might be
a lot harder to persuade them to bring me back again. For one thing,
I would have been a PI, a prohibited immigrant, illegally present in
their country, and therefore liable to the due process of law. I raised
my voice – not quite to the point of shouting, but as if addressing a
public meeting – and gave them back some bad eyes of my own.

'Oh no you don't,' I said. 'I knew you'd try this one on. I'm a
passenger in international transit, and as such you have no rights over
me whatsoever. My high commission is fully appraised of where I am,
and why I am here, as is the press, both here and in Nairobi. And if

any of you so much as lay a finger on me, you are liable to start an international incident.'

Now this, of course, was not entirely on the level. There was going to be no international incident on my behalf; or if there was, it was likely to be only a very small one. And I could hardly see any front-page headlines prompted by my being lifted from a transit lounge. But my counter-attack had very much the desired effect, for the three of them stopped in their tracks, with nobody quite sure of what to do next. In addition, two Danish men who had just sat down in the cafeteria pricked up their ears, and asked me what was wrong. I called them over to explain. Whereupon the younger of the two, who looked about seventeen, informed Squinty-Mouth that he also was a journalist, and would undoubtedly get a lot of space in the European newspapers, and air time on the BBC and Deutsche Welle, if they tried to arrest me illegally. And it worked. There were a few words muttered between the three officials, and then they turned to leave. But I called them back. Now was the time to press home the advantage.

'And Mr Immigration Chief, sir. Since it appears that I am going to have to spend the next two days sitting in your transit lounge, I would appreciate it if you would send me someone from Uganda Airlines, so that they can arrange to keep me fed during that period. And also, I would suggest that you provide me with a policeman, or someone who can guard me, so that you can rest easy that I'm not going to try to sneak into Uganda while your back is turned.' I didn't mention that the policeman would be as much for my protection as theirs.

'I'll see,' he said. But a policeman and a steward from Uganda Airlines arrived within the hour.

Meanwhile, I sat down with the two Danes who'd saved my bacon. They were kind to me; they bought me drinks, and the older man gave me a handful of Ugandan money – I'd spent the last of mine on that final bottle of beer. He also phoned the British High Commission, and came back later to tell me that Gordon Brown was advising me to keep cool. 'He said that you tended to exaggerate the dangers a little bit. I told him that I'd seen you almost being taken into custody, and he replied that you should contact him if something actually happens.'

'Well, thanks a lot, Gordon,' I said. But overall, I knew that both the high commissions in Nairobi and Kampala had done all right by me. It turned out later that Gordon had actually driven down to the airport twice, once on Wednesday, and again on Friday, so I could hardly expect him to come running yet again. Anyway, for the time being at least, it seemed that I was safe.

Presently the Danes set off for their hotel, and since there were no more flights due to leave from the airport that day, I was left to chat with the police guard. And then, when he went off duty at six o'clock, I was quite alone in the huge departure hall. For the first time since the beginning of the saga four days earlier, I had a chance to sit down and try to work out just why I had been expelled. The first explanation that sprang to mind involved my several clashes with Military Intelligence. Most significant, of course, had been the business of the 'Killing Fields' article: perhaps it had been decided beyond reasonable doubt that I must, after all, have been the author, and Katsigazi had merely made good his threat. In addition, there had been the botched Gulu report, my attempts to help Arthur Stern, the cattle-rustling episode, and my other brushes with authority such as at the Speke fire, and the meeting with Sue's sister. The second possibility involved higher authorities: perhaps my repeated attempts to visit the Luzira detainees, and my list of questions to Museveni, had been perceived as tweaking the lion's tail a bit too hard. The third possibility, of course, involved the sensitive subject of AIDS. It was not inconceivable that in certain circles I was felt to be asking just too many awkward questions; that my articles were considered to have 'spoilt the good name of Uganda'. And if the problem had indeed been the AIDS research, this might explain why Kenya, also, had seen fit to expel me.

Then I began to think of all the other work that I had been planning to do for the book: the interviews with doctors and researchers, a trip along the trans-African highway with one of the truckers, a meeting with one of the witch-doctors from Kyotera and, most important of all, the trip to Kalisizo to see the health education and home care being done by Robert Sango's team. I realised that none of this would now get done; indeed, that unless someone could bring my notes and tapes out of Uganda, there was not going to be any book at all.

Later, I stood and watched as the sun, in a defiant blaze of orange, was snuffed out in the vast expanse of Lake Victoria, and I wished that I was not separated from the sounds and smells and fresh air by 12-foot-high panes of glass. Meanwhile, on the radio, the safe middle-class voices of my homeland gave the latest news about the hurricane, the reception now so clear that it seemed as if the newsreader was standing by the window beside me. It was a discordant experience: on one level I felt profoundly sad that I would soon be leaving all this behind; on another, I felt tired and nervous about what the next thirty-six hours would bring, and eager to be back in England. I began to wish that there was a phone in the transit lounge, so I could check how things were going with Sue – whether she had a ticket, whether she was booked on the Sunday flight, whether, indeed, she had even managed to locate her passport. But on reflection, I saw that it was as well that I couldn't do so; there was always the chance that I would end up giving her away to the authorities, and of her being arrested on arrival at the airport, merely for being my girlfriend. It was only when the replacement policeman appeared at around eight o'clock that I realised that I'd been guarding myself for the past two hours.

On the Saturday morning, to my amazement, Jack Maumbe-Mukwana wandered in. He told me that he had popped by to get some whisky for a dinner party he was holding that evening, though why he should have to come to Entebbe to purchase in dollars, rather than buying for Uganda shillings in Kampala, I had no idea. In any case, he sat down with me for twenty minutes, and listened to my account of what had happened, and then told me how sorry he was, and asked me what I thought might be behind it. I told him my ideas, and he commented that the country had a very open policy about AIDS, so he didn't think it could be that. He promised to look into the matter on Monday, and see what could be done. I pointed out that, barring further hurricanes or acts of God, I would be in England by then. Unless, of course, there were any further attempts by security personnel to remove me illegally from the transit area – and I nodded towards the Two Stubbies, who had sat down attentively some 20 yards away.

'You've got to understand that I'm just a deputy minister,' he said. 'I have absolutely no authority over these boys.' And as he got up to go, the two intelligence officers also rose, and he said, for their benefit, as much as mine, 'No, I'm sure that these officers won't be harassing you at all, Mr Hooper. You can be assured of that.' And he walked out with them. I felt somewhat reassured.

A number of flights left for other destinations during the day, and I knew several of the passengers; two or three of them promised to phone journalist friends of mine when they landed, which was another reassurance. I also began to make friends with some of the other officials on duty, and one of them told me about the several different types of security personnel who were present at the airport. There were the traditional ones – immigration officers, police, and airport security; and then there were the rather less official ones, from Military Intelligence and the President's Office. The Stubbies, I was told, were from the latter category, and my informant apparently disliked them almost as much as I did. Later I was told that, in an attempt to find out what I was up to, they were asking questions of anyone who spoke to me, and that they were saying that I was 'felt to be subversive'.

Subversive or no, I was becoming quite hungry. Towards the end of Saturday afternoon, after the departure of the last flight, I was suddenly presented with a large bill, in dollars, by the airport restaurant, which had been supplying me with my meals. This was surely a try-on, for Uganda Airlines had already undertaken to feed me during my enforced stopover, but the Asian manager persisted. In the end I refused to pay, agreeing only to countersign all the bills. And that evening, the meal that I was brought from the upstairs hotel restaurant consisted of a dry chunk of meat, a spoonful of gravy, and two hard pieces of potato. I sent it back in disgust, and it duly came back with an extra piece of potato. Someone had decided that I was going to suffer a bit on my last night in Africa.

But I didn't. Instead I had a party. There were two police guards with me that evening, and some members of airport security wandered in to join us, and I broke out the bottle of tequila. Someone went upstairs and managed to find some salt and lemon, and someone else brought a couple of bottles of beer. And that's how I spent my last night in Uganda, just as I had spent the first one, nearly eight years before: drinking and talking; conversation and good fellowship.

Someone explained at length just how it was possible to survive on such paltry salaries, how tips and favours and blind eyes kept the wolf from the door. I told them about Slim: how it was caught, how to avoid it, how many people had so far died from the disease, how many were probably already infected. I pointed out that, if we took ourselves to be an average group of urban adults from this area, then the probability was that at least one of the seven of us sat around the table already had the virus.

Later, they asked me why I'd been thrown out of the country. I thought about that one for a while, and finally told them it was probably because of a certain lack of tact. That when you worked as a reporter in a foreign country, it was generally accepted that you didn't criticise that country too much: you didn't say there was too much killing by the army, too much corruption, too much Slim disease. And that while I had never, I felt, been overly critical of this government, which I still believed to be a considerable improvement on its predecessors, I retained the right to ask questions, and to make critical observations, just as I had criticised Obote's government in the Minority Rights Group report. For as soon as one lost the freedom to comment upon the fact that the resistance committee system was not working well in some areas; that there was still fighting in much of the north and the east; that respect for human rights had deteriorated during the previous nine months; that people were being thrown into prison illegally; that one of the reasons why AIDS was spreading so fast in the country was that a lot of people were having sex with more than one partner; that some of the officials appointed to help fight the disease were dragging their feet due to political cowardice . . . as soon as one felt constrained not to mention such issues because one knew that this was a Third World country which had been exploited by its colonial masters, or because one liked its people, and knew that they were poor in a way that most Westerners couldn't even imagine, or because one had a nice house, and a regular income, and a good bunch of friends, and one didn't want to lose them – then one had sold out the very principles that a journalist was meant to uphold.

The tequila was finished, so I rummaged in my bag, and brought out the bottle of calvados, pouring a tot into each of the seven plastic beakers on the table. I knew that I was getting carried away with my own rhetoric, that some of those present had lost my train of thought several clauses ago, that, to an extent, I had appointed my own judge and jury, and was making an impassioned plea in my own defence. But it seemed very important, on my last evening in a country which I loved but which had twice rejected me, to try to explain to some of its citizens – and perhaps to myself – why I had done what I had done, why I had had problems. We talked some more, but presently there was the sound of footsteps approaching slowly up the stairs from the ground floor, and then a small, sturdy figure began moving through the darkness towards us. When he passed in front of the lamp on the far wall, I could see that it was indeed the Shorter Stubby. But he just kept on coming, in silence, until he was standing 4 or 5 feet to one side of me. Nobody around the table said anything, though there was a general straightening of bodies in seats. He was as a headmaster arriving behind the bike shed, an angry god descending among his flock.

'So, Mr Hooper. We seem to be having a little party.'

'Yes,' I replied, looking straight ahead, not at him. 'We do, don't we? Sorry we forgot to invite you.'

There was a long, long pause, during which the Stubby looked from one to the other of the assembled officials, and they shrivelled before my eyes. Then I could feel him turn back to me, and I realised that he was drunk; I could even smell the whisky fumes. And I knew that he wanted to say something back to me, something witty and acerbic, but nothing suitable had come to mind. Finally, he barked two names, together with a clipped order in Kiswahili. Two of my drinking companions sat up straight and put on their berets; one had to tie up his boots as well. Stubby looked on in disgust. Then he walked away, quicker now, with the other two following, the policeman still trying to put on his belt as he went.

There was now an unmistakable mood of nervousness around the table, and nobody wanted to talk any more. After a while, a couple of my companions began to fall asleep. Finally, I asked one of the airport security men whether they were going to be in trouble for talking to me, or drinking with me.

'We could be. I don't know; this man is very upset with us, as you can see. Maybe he is upset with you too.'

If a problem was going to develop, it didn't seem a good idea for us all to be asleep. I suggested that we took it in turns to stay awake, and they agreed. It was now half-past one; the policeman and myself would wait up until half-past three, after which the other two officials would take over. But at this point the first policeman hurried back, and told two of the others to go with him. 'Looks like he's really wanting to know what I was saying, doesn't it?' I asked the junior policeman, when they'd left. The seventh man was now curled up on a row of seats, fast asleep.

'Don't worry. Nobody's going to tell him anything,' he grunted. But some ten minutes later, he started walking across towards the stairwell.

'Hey, where are you going?' I asked, nervous now for the first time about my own safety.

'I need some cigarettes,' he called back. 'I won't be away long.'

'Well, make sure you're not. Remember you're supposed to be guarding me.'

Fifteen minutes passed, then twenty, and by this time I was getting really worried. I realised that the Stubbies had called everyone away so that there would be no witnesses when they came upstairs to kidnap me. I was furious with myself for letting it happen; I should have hung on to the last policeman at all costs. Eventually, I woke the other man, who was airport security, but he seemed drunk, and not able to understand the importance of what I was saying. Almost as soon as I stopped explaining to him, he fell asleep again.

After a while, I heard a noise from the far end of the concourse. There was surely someone there in the darkness, trying to move very quietly. Jesus, would they be prepared to shoot me in here? It wouldn't be difficult to set up: I had been attempting to escape, to grab a gun; there had been an unfortunate accident.

More scared now than I cared to admit, I decided to confront my fears by walking towards the noise. Better at least to see who I was up against. Very slowly, and as quietly as possible, I slipped down the outside walkway, but keeping well away from the windows. Thirty yards, 40 yards – I had nearly got to where the sound had seemed to come from. Just here was a display area, where some of the residents (or former residents) of Uganda's national parks were standing in stuffed splendour: this end of the lounge had no lights at all, so the tableau was illuminated only by the moonlight shafting in through the great windows.

There was a huge lion with shaggy mane, a rhino, then a buffalo, and a hippo with its jaws gaping wide enough to munch a man in two; there was a kudu, an eland that looked too long to be ecologically viable, and a few other examples of assorted gazelles. I started to walk around the barrier surrounding the display, and then, suddenly, I heard it again. Unmistakably a human noise, somewhere behind me, near to where I had just walked. It sounded as if it was coming from floor level.

I moved back quickly now, to confront my nemesis, and was just in time to see a movement under one of the long airport sofas. I actually jumped backwards. But I stayed close enough to watch, and very slowly, as my eyes adjusted, I made out the figure of a man curled up underneath the seat, partly covered with an army overcoat, but still clutching his rifle. Presently he made another noise and then turned over, and I could see from the face that it was not a man, but a boy of perhaps sixteen or seventeen. A *kadogo*, a boy soldier. He must have been on guard duty, and had probably crept inside hours earlier, to grab some sleep in the warm. I walked back to where my bags were stacked, to get some sleep myself before the morning. The policeman came back at around three o'clock, and said sorry for being so long; he hadn't managed to find cigarettes anywhere.

Come the morning, I was sweating so much that I had to take two showers in the men's washroom. Then the passengers started filing through into the departure lounge. Once again, Ann was one of the first through, and I asked her, in a muttered undertone, if she'd seen anyone who looked like Sue outside at the check-in counter.

'I'm sorry, Ed. I really couldn't say, there were so many people waiting out there. I should think that quite a lot of people aren't going to get on.'

'Don't say that, for God's sake.'

'Hey, you really are nervous, aren't you? Let me buy you a beer, or a coffee or something.'

I asked for a coffee. I couldn't bear to be talking to anyone, but I couldn't sit still either. What I really wanted to do was pace up and down, but it wasn't the place or time. Then the taller Stubby came across and asked, most politely, if he could borrow a copy of *South* magazine that he'd seen me reading.

'Yes, of course. Take it if you like.' But he brought it back, again most courteously, half an hour later.

And then the flight was called. The passengers moved *en masse* towards the steps down to the tarmac. I could see that someone else had just arrived at the immigration desk: an attractive young woman of about Sue's height, but in a jacket that I'd never seen before, and with a curtain of long braids that covered her face as she bent down over the departure form. Then one of the security men came and demanded my passport, and I refused, saying that there was no conceivable basis for such a request.

'Come on, Mr Hooper,' he said. 'Everything's gone very well so far. Let's not have any problems at the end. I have to give your passport to the pilot of the plane, to hold until you land at London. If you refuse, we'll just have to pull you off the flight, and you'll wait here in the transit lounge for another few days.' I handed it over, and by the time we started moving down the steps, I could no longer see the woman with braids.

So it was not until we were already on the plane that I turned round, and knew for sure that it was Sue. She was in a seat six rows or so behind me, looking absolutely ravishing, and as we looked at each other, she made no acknowledgment at all. And for the first half-hour after take-off, I stayed in my own place, still feeling nervous, but chatting away to Ann. Then, looking out of the window, I saw the line of hills near Moyo where the Nile swings through in an enormous elbow from west to east and back again, and then resumes its flow northward. I had seen this place many times before from the air: Nimule, on the Sudanese border. We were out of Ugandan airspace.

Holding the remaining half-bottle of calvados, I went back to where she was sitting, in the row of special seats with extra leg-room. There was a cabinet minister sitting on her right side, chatting and laughing away, with the light of pursuit in his eyes. The seat on her left was empty.

'Excuse me, madame,' I said, using the Ugandan style of address for ladies. 'Would this seat be free?'

'Oh yes. You are welcome,' said she.

I apologised to the minister for interrupting, sat down beside Sue, and gave her a good long kiss. Then I poured some calvados into two airline beakers, and proposed a toast to our forthcoming adventure in England. Sue stopped me with her hand.

'What's an adventure?' she asked, and I had to think for a bit.

'Well, it's having a good time, with lots of excitement and getting into trouble, and getting out of trouble again ... that sort of thing,' I said finally.

'It sounds like what we do in Africa,' said Sue. I could feel my skin tingling. We touched beakers and drank.

27 · LOOSE ENDS

Settling down in England was not easy. The foremost problem was finding somewhere to live. My parents had just moved into a retirement bungalow by the sea, where the only sleeping space for Sue and me was in a corridor, end to end. This didn't work for long, so we tried hotels and bed-and-breakfasts, but we didn't have enough money to live like that for more than a couple of weeks. Friends, who in the past had been quite happy for me to spend a night or two in the spare room or on the sofa, were less keen to help out now that one person had become two. And there was no point in looking for a flat in London until I'd decided how I was going to earn my living.

Thus we spent a month lugging our several items of luggage to and fro across southern England, staying a night here and a weekend there. Sometimes we could pretend that it was just a holiday, as when we arrived in Lewes for the town's Guy Fawkes celebrations, but for most of the time we knew full well that it was not. The strain began to tell.

The crunch came one weekend, which we spent at a fairly remote youth hostel on top of the South Downs; it was supposed to be a 'Real Ale Weekend', though we were both too busy sulking to join in any of the fun. Instead we spent the whole three days in tight-lipped, furious silence. Every day between ten and five we had to vacate the hostel, and instead of inflicting our filthy moods on the other hostellers we marched off together, still in silence, up and down hills, into marshes and bogs, through gusts of rain and the bitter November cold. Come the Monday, Sue had had enough of England, I had had enough of Sue, and I phoned Uganda Airlines to book her flight back to Entebbe.

The situation was saved by my parents, who invited Sue to stay with them for a few days while I took off to see an old friend in Somerset. And suddenly the luck changed. On the very next day, I came across a sixteenth-century farmhouse beside a church in a quiet village, which was available for winter let. A week later, on 23 November, Sue and I moved into our new home; it was not a day too soon.

I made some discreet enquiries at the Uganda High Commission in London, and within a few weeks it became apparent, without anything being said, that my expulsion was not about to be rescinded. I had to bow to the inevitable. I would not be going back. No longer was there any point in denying authorship of the *New African* article.

Having abandoned all hope of returning, the next question was whether or not I would still be able to write the book. Fortunately, a few weeks later, Dave arranged for someone to hand-carry the tapes and notebooks on AIDS back from Uganda. And afterwards, down in Somerset, I spent a couple of days at the big oak table, skimming through the material. I had failed to get around to certain things, certainly: in particular I would like to have seen Robert Sango in action. But on the other hand my expulsion had provided a deadline for my research, and a natural conclusion to the story. It had also, effectively, transformed the book from third-person reportage to first-person narrative. I decided to go ahead.

At around this time, I took Sue along to the Hospital for Tropical Diseases in St Pancras, so that we could have our blood checked, once again, for the presence of HIV. It was Sue's third test, and my eighth.

In mid-December 1987 I left Sue in Somerset and headed off to Geneva to visit the WHO's Special Programme on AIDS. It turned out to be a hive of activity. Never before had I seen United Nations personnel with such a sense of urgency: I was impressed. So was Ian Pett, a relief worker friend whom I bumped into in the cafeteria; it turned out that he had just been signed up. In his customary tones of mild surprise he told me: 'It's actually a remarkably calm and good-natured programme: busy, but not frantic. And there's a degree of inter-professional respect which is quite exceptional. It could be the beginning of a great human enterprise.'

I did a lot of background research in Geneva, both at the WHO and elsewhere. Most experts reckoned that between 5 and 10 million people were already infected with HIV worldwide, but forecasts of the future extent of the global epidemic seemed to be rising all the time. The best ball-park estimates for 1991 (five years after the beginning of an effective global response) were of between 10 and 100 million HIV carriers, and at least a million actual cases of AIDS. Just over a third of all future HIV infections were considered to be potentially preventable by health education and other interventions, but it was only by the late 1990s that any such interventions would begin to make a dent in the rising curve of AIDS cases. It was feared that as many as half of those infected with HIV were African, and also that because of the low level of general health care, the rates of progression from HIV to AIDS would turn out to be faster in Africa than elsewhere.

It was on my last day in Geneva that I remembered that Barry Baxter, who had briefly worked for the ACP in Entebbe, was now working for the SPA as a country administrator. I located his office, and within a few minutes he was telling me all about the events which had led to his leaving Uganda four months earlier. It was an interesting tale.

He had actually been interviewed on two occasions by Mike Rukeba. On the first, in mid-1986, Rukeba had presented an identity card from a committee investigating corruption, which operated out of the President's Office. He had questioned Baxter – then working for the Ministry of Education – about the alleged theft of the seventy-five bags of cement, and Baxter had protested his innocence, saying that some of the Ugandans who had identified him as the culprit were perhaps themselves the ones responsible. Then, almost a year later, by which time Baxter had just started working for the ACP, he was summoned into the office of Dr Okware, to be questioned once more by Rukeba, who by this time had a card showing him to be a reporter for *New Vision*. This second interview was followed a few days later by Rukeba's front-page revelations, and shortly afterwards Baxter was told that the Ministry of Health had declined to approve his appointment.

Finally I had evidence of what I had always suspected: that Mike Rukeba had more than one hat to wear. His newspaper article had cited 'an NRA intelligence report' from August 1986 as evidence of Baxter's guilt; it seemed likely that he himself had submitted this report after his original interview with Baxter, and that his second hat was that of an intelligence operative working either for the military, or for the President's Office. The intelligence report was dated just one month after his journey down to Kyotera, as a journalist, with Jonathan Wright and myself, so it also seemed likely that Rukeba was not averse to wearing both his hats at once, and that his specific security role might include keeping an eye on the foreign press. It occurred to me that he might also have had a role to play in my sudden departure. His comments in the street that last time I saw him began to take on a whole new significance.

I did not, however, have a chance to follow up further, for suddenly the SPA Press Officer burst in and announced that Jonathan Mann was free to see me straight away. I had been waiting three days for this opportunity, so I closed the notebook, took my leave of Baxter, and set off upstairs to Mann's office.

This was the man who, more than any other, would determine the course of the world's response to the epidemic. And he certainly cut an impressive figure: moustachioed and well groomed, he looked rather like a spruced-up Groucho Marx. He was also more candid than one had any right to expect from the front-man of such an enormous programme, possibly because of his relative youth – forty years – and his previous experience as head of an AIDS research programme in Zaire. Whatever, it seemed he was capable both of admitting mistakes, and of admitting to personal opinions, both of which are unusual tendencies in the more rarefied strata of the UN. Of course he had to be a politician in order not to offend the more sensitive and conservative of governments, but he was also prepared to speak out when necessary, as he had demonstrated during his implicit criticisms of Reagan and Bush at Washington.

He began by telling me about the history of WHO's involvement with AIDS. The earliest significant date was April 1985, when the First International Conference on AIDS was held at Atlanta. It was there that WHO first canvassed researchers and scientists about the best means of response, and in early 1986 the creation of a separate WHO AIDS unit was approved. It began operations in June, with Dr Mann and his secretary working out of an office in the Communicable Diseases Unit. By February 1987, the Special Programme on AIDS was officially designated, and by the end of the year, the SPA was collaborating with over a hundred countries, including all those in sub-Saharan Africa. By 1988, its budget had swollen to 66 million dollars and it was working at some level with 142 countries around the world. When I commented that many doctors and scientists were saying that in terms of AIDS, the WHO had taken two years too long to get into gear, Mann did not disagree.

'But I think we've seen an incredible acceleration in this programme since the end of last year: we've made up for lost time with a vengeance.'

Mann was also frank about the difficulty of getting accurate figures for the incidence of AIDS in Africa, and conceded that in the past, apart from the obvious difficulties in recognising, diagnosing and getting laboratory confirmation, many governments had simply been reluctant to report their cases. But all this had now changed, he said, with thirty-seven African countries now acknowledging at least one case of the disease. And as for seroprevalence: Africa was actually showing the way to the rest of the world, with the national sero-survey now being field-tested in Uganda.

When I asked what struck me as being the crunch question, concerning the efficacy of health education about sexual activity, Dr Mann declared himself 'a sceptical optimist'. Then he added, 'People can change. Look at cigarette smoking in the US, and exercise patterns around the world. AIDS *can* be stopped. Governments and health systems have the responsibility to ensure safe blood, and that needles, syringes, and other medical instruments are always kept sterile, so that they do not contribute to the spread of infection. But the bulk of the responsibility is personal, and has to do with sexual practice: the number of sexual partners, the choice of partners, the use of condoms. These are the messages that people throughout the world need to hear. This is not a disease that can spread without people having any control. This is a disease of human behaviour.'

Soon after arriving back from Geneva I contacted the Carswells, Wilson and Margaret, and we arranged to meet up in central London the following afternoon. It turned out to be a chill, blustery day, and because the meeting-place that we had chosen was closed over the Christmas period, we ended up going to Canada House, where a kindly official allowed us to do the interview in the warmth of the foyer. It was an ironical venue, for Canada House lies just 50 yards from the Uganda High Commission in Trafalgar Square; the three of us, who had all been shown the door by that country, almost felt as if we should lower our voices.

First I asked Wilson Carswell for a little background history of the AIDS epidemic in Uganda, and he warmed to the task. He related how in early 1984, following a tip-off from a Zambian colleague, Dr Anne Bayley, he had checked through the well-kept medical records at Makerere, to find that there had been a sudden increase in the aggressive form of Kaposi's sarcoma over the previous two years. Later he sent samples of this new form of KS to Porton Down, where they were tested by Bob Downing, the virologist who later joined the ACP. In October 1984, Downing reported back that the samples (like those sent him by Anne Bayley) had contained HTLV-3, the early name for HIV. The following month, Dr Lwegaba alerted the health ministry to his fears about Slim disease, and an article about the Rakai epidemic appeared in the *Star* newspaper. In January 1985, President Obote instructed the Disease Surveillance Sub-Committee to investigate, and a team of doctors was sent down to Kasensero, where they concluded that the epidemic was due to poor sanitation. They also, however, took blood samples, which were later – at Carswell's prompting – tested by Downing in the UK, and found to be seropositive. Carswell duly informed the Minister of Health that he had AIDS in Uganda, whereupon he was himself appointed to the Disease Surveillance Sub-Committee.

That June, Anne Bayley and Bob Downing were visiting Uganda, and together with Carswell, and Ugandan doctors like Roy Mugerwa, Nelson Sewankambo and David Serwadda, they made a field-trip to the south-west. They had actually intended to visit Sanje (John Katamba's village), which was already known to be badly stricken by Slim, but they never got further than Masaka Hospital, where they apparently found 'wards full of AIDS victims'; all twenty-nine of those they tested later proved to be seropositive. This field-trip provided the basis for a medical paper that appeared in the *Lancet* in October 1985, which was the first published report of 'Slim disease' in the international medical press, and which concluded that it was 'not unlike AIDS'. I noticed, however, that Dr Carswell seemed embarrassed about the article, and when I located it in a medical library I realised why. For although the authors found that all those patients who presented with Slim disease, ARC, or aggressive KS tested positive for HTLV-3, there were also some rather dubious findings, such as the Tanzanian traders who, most unusually, 'admitted to both heterosexual and homosexual casual contacts', and the four out of ten 'sexually immature control patients' (one nine-, one eleven- and two thirteen-year-olds) who tested seropositive. The paper also suggested that since aggressive KS had been reported in Uganda from as far back as 1962, then AIDS might also have been present, even endemic, since that time. But these were early days for AIDS research in Africa, days when the papers of Biggar and Saxinger were still seen as seminal texts.

By December 1985, Dr Carswell had collected 110 confirmed cases of HTLV-3 from Kampala, Masaka, Rakai, Gulu, and other of Uganda's districts, and he briefed a meeting of senior medical staff from the Ministry of Health, including Louis Ochero, who was in charge of general health education, and Dr Okware, the secretary of the Disease Surveillance Sub-Committee, about the AIDS epidemic in the country. One month later the NRA took Kampala, and in February 1986 the new Minister of Health, Dr Rugunda, appointed Dr Okware to take over as the sub-committee chairman. Meetings continued to be held on a bi-monthly basis until September, when President Museveni (possibly alerted to the scale of the epidemic by the Rakai DA, Bob Kagoro) began to take a personal interest. Rugunda had Okware convene the sub-committee to brief the President, Carswell's own studies on antenatal mothers, blood donors and geriatrics were cited, and Museveni apparently responded very favourably. He promised a separate AIDS line in the next budget, and having been told that it cost 2 dollars to carry out an HIV antibody test, observed that it would therefore cost only 32 million dollars to test the whole population. 'We can afford it,' he apparently commented. But the money – actually a vast sum for a country in Uganda's economic state – was, of course, never made available.

But Museveni did authorise the upgrading of the Disease Surveillance Sub-Committee into the National Committee for the Prevention of AIDS; Dr Okware was still its chairman, but there was no longer any room for either Carswell or Goodgame. The inaugural meeting was held at Kampala City Hall that October; UNICEF, which then appeared likely to be the lead agency in terms of international assistance, was represented, but WHO was not. At the start of 1987, however, a preliminary visit by a WHO team led by Manuel Carballo laid the groundwork for initial co-operation with the Ugandan government. In February, the visit of a second team, featuring Bob Downing, led to the drawing-up of the justly praised five-year action plan, which was subsequently used as a model for many other developing countries. It also led to the donors' conference, and to the establishment of the world's first national AIDS Control Programme, but by then the Carswells had already left Uganda for the last time.

I next asked Wilson about the events which had led up to their departure. Who had been behind the February attack on their home in Kampala? He told me that it had indeed been perpetrated by uniformed soldiers of the NRA, and that this had been confirmed by a European who saw two soldiers leaving the house at around that time, and by the cook himself, who briefly recovered consciousness in hospital before his death. Apart from the two murders, there had been just one item stolen – the printer from their computer, though the whole computer room had been turned upside down, with books and papers thrown all over the floor. So what had been the motive? It was possible, Wilson said, that the previous month's article in the *Topic*, accusing him of being an American agent, could have been responsible. 'The immediate reaction of some European friends of ours,' added Margaret, 'was that it was a warning to us to get out while we still could. At the time we didn't see it like that . . . we were just stunned.'

Wilson Carswell commented that the quotation in the *Guardian* could not have been responsible, because the attack had taken place a couple of days before the appearance of the article. But I pressed him about the quote: had he actually said it; had it been on the record? He was reluctant to go into details, but he eventually said that his conversation with Murtagh had been for background use only, and that although he had made both remarks, about the Apocalypse and about parking space, the latter had actually referred to Uganda's chronic petrol shortage. About three weeks after the Murtagh piece came out, the Carswells were officially told they were no longer welcome in Uganda, though no explanation was ever provided.

I asked if there was anything else which could have contributed to the authorities' animosity. Wilson told me that two of his research proposals on AIDS had been given short shrift by the powers-that-be from as early as mid-1986; on one occasion, Dr Okware had responded to a proposal for an epidemiological study in Rakai with the accusation that Wilson was simply interested in getting a project Land-rover. 'But I think the Ugandans had wanted us out for some time,' he continued. 'Because we were talking about AIDS generally, AIDS is very bad news, and if we weren't there, there would be no bad news, and things would obviously get better.' It was not the only time in our three-hour conversation that Wilson Carswell was bitter and ironic about the treatment he had received, and it was not difficult to feel some sympathy. For the fact was that he had played a key role in helping Uganda respond to the threat of AIDS. He had helped identify the two main local forms of the disease; he had alerted others, notably the relevant ministers of health, to the epidemic; he had helped to fund research initiatives by Ugandan doctors out of his own pocket. He had been the prime mover behind the delivery of Uganda's first two ELISA machines, and the training of Sister Nellie in England. In return, he had been excluded from the NCPA, and later expelled from the country. Was it simply that others had been jealous of his pre-eminence? Or had he, as some claimed, trodden on too many colleagues' toes, and been cavalier in his research methods? As with many Ugandan affairs, my own expulsion included, the answers to such questions were not clear-cut, and depended very much on where one happened to be standing.

The Carswells both criticised the ACP in Uganda for its lack of urgency. 'The house is on fire, and they're still painting the fire engine,' said Margaret.

'No they're not,' corrected Wilson, 'they're just arranging a contract with the paint suppliers!' More specifically, they felt that having an NCPA which met twice a month to discuss AIDS was quite inadequate, when the minimum that was needed was a large body of people working full time. As for Dr Okware, Carswell dismissed him as a typical bureaucrat. 'He can't decide whether it's a big problem, and Uganda needs help, or if the whole thing's being overstated. So he veers from one to the other. When the WHO comes, it's a big problem. When he's away in Australia, he says there's no infection in the rural areas, and Ugandans don't use condoms.'

'And how do you see Uganda in ten years' time? How is all this going to turn out?'

'Ask Museveni,' said Wilson. 'He's in charge. He'll determine to a large extent what happens to young people in Uganda. And the big aid agencies, like WHO and UNICEF. There's so much work to be done, and they ought to do it together, laying off work to each other like bookies laying off bets. Instead, they're busy empire-building and having arguments.'

Then I turned to Margaret Carswell, and asked her the same question. She took a while before replying.

'There's two schools of thought. One is that AIDS is just another disease in Africa, to be seen in the context of measles, TB and so on. The other is that it's a very big problem, and maybe even a threat. I myself subscribe to the latter view. If they're right, we're being hysterical. If we're right, they're being complacent. We can't both be right; only time will tell.'

It was around this time that the Hospital for Tropical Diseases sent a letter to inform Sue and me that we had both once again tested seronegative for HIV. Perhaps for the first time, it struck me just how fortunate we had been; many others had given the virus a lot less opportunity to get into their systems, and had not got off so lightly.

But as it turned out, we were still not quite in the clear. Since the end of 1987, several research teams have reported the existence of a very small number of individuals who continue to present as seronegative on the standard antibody tests, but who prove to be HIV carriers when assessed by a more sensitive test that detects the genetic material of the virus. There are several implications.

On the one hand, it may be that such 'silently infected' persons are in fact the lucky ones, among whom HIV will not replicate, and AIDS will not develop. On the other, such findings inevitably raise questions about the reliability of all testing methods that assess seropositivity by checking for HIV antibodies, including ELISA and Western blot. All of which has left many people, Sue and me included, wondering whether they can be certain that their bodies really are free of HIV.

The 1988 AIDS conference circuit had begun. In May, the WHO was scheduled to host six different AIDS-related conferences in Geneva, together with the World Health Assembly, much of which would doubt-less be devoted to the same topic. And AIDS had become big business too; some privately organised conferences now cost upwards of 400 dollars to attend, though of course the press was admitted free. In January 1988, there was a particularly important AIDS conference held in London, a summit conference for ministers of health from around the world. Uganda was represented by Dr Batwala, the deputy minis-ter, who delivered a speech which lambasted the international press for exploiting Uganda's policy of openness 'for purposes of disinformation and propaganda'. Also representing Uganda was its ACP director.

Probably my main reason for attending the conference was to procure my long-awaited interview with Dr Okware. By this stage I had a very substantial list of questions for him, to which many emendations had been made over the months. I spotted him quite early on the opening day: he was busy castigating a reporter from ITN for some injustice in his coverage, and seemed a little taken aback when he saw me walking towards him. He promised to talk to me the following day, during the mid-morning break.

Later that morning, Dr Okware delivered his speech on 'Planning AIDS Education for the Public in Uganda'. He gave a confident performance, and his analysis of the theory behind health education programmes was compelling. And yet there were so many subtle misrepresentations. Once again there were the claims that AIDS was 'rare' in the rural areas; that the press gave 'distorted information'; that 'nothing must be hidden from the people'. As proof of the success of Uganda's HE programme, Dr Okware claimed that attendance at STD clinics had dropped from 'long lines in 1986 to only a few people a day in 1987', and that night clubs were 'complaining about lack of clients' – both claims where the kernel of truth had been spoilt by the worm of exaggeration; there is not, for instance, a single STD clinic in the country. Upstairs, in the HE exhibition, Uganda's display stood out as by far the best organised, the frankest, of any of the African nations. Meanwhile, downstairs on the conference floor, Okware was indulging in what Margaret Carswell refers to as 'the sort of window-dressing openness at which Uganda excels'.

And of course, I was never to get to ask the doctor any of my questions either. The next time I saw him, he told me: 'I've promised to see you, so you don't have to worry on that score.' But over the three days of the conference he came up with an impressive range of excuses. First he claimed that he'd offered to see me once in Entebbe, but that I hadn't turned up. Then, for good measure, he added that surely he'd already answered all my questions, months before. Later, he was too busy doing paperwork for the minister; then he promised that he'd phone me that evening (he didn't); and finally he told me that I should contact him at his hotel (it transpired that he'd moved out the day before!). On the last day of the conference, I managed to corner him during a coffee-break, and pressed him for a straight 'yes' or 'no' to my interview request. 'You write in your book that Dr Okware was unable to see you because of other commitments,' he told me. In the end, Dr Okware simply caused us both a lot of aggravation and wasted time. But it was hard not to see a parallel between his weak-willed refusal to refuse, and the national policy of not informing seropositives of their status.

Later in 1988, at the Third International Conference on AIDS in Africa, held in Arusha, Tanzania, Okware told his audience that among a group of Ugandans he had studied, the average number of sexual partners per person was 5.6 over a period of five years. Then he added: 'I think that one sexual partner per year is the minimum required to meet the physiological needs of an African. This is irrefutable evidence that we are not really promiscuous.' Although many of the audience laughed, other listeners felt that this was actually irrefutable evidence that the director of Uganda's AIDS Control Programme had still not fully grasped just what constituted 'risk behaviour'.

Over a year after my return to England, I found that I was still preoccupied with my expulsion, and the events leading up to it. During this time, I had virtually lost touch with Arthur Stern; he had written to me briefly soon after my return, but it was a strange letter, disembodied and full of embarrassment, as if he would really prefer to forget about Uganda altogether. Then, towards the end of 1988, I wrote to him again, saying I'd like to keep in touch, and suddenly we were exchanging regular letters and phone calls. What I'd failed previously to realise was the extent to which Arthur had been traumatised by his Ugandan experiences – and the degree to which he had become simply unable to cope with the spawning repercussions. Apart from my own adventures, and those of the people who'd been arrested with him, Arthur's fisherman friend – the one who used to take him out in a dug-out canoe – had been held in custody for a lengthy period, and Dr Gerry Kambites, a Canadian priest with whom he'd stayed on one of the islands, had been summarily ordered to leave Uganda some months later. Arthur had dipped his oar into Lake Victoria, and the ripples were still being felt on distant shores. Not surprisingly, he had

responded by consigning all this information to the burgeoning internal
file marked 'Unwanted'.

But now, at my request, he began to open that file, and some
interesting material came to light. Firstly, Arthur told me that his
captors still seemed preoccupied with the figure of Andrew Kayiira,
killed three months earlier. Apparently the Sese Isles, traditionally a
stronghold of the ancient Kiganda kingdoms, had also been an area of
strong support for Kayiira and the UFM. Arthur had stayed briefly at
a police post which was riddled with holes, the result of a UFM attack
in the days of Okello. And secondly, the question which, more than
any other, had obsessed his captors during his interrogation at Basima
House had concerned the way in which he had got his money. Early in
the proceedings, he had let slip that I had once brought 500 dollars in
cash (from some friends of his in London, who in turn had received it
from his parents), and the MI people apparently kept returning to this
point. He was eventually brought a statement to sign; everything was
accurately recorded, save that the reference to me and the money was
so vague that it could easily have been misinterpreted to read as if
I'd been financing him on a regular basis. Arthur objected, and the
officer-in-charge got angry, saying it was of minor importance. Finally
he made a token change to the text and Arthur, still exhausted by the
hepatitis, signed at the bottom.

A pattern, of sorts, had begun to emerge. If the MI officers were still
concerned with the Kayiira affair, they may possibly have suspected that
Arthur and Gerry Kambites, both of them North Americans, were trying
to organise some right-wing UFM opposition to the NRM regime based
on the scattered Sese Islands. The fact that I had brought out money
to Arthur may have led them to conclude that I was paymaster for the
operation. With the signed statement, the intelligence boys would have
had some hard evidence to back such a theory.

Arthur now felt guilty about having involved me at all, let alone
having signed the statement, but I knew what pressure he must have
been under, and was glad that he had now told me the full story. But
it made me realise that my days had probably been numbered from the
time that I returned to Uganda in June. No wonder that during my last
four months in the country, I had only to turn around to bump into an
intelligence officer, or a watchful pair of eyes.

One night, I woke suddenly with the strong impression of the
face of the security official at the airport, the one who seemed to
know so much about my past. I could still see the pale skin, the
slightly protruding eyeballs, and the large lips. In fact, I realised with
a start, the face was that of Patrick Karegeya. To this day, I have no

idea whether the two faces had become muddled in the dream, or if
it had indeed been Karegeya who used to question me knowingly as I
left the airport, a Karegeya whom I never recognised because I never
expected to see him there. Certainly, if it had been him, my failure to
know him, and my hostility, must have seemed very strange: another
entry in the file, another nail in the coffin.

I also began to wonder why back in June the deputy minister,
Maumbe-Mukwana, had sent me up to Basima House with a note
asking Karegeya to release Arthur into my custody. On reflection, it
seemed an extraordinary and irresponsible action for a minister to take.
But if Arthur's case had been widely discussed in ministerial circles, and
if Maumbe-Mukwana was aware that he had already been released and
driven to the Kenyan border, then the incident made more sense. In
that case, the note would have been a nice ploy to get me up to Basima
House so that I could be checked over as well. Pursuing this scenario,
Maumbe-Mukwana's arrival at the airport while I was stuck in transit
would have been anything but coincidental. It would have been confirmation that a man rumoured to be close to the President was himself
following my case, and playing a part in its resolution. The decision to
expel me, I suspected more and more, had either been instigated, or
approved, from the top.

All this was extremely hypothetical, though soon afterwards something happened which seemed to tie together some more of the loose
ends. I was up in London, talking to a journalist friend who had recently
returned from Uganda, and I was telling him the story of my arrest,
my escape from the OAU building, and my eventual interrogation by
Commander Katsigazi. When I first mentioned the name he looked up
with a start.

'Well that's interesting,' he said, 'because your man Katsigazi has
just been arrested for murder.'

It turned out that six men had been held in all, of whom Lieutenant
Katsigazi was the most senior. (The NRA had abandoned the security
device of referring to all its officers as 'commander' some months
before.) The six were accused of involvement in the death of a civilian, Kasirye, whom they had been questioning in connection with the
Kayiira murder. The five juniors had apparently been held in barracks
for several weeks; Katsigazi himself had been placed under house arrest.

'In fact, it looks as if Katsigazi wasn't part of Military Intelligence
at all,' my friend explained. 'We think he was actually in charge of
something called the Internal Security Organisation, which he was
running from the old OAU building. It appears to have been basically
a torture centre. There were beatings, electric shocks to the genitals,

kandooya, people being starved and shut up in cupboards for days on end; one man even had his testicles stapled together. A lot of people seem to have died or disappeared. It's probably just as well you didn't see too much while you were there.'

It appears that Katsigazi was never placed under proper arrest, nor was his case ever brought to court, despite promises by his boss, Jimmy Muhwezi, the overall Director-General of Intelligence Services, that it would be. In fact, if Katsigazi had been prosecuted, it would have been the first time that an NRA officer had been charged for systematic human rights violations, as distinct from acts of army indiscipline.

In March 1989, more information came to light when Amnesty International issued a report on Uganda's human rights record in the three years since the NRM takeover. It turned out that Arthur, also, was probably lucky not to have seen too much, for the report described horrific cases of torture by Military Intelligence officers. A man who had been arrested in Kampala was allegedly tied *kandooya*-style, taken to Basima House, and then killed by having a 6-inch nail driven into his head. Another man is said to have been killed at the same place by having a nail hammered into his penis, and by being stabbed in the stomach with a knife. All this, it seems, was taking place despite the fact that the NRM government had specifically withheld powers of arrest and detention from the new security services, which Museveni had promised would be a departure from their hated forerunners like Amin's State Research Bureau, and Obote's National Security Agency. It appeared that nothing had changed, that the same horrors were still being perpetrated by the very organisations whose brief it was to protect the people.

Neither did the rest of the Amnesty report make pretty reading, despite noting in its introduction that there had, in many ways, been a 'significant improvement in respect for human rights' under the NRM government. A number of extrajudicial killings and massacres by the NRA were documented, in the course of a 'brutal and indiscriminate campaign against rebels and their alleged supporters in the north and east' during 1986 and most of 1987. Neither had the anti-government forces behaved any better; throughout the conflict, Amnesty had apparently received reports of killings by various rebel groups.

In June 1987 the government initiated a new approach, offering the rebels a general amnesty which was eventually extended up to April 1988. During this period, there was apparently a tangible moderation of

SLIM

human rights abuses by both sides. Thousands of rebels and ex-UNLA soldiers surrendered, and were either sent back to their villages with seeds and agricultural tools, or dispatched to 're-education camps' prior to being inducted into the NRA. One rebel group which did not respond, however, was the Holy Spirit Battalion. In fact, the remarkable long march of Alice Lakwena and her supporters only came to an end in November 1987, and they managed to approach within a few miles of Uganda's second city of Jinja before the NRA finally routed them. Alice herself escaped to Kenya, where she was given asylum; the legend lives on.

In June 1988, the UPDA agreed to a full cease-fire and peace accord, which left only the Uganda People's Army and Joseph Kony's 'Holy Spirit Part Two' still fighting in the east and north respectively. But hostilities resumed in October 1988, when the NRA mounted a major new offensive in Gulu district, which reportedly employed classic counter-insurgency tactics such as scorched earth. Many were surprised that such an offensive should have been mounted, given the previous success of the amnesties, and the small number of rebels who were still fighting in the bush; one observer described it as 'using a sledgehammer to crack a nut'. In the course of the operation fields and granaries were burnt, and several groups were apparently incinerated inside their huts, including forty-five prisoners in one particularly gruesome incident. In addition, in another ugly memory of Luwero, over 100,000 people were displaced to camps around Gulu town, where conditions were apparently poor and food in short supply. Reports coming from the eastern districts of Soroti and Kumi at around this time told of similar devastation, and similar hardship among the civilian populations; one report by a human rights organisation spoke 'conservatively' of 1 million rural people being displaced by war in six northern and eastern districts.

Despite the peace accord, and the subsequent release of over 2,600 lodgers from Luzira, new arrests brought the number of NRA lodgers held illegally in civilian prisons at the start of 1989 back up to nearly 3,000. The Amnesty report declares that these would appear to be largely men who had been rounded up on suspicion during army sweeps, rather than actual rebels or rebel supporters. In most cases no charges were made, neither were records kept of arresting officers or the reasons for arrest. And despite the government's earlier announcement that it had released ninety-four children under the age of fourteen, other child lodgers apparently remained in custody. The report also notes that several persons freed by the courts (like the three UFM men accused of Kayiira's murder) had been redetained immediately afterwards by the army. Some prisoners, however, were better treated, among them the

journalist Francis Odida, who was released from custody on grounds
of ill health.

In February 1989, the NRM pulled off a major tactical coup by
staging, at short notice, the elections which had been promised within
four years of its assumption of power. But they turned out to be rather
different from the democratic elections that most people had envisaged.
The polls that were staged were for the resistance committees at village
level (RC1s); no political parties were allowed to participate, nor was
electioneering permitted; and a queueing system was adopted because
of lack of resources for a secret ballot. A college of those elected to the
RC1 then elected those at parish level (RC2), and so on through sub-
county, county, and district level to the National Resistance Council,
the NRM's parliament. The fact that fourteen government ministers
were removed from office suggests that the election was a genuine
expression of popular will, albeit one that was made within the context
of the NRM system.

Meanwhile, the NRA continued to grow: by early 1989, the estimate
was 80,000 and rising. Most of Uganda's ethnic groups were now represented, though some three-quarters of the NRA's High Command
were apparently still westerners. Discipline, however, appeared to be
weakening, as it became ever harder to trace who was doing what to
whom and why. The worst fears were that when the dust settled in
districts like Gulu and Soroti, the devastation would turn out to be
not unlike that of Luwero in Obote's days. As Ugandans are fond of
saying: 'When the elephants fight, it is the grass that suffers.'

28 · ONLY THE BEGINNING

Strange things happen when a community is frightened. During 1988, thousands of people began flocking to the village of Mbuye, near Kyotera, in Rakai district, where an AIDS cult had sprung up. A local businessman claimed to have seen miracles there: 'The sun moves this way and that. Rosaries fall from the sky; burning crosses . . . funny rainbows.' Others claimed that they had seen visions of the Virgin Mary, who had revealed to them that Slim was a divine punishment for adultery. Others again said that the Virgin had promised to return the following month with a cure. There are no reports of her having done so.

Throughout 1988 and 1989, reports such as this one continued to feature regularly in both the Ugandan and the British media. Rakai district prompted particular interest. According to Catherine Bond, in mid-1988 Rakai officials were estimating that 3,200 people (well over 1 per cent of the district's population) were dying of AIDS each year; but one year later a foreign aid worker just returned from the area explained that the situation had grown much worse, that thirty people were now dying of AIDS every month in many of the parishes of Rakai and Masaka, and that several households now comprised just the grandparents and grandchildren, the whole intervening generation having been wiped out. Catharine Watson, meanwhile, reported that in the worst-hit rural areas crops like maize, coffee, potatoes and cassava were already in decline, because there were not enough healthy people left to dig the *shamba*s, as well as attend funerals and look after the sick. (The perennial *matooke* trees, on the other hand, were continuing for the time being to provide food without needing very much attention.) Also in 1989, the Rakai project sponsored by Columbia University had to be suspended by the ACP 'because people were running away from the teams of researchers' – apparently because of a proliferation of rumours about American scientists deliberately 'planting' HIV in Rakai. Within a month the Columbia project had resumed, but Dr Okware told

a reporter that the influx of so many foreigners on AIDS research programmes 'may have increased the suspicion of local people', and soon
afterwards it was announced that no further research teams would be
allowed into the area.

However, the widest coverage of Slim in the Ugandan press coin-
cided with World AIDS Day on 1 December 1988. Four bands paraded
through Kampala city centre, followed by processions of people bearing banners with messages like 'Dance, Prance, But Don't Chance'.
A couple dressed in wedding clothes carried a huge banner decorated
with 'Love Carefully' and the big red heart. But most important of all
was President Museveni's address to the nation, read by Prime Minister
Samson Kisseka.

It was a particularly hard-hitting speech, and one which was presumably influenced by the preliminary results from the national sero-survey,
which should by then have been on Museveni's desk. It spoke of AIDS
as 'potentially a more serious threat to the security of the individual
than any social or military crisis'. Specifically, the President enjoined a
return to the 'social behaviours of our ancestors which forbade immo-
rality and irresponsible communal sexual lifestyles'. He recommended
that resistance committees should deal with prostitution and adultery
by fining offenders goats or cows, or by imposing corporal punishment.
He ordered the closure of unofficial clinics which might encourage the
spread of disease through dirty needles. He threatened new harsh laws
against people such as 'AIDS-infected sugar daddies and sugar mum-
mies' who knowingly spread the virus. Finally, he ordered government
officials to speak out about AIDS wherever possible, and especially when
addressing public rallies.

In Kenya, meanwhile, World AIDS Day got a different approach, with
the Minister of Health opening Kenya's new ACP offices at Kenyatta
National Hospital, and Dr Mueke, the ACP co-ordinator, stunning
reporters by announcing that Kenya now had 3,276 cases of AIDS,
or almost three times the previous official figure. Two months later,
in February 1989, papers read at KEMRI's annual medical conference
revealed that 44 per cent of 'sexually promiscuous women' on the coast,
and 27.5 per cent of those in Nairobi, had tested sero-positive, as had
24 per cent of blood donors and food handlers tested at Busia, a major
truck-stop on the Kenya/Uganda border. In March, it was announced
that Kenya now had just under 6,000 AIDS cases (a fivefold increase in
three months), and some 160,000 to 200,000 HIV carriers, or nearly 1
per cent of the entire population. It was apparent that a complete change
of approach had taken place; the Kenyan ACP clearly intended to reject
the old policies of secrecy, and henceforth wear its heart on its sleeve.

At the same time, more money was being pledged by donors; the estimated ACP financing for 1988 ended up at over 7 million dollars. And thus, after spending most of 1987 and 1988 deciding how to implement the WHO guidelines, Kenya began 1989 by embarking on a nationwide public education campaign, combined with special lessons on AIDS in schools. Twenty AIDS counsellors were appointed, together with 300 AIDS teachers, who were to recruit and train a further 5,400. A decision was taken to concentrate on cleaning up the blood banks at the country's various hospitals and clinics – partly, no doubt, in order to alleviate tourists' fears of contracting HIV through transfusion. Another area where Kenya adopted a different approach to that of Uganda was in the establishment of sixty-four blood-screening centres, where Kenyans could go to get themselves checked for HIV infection. Dr David Ndeteyi, of the National AIDS Committee, told the *Daily Nation* that 'the good news' about HIV testing in Kenya was that 'if professionally guided, most people will voluntarily opt for the test, accept the result, and above all, opt to live responsibly.'

As I write this, in August 1989, it is rather more difficult for me to comment about the progress being made by the ACP in Uganda. This is because I have apparently been declared *persona non grata* not only by the government, but also by the ACP itself; not one of the dozen or so letters which I have written to people working on the programme has been answered. Fortunately, others involved in the fight against AIDS have been more helpful: replying to enquiries, giving interviews, and sending batches of documents.

Due to the time-span covered, this book has inevitably emphasised the often faltering responses to AIDS which I personally witnessed during the early days of the ACP. It would appear, however, that since 1987 the Ugandan programme has made considerable progress. There are now five people, including two seconded from WHO, working permanently under Louis Ochero in the health education section, the linch-pin of the entire ACP. 'Training of trainers' workshops for groups as diverse as prison officers, university students and agricultural extension workers are being held, as are district-level training sessions. One of the key points is that each group of trained personnel is meant to 'cross-fertilise' others.

Already there are some telling clues to indicate that the population is becoming more aware of the dangers. The results from the 1987 Kasangati KAP study, conducted before the HE programme was properly underway, demonstrated that over a quarter of those questioned had had two or more sexual partners in the previous six months, and it also revealed some alarming gaps in popular perceptions about AIDS. Seventy-one per cent of respondents thought HIV could be transmitted by sharing clothes, while only 59 per cent identified sexual contact. And 37 per cent believed that insects could transmit the virus (though when a similar study was conducted in the United States, also in 1987, fully 40 per cent thought insects were carriers). By contrast, Catharine Watson has reported that in a KAP survey of some 200 Ugandans conducted in 1988, 90 per cent knew that the best way of avoiding AIDS was to have sex only with a single faithful partner; that even in a remote village, over 30 per cent of the people could correctly name at least three ways in which HIV was transmitted. Watson also reported that Ugandans were actively changing their sexual habits, as evidenced by the fact that there had been a substantial reduction in the incidence of STDs, at least in Kampala. This, she said, suggested not only that there had been fewer sexual contacts, but also that the genital ulceration that facilitates HIV transmission was now less common.

Condoms have continued to be a sensitive subject. In the past, Dr Okware has pointed out somewhat disparagingly that the 2 million brought in by USAID in early 1987 were 'not enough for one-third of the adult population to swing into action for one night, let alone have sex more than once'. Nevertheless, since October 1988 there has been some acceleration of the condom programme, with almost 10 million scheduled for delivery to Uganda's ACP in the twelve months following, to be distributed mainly from family-planning clinics and hospitals. However, Museveni's known misgivings about condoms are apparently causing serious repercussions for the army. It is reliably reported that hardly any condoms are being distributed to the troops, despite the Radio Katwe rumours about current levels of HIV infection in the NRA being more than twice those recorded in early 1987.

In addition to co-ordinating the HE programme and arranging medical supplies, the ACP has also overseen the national sero-survey, implemented a sentinel surveillance system at many of Uganda's major hospitals, imported 3 million pairs of gloves and rubber boots for health workers and midwives, organised the rehabilitation of both the VRI and the central blood bank at Nakasero, Kampala, and installed ELISA machines for blood screening at twenty-eight different centres around the country. It is conceded, however, that due to such problems as equipment failure, missing reagents, inadequately-trained staff and poor supervision, only six or seven of these screening centres produce consistently reliable results.

The total ACP budget for 1989 topped 18 million dollars, a considerable increase on the two previous years. This included 10.5 million dollars in WHO-administered funds, over 7 million dollars in bilateral assistance, and 0.5 million dollars from the Ugandan government. It remains to be seen whether all the money will be released, and utilised, as scheduled.

In December 1988 a well-compiled review of the first full year of operation of Uganda's ACP was published, co-written by members of the NCPA, and visiting WHO consultants. The review acknowledged that the ACP had provided strong leadership for the national effort against HIV transmission and AIDS; it commended the political commitment of the Ugandan government and, in particular, the President. But it also expressed concern about a number of aspects of the programme. Some of its more significant recommendations were: the need to decentralise the ACP, and to intensify its activities at district level; the need to provide more patient care and counselling; the need to obtain more KAP information, and to utilise such information in future planning; and the need for reassessment of the use of condoms as part of the national preventative strategy.

Another of the review recommendations was that the ACP should increasingly concentrate on co-ordination and technical back-up, leaving more of the implementing role to non-governmental organisations (NGOs) like church groups and voluntary agencies. A clue to the reasoning behind this lies in the continuing debate about whether or not to inform seropositives. In July 1989, over two years after the inception of the ACP, the NCPA ethics sub-committee, now chaired by Sister Miriam Duggan, was still battling hard to establish a consensus national policy on HIV testing, still promoting the idea that trained counsellors would allow more subjects to be informed of their results. Meanwhile, very little actual progress has been made: Uganda currently has just three AIDS counsellors, all of them trained as a result of initiatives by the NGOs.

Apart from the ACP, the single most important AIDS control input has been that of UNICEF which, in late 1987, initiated its programme of AIDS education in schools. Special workshops were established, where science teachers from many of Uganda's 7,000-odd primary schools were trained to teach a brand-new health syllabus that includes extensive information about AIDS and other STDs. The syllabus is designed to encourage class participation, and Ugandan children of all ages are nowadays acting out the effects of HIV on the immune system, telling stories, drawing posters, presenting puppet shows for their communities, and even learning how to care for AIDS patients. The response, even from young children, has apparently been 'excellent', and the government was so impressed that in early 1988 it sanctioned the adoption of an emergency education programme for Uganda's 800 secondary schools, even though the appropriate health syllabus had not at that stage been finalised. The scheme is not, however, a complete answer to the problem of sensitising the next generation, for only about 40 per cent of Ugandan children ever attend school. In addition, critics claim that the programme has been far less successful in up-country districts.

UNICEF has also played a major role in the Ministry of Health's training programme for the thirty-three district health educators. Because of the late start made on this programme, and its urgency, the DHEs were sent out to work in their districts in June 1988, half-way through their training, before returning to complete their classwork in September. All were fully trained by the end of 1988, and already some are making an impact: in districts like Masaka and Rakai there is now apparently a much more integrated response to the AIDS threat, involving collaboration between the DHEs, local hospitals, schools, church and women's groups, resistance committees, and community-based health programmes.

The assistance given to the ACP by NGOs is finally being acknowledged, and the churches and voluntary agencies are now actively encouraged to submit appropriate proposals for funding. One of the best initiatives has been the 'Answers' campaign of Rick Goodgame and the Baptists: apart from the Bible inserts, 'Answers' is now being produced as an eight-page leaflet which has been translated into twelve Ugandan languages. By late 1988, some 4 million copies had apparently been distributed, and almost 200,000 people had attended related discussion seminars.

Ninety-two per cent of Ugandans are said to be regular attenders at a place of worship, which indicates that the churches and mosques have a vital role to play in the fight against AIDS. As an illustration of the seriousness with which the situation is viewed, some of the nuns at the Catholic hospital of Nsambya are now privately advising their young patients that the use of condoms is acceptable and even advisable as a precautionary health measure. And the Joint Medical Stores, which co-ordinate supplies for mission hospitals of all denominations, are now providing drugs and dressings for AIDS patients at government hospitals as well.

Most of the NGO's efforts are being concentrated in the hitherto somewhat neglected areas of patient care and counselling. All of the Kampala mission hospitals, together with Kitovu in Masaka, have now established special AIDS clinics where urban patients and seropositives can go for counselling, care and support. But for PWAs in rural areas, or those living far from hospital, the only support available is that offered by the mobile AIDS units. The first such unit, the Land-rover delivered to Nsambya Hospital by Tom Rayner, did sterling work for over a year before finally succumbing to Uganda's potholed roads. Since then the Catholic relief agencies Caritas and Cafod have financed another such vehicle based in Nsambya, and two mobile clinics based at Kitovu; several other hospitals hope to have their own units operational shortly. By mid-1989, the Kitovu clinics had made over 6,000 home visits in Masaka and Rakai, tending to a total of over 1,000 AIDS patients. They concentrated their efforts on dispensing therapeutic medicines and providing easily digestible food; doing simple surgery such as the excision of abscesses; examining those who feared that they might be infected; and praying with patients 'to whichever God they know'. In some parishes, however, the arrival of a mobile AIDS team still provoked hostility, because frightened local people often viewed it as a harbinger of doom.

Paediatric AIDS is another area of major concern, especially since clinical diagnosis of AIDS in infants is much more difficult than in adults. Approximately 20 per cent of Uganda's urban babies are now born HIV-positive, though thankfully about two-thirds of them are carrying only antibodies from the mother's blood, rather than the virus itself. Hanni Friesen, formerly of Rubaga, is now working as a paediatric consultant for the Save the Children Fund; her experience in this field is much needed, for Mulago Hospital is now admitting at least three babies with AIDS every day (as against roughly twelve adults), and some 300 infected infants are regularly brought to its AIDS clinic. Meanwhile, four different voluntary agencies such as SCF and the Uganda Red Cross are helping to provide care for Uganda's 'AIDS orphans'; SCF have apparently recorded over 30,000 orphans, many of whose parents are likely to have died of AIDS, in Rakai district alone. In some areas, up to 26 per cent of children have lost at least one parent.

Perhaps the most remarkable independent effort in Uganda's fight against AIDS, however, has been that mounted by The AIDS Support Organisation (TASO) which, supported by funds from ActionAid among others, is the first such indigenous self-help group to be established in Africa. It was started in November 1987 by a physiotherapist, Noerine Kaleeba, whose husband was already dying of AIDS after being transfused with infected blood. Mrs Kaleeba discovered that many of the AIDS patients at Mulago had been abandoned by their families, and were thus missing the extra supplies of food which relatives traditionally bring in to supplement the meagre hospital diet. She began by supplying meals to some of these neglected patients, and before long her initiative had grown into TASO.

The organisation now provides counselling and material support (like soap and bed-sheets) for those HIV-positives and PWAs who attend its day centres at Mulago and Masaka hospitals, and makes regular visits to another fifty clients who stay at home. TASO provides therapeutic drugs to alleviate such symptoms as oral thrush, diarrhoea, and headaches, but it is also investigating herbal medicines, including one known as 'red wine', which seems to be having beneficial effects on several of its clients. Most important of all, however, is the self-belief which TASO tries to instil, encouraging its clients not to drop out of society, but instead to carry on earning an income, going to work, going to the market, taking part. In this respect, the organisation is highly successful, perhaps because the majority of its volunteers are themselves seropositive. Twelve of its original sixteen staff have themselves died of AIDS in the last two years.

It will be some years before anyone can determine whether the massive effort against AIDS being made by countries like Uganda is managing to turn the tide. But when I returned to WHO headquarters in Geneva in February 1989, I was not greatly encouraged. There was not the same feeling of élan, of a great human enterprise underway, that I had discerned at the end of 1987, and several people at the GPA (the SPA had gone global the year before) told me how tired they were feeling. 'There's a sense of depression nowadays,' one official told me over dinner. 'We're all getting stale; everyone's waiting for a medical breakthrough. It's only Jonathan Mann who keeps us all going. And we keep getting reports from Africa saying that people are beginning to feel over-pressurised by the constant barrage of information. More and more people are apparently being fatalistic, blaming the mosquito and so on.

'I'm afraid that over the next few years, the problem will get so bad that more and more governments around the world will begin saying: "It's your own responsibility. We've screened blood transfusions, we've supplied clean needles, we've warned you of the dangers – and you didn't pay attention. A lot of public services for PWAs are going to dry up, as governments become overwhelmed, and begin to leave each person to fend for themselves. And as for the West helping the Third World, no way. Within a few years the West will have too many of its own AIDS cases to bother about Africa. Europe and

America will be spending all their money on their own control pro-grammes.'

Thankfully, not everyone felt this way. There was much enthusiasm about the success of World AIDS Day the previous December, and Patrick Friehl, the man in charge of condoms, showed me a polyurethane 'female condom' which was causing a lot of excitement. It looked unwieldy, but he told me that field-tests were going well, and that it could represent a major breakthrough for AIDS control, since women were far more reliable about condom use than men: in one study of disparate couples (one partner seropositive, the other seronegative) by a factor of more than three.

The main reason for my visit to Geneva was, however, to try to find out the results of Uganda's national sero-survey. I already knew that there had been several logistical problems: insecurity had prevented the survey being carried out in most of the north and east, whilst the degree of panic which the arrival of the testing teams prompted in some southern towns had made it necessary to erase the words 'AIDS Control Programme' and 'Zero Grazing' from the project vehicles. Nevertheless, by the end of 1988 the sero-survey had been completed and analysed, and half a dozen people in the GPA had been informally briefed about the results. However, none of them was willing to say too much. I was led to believe that the final report had gone from Okware, to the new health minister Adoko Nekyon (ironically Milton Obote's cousin, but also a staunch NRM supporter) and thence to President Museveni, with whom the final decision about whether to release it now rested. All this did not sound terribly encouraging.

But I did manage to get a few clues. I spoke with Jim Chin, the GPA's chief of surveillance and forecasting, and to his colleague Steve Lwanga. They had prepared a mathematical model for a country of roughly Uganda's size (16.1 million population) and demographic make-up of rural and urban, and, using base-line data gathered from a smaller sero-survey carried out in Rwanda, had extrapolated the likely number of HIV-positives and AIDS cases over a five-year period. The results were quite alarming, and on a completely different scale from anything to which the WHO had previously put its name. Assuming that the transfer rate of HIV to AIDS remained constant, the model forecast that by 1991 Uganda would have 1.06 million HIV-positive people, and a cumulative total of 95,000 AIDS cases. (Extrapolating to the whole of Africa, such estimates would suggest roughly a million cases of AIDS in that continent alone by the end of 1991.) Dr Chin added that the model had been based on 'the most conservative estimates', and that in the light of Uganda's sero-survey results, it might be necessary to revise these estimates 'significantly upwards', even to double them.

Other WHO officials in the know all hinted that the sero-survey results had been worse than expected. One spoke of 'appallingly high' levels among young people in urban areas, and of over half the young women in certain towns now being HIV carriers; other reliable sources testified to urban seroprevalence levels of 25–30 per cent among adults in Kampala, and 40 per cent among those in Masaka. The final results from Dr Konde-Lule's Kasangati survey, conducted back in August 1987, were no less alarming. They indicated an adult seropositivity level of over 10 per cent, rising to 16 per cent among females aged between thirteen and twenty, and this in a rural (or, according to some, semi-rural) environment.

But it was not until the AIDS conference held in Montreal in June 1989 that a poster prepared by the Ugandan VRI briefly appeared, disclosing a few of the official sero-survey results. Apparently 12.1 per cent of rural adults tested in Central province, 6.6 per cent of those in West Nile, and 5.7 per cent of those in Western province had proved seropositive; no figures were given for urban areas, though seroprevalence was said to be 'high'. Extrapolating from this, it would seem likely that at the time of Uganda's sero-survey about 8 per cent of the country's rural adults, over 20 per cent of urban adults, and perhaps 5 per cent of the total population (that is 800,000 people, including infants) were already HIV carriers.

If indeed such a percentage of the nation was infected in late 1987 and early 1988, then the repercussions are not only grim for Uganda, but also for other countries. Many scientists believe that despite the concomitant risk factors that particularly apply in Africa – like the high prevalence of GUD which facilitates HIV transmission, and the low general standard of health care which makes it easier for opportunistic infections to take hold – it is only a matter of time before continents like Europe, America and Asia get their own widespread heterosexually-transmitted AIDS epidemics. One can only imagine what the response would be if one in every twenty Britons or Americans – men, women and children alike – was found to be infected with the deadly virus.

The officially-reported totals of Ugandan AIDS cases remain comparatively low. As of August 1989, the WHO had been informed of 6,772 cases, although considerably more confirmed cases – 9,145, to be precise – had already been recorded by the Ugandan ACP in its surveillance report of 30 June 1989. The reasons for the discrepancy were not clear. Of the 9,145 cases, 11.6 per cent were paediatric, consisting of 1,017 under-fives, and 46 children aged between five and eleven. The ACP has itself acknowledged that there is under-reporting, and this is evidenced by the fact that only just over 500 cases were recorded from among the 270,000 residents of Rakai district. Officials in Geneva believe that the actual number of AIDS cases in the country could be roughly five times greater, and that the totals are probably doubling every twelve to eighteen months.

Although there is still no official figure, or estimate, for Uganda's population of HIV carriers, it is certain that the number is very high, (probably 1 to 1.5 million people by mid-1989) and that there is a growing epidemic in rural areas. One hopes that President Museveni will have the political courage to release the national sero-survey results in due course.

Uganda is a war-ravaged country, still in a state of economic collapse, with correspondingly limited health care resources. According to the IMF, there is just 0.64 dollars available to provide for the annual health needs of each Ugandan citizen; even if one were to add on the current ACP budget, this would still work out at rather less than 2 dollars per head per year – roughly what it costs to conduct an ELISA test. To take a contrasting example from the Western world: the cost of medical treatment for about 440 American PWAs, at 65,000 dollars per head, could finance Uganda's entire health care budget, including AIDS. If the loss of lifetime economic productivity of PWAs were also to be taken into account, then Uganda's total health and ACP expenditure could be equated financially with the deaths of just forty Americans from AIDS.

But of course, as Dr Okware and others have pointed out, Uganda also has many other preoccupations in the sphere of health. Malaria, measles, sleeping sickness, cholera, dysentery and other diarrhoeal diseases: all are major causes of sickness and death, all make additional demands on that budget. In the light of such demands, the 10-million-odd dollars from the health ministry and the 18 million dollars from the ACP comprise a grotesquely inadequate total.

At Kalisizo health centre there is no borehole and no diesel generator; mains electricity is intermittent. Kitovu Hospital, Masaka, has been entirely dependent on rainwater since its water pipes were destroyed in the 1979 war. Given such working conditions, the response made to the AIDS problem by Ugandan doctors and health care workers has been exceptional. One such man, hard-working and committed, is Dr Anthony Lwegaba, the former DMO of Rakai, and now the NCPA official with special responsibility for Rakai and Masaka. Some time ago Dr Lwegaba had the temerity, in an interview with a foreign newspaper, to mention that his salary and the salaries of his colleagues were little more than a joke – a comment for which he was subsequently reprimanded by his minister and by the director of the AIDS Control Programme. In Uganda, the average salary for a doctor of Anthony Lwegaba's status is currently about 15 dollars a month at official rates, and less than half that in terms of real buying power. But he is one of the lucky ones. Because he is working for the ACP his wages will be topped up by a WHO bonus, and he will enjoy the luxury of occasional trips to conferences abroad, and the accompanying foreign exchange allowances. The majority of his colleagues survive on their salaries alone – salaries which sometimes do not even arrive on time.

I stress this because it is important that the instances of apparent inertia or slow response that have at times featured in this book be seen in their proper context. By and large, the doctors and nurses who run Uganda's health service at grass-roots level are battling tirelessly and bravely in the face of an overwhelming epidemic. Perhaps even more crucially, in Uganda – or at least in rural Uganda – AIDS is not treated as a stigma in the way that it still is in the 'developed' world. All over the country, men and women have eventually gone back to their home villages to spend their final months or weeks, and then to die. Local communities have, almost without exception, rendered the impossible 2-dollars-a-head equation viable by overcoming their fears, and looking after their own sick people.

So much for the grass roots – now what of the leadership? President Museveni's personal interest and interventions have, by and large, been indicative of a clear-headed and pragmatic response to the potential disaster that Slim represents for his country. His initiative in addressing rallies in the worst-affected areas, and instructing his officials to do the same, have more than counter-balanced some of his more questionable statements about 'banning' extramarital sex, even if his blind spot about condoms remains cause for grave concern. The government, meanwhile, deserves credit for its decision, from the outset, not to deny the epidemic in the manner of so many other countries, both in Africa and elsewhere. That courageous policy was rewarded in practical fashion by the generous pledges made at the 1987 donors' conference, which allowed the Ugandan ACP to begin a relatively effective and early response.

But as I have related, after that initial openness there was something of a tendency to shut up shop. The Carswell affair is a case in point. Dr Carswell has his supporters and his detractors, but he undoubtedly played a vital role in Uganda's first reactions to the epidemic. And in the end, it would appear that his main error may have been that he was the leading figure in the AIDS field at a time when Ugandan doctors – like Okware, Mugerwa and Sezi – wanted, understandably enough, to take charge of their own programme. It may even have been that, once AIDS was identified as a potential source of large sums of foreign exchange, his occasionally prickly presence became obtrusive, 'that he made the pool too clean for others to fish in', as another doctor put it. Nowadays, ironically, he seems to have been restored to favour; people are beginning to comment that 'his only mistake was to speak out two years too soon'.

After his expulsion, and after the successful donors' conference, a lot of Uganda's much-vaunted openness about AIDS became more rhetorical than real. In this book, I have focussed on the obstructiveness of Dr Okware, the ACP director, mainly because his was the desk at which the buck stopped, and thus his was the obstructiveness which I personally encountered. This is also, however, a reflection of his particular distrust of reporters, and his tendency to view them as opponents rather than as potential allies in the broadcasting of information – except, that is, on high-profile occasions such as the visit of the SCF president, Princess Anne.

As I write this, in the latter half of 1989, there does seem to have been a great improvement in the co-ordination and implementation of Uganda's ACP. However, there are still some basic policy decisions about which it would be interesting to question the programme director. Why, for instance, has he been so secretive about seropositivity figures, when to be so has only encouraged speculation? Why could he not have announced those that he knew, explained to which groups they applied, and added that until the national sero-survey was completed, none of them constituted a truly representative sample? Why has he placed such stress on not informing seropositives? To sensitise the whole community is an admirable aim, but surely health education alone is not enough, when counselling HIV carriers has been proved by the Pumwani team to be a further potent weapon against the spread of disease. Why – except to flatter the President – has he played down the usefulness of condoms, when their distribution, at least among groups of prostitutes, truckers, soldiers and the sexually mobile young, could have dramatically reduced the rate of spread? And why has he tried so hard to deny the reality of the spread of HIV to rural areas, a crucial policy error in that an effective response has thereby been greatly delayed? Dr Okware has held down a highly sensitive post for over three years now, but one wonders if he would not have served his country better by being more candid, and by striving less hard to put an optimistic gloss on the situation.

*

In the course of my three years of researching this book, I have spoken with a number of experts in their fields, many of whom have what would seem to be constructive ideas about how the countries in East and Central Africa can best confront the AIDS crisis. Some of these ideas are already being implemented but, I believe, too slowly; others have not so far been tried. I would like to conclude by mentioning the most significant.

The first and most practical intervention involves effecting a reduction in the prevalence of sexually transmitted diseases. The researches of several medical teams – notably Dr Plummer's in Nairobi – have shown conclusively that STDs, particularly those which involve genital ulceration, greatly increase the chances of HIV transmission. Plummer suggests that, largely because of the local prevalence of GUD, between 5 and 20 per cent of sexual encounters involving an HIV-positive female and an uninfected male in the urban African environment result in onward transmission of the virus. The comparable risk factor for Europe and America seems to be between 0.1 and 1 per cent. This is further proof that the promiscuity debate is, in many ways, a red herring. The major reason why HIV spreads so much more easily in Africa than elsewhere would appear to be simply that more of the population have genital ulcers – a testimony to the low level of basic health care that has obtained over several decades. Since genital ulcers can be readily treated by antibiotics, this represents a practical point of intervention, and one which would be affordable both by African health ministries, and by concerned Western donors.

It also raises the question of whether AIDS control in Africa should not have been approached, from the outset, from the perspective of an STD programme. Any such programme would, however, have to be carried out with the utmost care. Another reason for the appallingly high prevalence of STDs in sub-Saharan Africa today lies in the indiscriminate prescribing of antibiotics that goes on in unlicensed clinics, and the widespread availability of pills in market-places: both factors have assisted the development of resistant bacterial strains.

Dr Plummer has also reported that uncircumcised men are far more likely to have genital ulcers than circumcised men, and that an uncircumcised man with genital ulcers has a 43 per cent chance of getting HIV from a single encounter with a seropositive woman. The gist of his message is that the foreskin provides a safe, moist environment for the virus, which might help explain the high prevalence of HIV in Uganda, Rwanda and Burundi, where male circumcision is less commonly practised. My second point is therefore that, at least in such parts of Africa, a campaign to encourage male circumcision at birth might prove beneficial.

The third suggestion is that Africa's hospitals, clinics and health centres should be furnished with enough needles and syringes to reduce accidental transmission through injection to a minimum. And that unless screened blood is available, transfusions should be restricted to circumstances where a patient would otherwise be likely to suffer death or permanent disability. This is particularly important in the light of the recent rapid spread of resistant strains of malaria, and the consequent increase in the numbers of African children being transfused because of severe malaria-related anaemia. Similarly, in the light of high prevailing levels of HIV, such practices as tattooing, cupping, shaving, ear-piercing, and in particular scarification (the therapeutic use of which appears to be increasing in Africa) should be discouraged, at least when performed by 'amateurs'; even circumcisions should be carried out only by trained medical personnel, using properly-sterilised equipment.

The fourth suggestion pertains to a subject hardly touched on in this book: the close, and as yet not fully understood, relationship that exists between HIV and tuberculosis. In fact, TB is probably the opportunist infection *par excellence* in the African environment, though it has taken a number of years for this to become apparent. One recent study found that, by 1988, up to 60 per cent of newly-diagnosed pulmonary TB cases in East and Central Africa were HIV-positive. And because TB is so infectious, the seropositive TB patients are in turn causing further TB infection in the general (HIV-negative) population. This additional disaster for Africa necessitates the strengthening of TB control programmes, and closer collaboration between such programmes and the national ACPs.

The fifth important point is that, so far, too much of the response to AIDS has been focussed in the health ministries and capital cities; there has been insufficient devolution to the provinces and districts. This is particularly important in a land like Uganda, where factors such as war and smuggling have already helped spread HIV to many parts of the countryside. One area in which Uganda is rich is human resources, and all over the country I have met competent and concerned doctors, teachers, health officials, missionaries and resistance committee members who, after training, would be more than capable of accelerating the dissemination of the AIDS message at a local level. Ninety per cent of Ugandans live in rural communities; 50 per cent are under the age of sixteen; in most cases there is still time for information to reach them before HIV does.

My sixth point is that as more people fall sick, the demand will increase for home-based care and counselling, of the type already being carried out so successfully by the mobile AIDS teams and TASO. Both medical and moral support are greatly needed by those people in the villages who are already bearing the brunt of the epidemic. The training of more counsellors, combined with the recent development of several cheap, easy-to-use HIV testing kits, should also facilitate the whole process whereby suspected HIV-positives and PWAs are counselled, tested, and then, if appropriate, counselled again about such important subjects as how to avoid passing on the virus to others. On this particular point the Kenyan attitude, of believing in the intrinsic responsibility of its people, is surely preferable to the negative approach of the Ugandan ACP.

The seventh point is that it is necessary to accept that not only prostitutes, truck-drivers and young urban migrants, but also such people as soldiers, businessmen and civil servants, who are often dispatched to different parts of the country, can all be expected to have a relatively high number of sexual partners. Correspondingly, these are the groups which are most prone to contracting and spreading HIV; an assertion which has already been largely confirmed by sero-testing. And a single seropositive can unwittingly wreak a lot of havoc. A paper presented at a recent London conference concluded that the Nairobi prostitutes studied by Dr Plummer between 1981 and 1985 were each likely to transmit HIV infection to a further eleven partners. These are clearly the groups at whom condoms should be targeted; by whom condoms would be most likely to be used; and among whom condoms would have the most immediate positive impact in reducing spread.

Finally, sadly, it should be accepted that as yet, in Africa, there is not really much of a glimmer of light at the end of the tunnel. Even the announcement in mid-1989 that AZT can help delay the onset of symptoms among early-stage HIV-positives only serves to buy a little more time for researchers to come up with a 'magic bullet'; the findings are anyway of little relevance to the Third World while the drug remains so expensive. This is therefore not the time for self-congratulation about imagined 'openness'; this is the time for further levels of frankness and candour, in Africa as elsewhere. Until an effective treatment for HIV and AIDS is found, governments should be encouraged to divulge as much information as possible to their peoples about the state of the epidemic, so that every individual is fully aware of the potential risks of sexual irresponsibility.

An exhaustively-reasoned article which appeared in the German journal

AIDS-Forschung in 1987 caused considerable controversy by predicting that 70 per cent of all sexually active adults in urban areas of Africa could become HIV-positive within ten years unless there were 'radical changes of behaviour'. The article stressed that if, as seemed apparent, all infected persons went on to get AIDS, the results of such widespread infection would be disastrous for the continent. Productivity levels would suffer from the sickness, early retirement and death of both skilled and unskilled personnel; families would sink into destitution as they became less and less able to pay for basic essentials, let alone for such extras as medical and funeral expenses; population growth would be reduced or reversed as more women and infants became infected; extended family networks would be increasingly unable to support those, like orphans, who were left behind. It was predicted that the impact of AIDS would become even more catastrophic as rural areas became infected, and local food productivity began to decline. Some observers were sceptical about the high figure of 70 per cent seropositivity, but by 1989 the scenario was already beginning to be realised in some areas. By that year, according to reliable sources including officials from the GPA, Uganda's ACP and the UK's Medical Research Council, over half the young adult populations of certain Ugandan towns and trading centres, and even of some rural parishes in Rakai, were HIV-positive. It seemed likely that one such place was Kyebe.

It has been calculated that the Western world currently spends roughly 200 million dollars per year on AIDS control in the Third World, which is the equivalent of what the British spend on their pets every thirty-six days, or what the planet spends on military apparatus every two hours. It is clear that the so-called developed world needs to invest some of its cash right now – perhaps the price of a dozen or so of its missiles – to help Africa combat the spread of the human immunodeficiency virus. If not for Africa's sake, then for purely selfish strategic reasons. For, as the *AIDS-Forschung* article puts it: 'We are still only at the beginning of this disastrous epidemic in Africa. Africa today foretells the future for all other continents, unless there is an effective worldwide strategy for prevention.'

Only the beginning.

The Fifth International Conference on AIDS, held in Montreal in June 1989, was apparently the largest medical conference ever held, with an attendance of over 10,000. It was reported that 1 in 500 American college students now displayed HIV antibodies, as did one of every sixty-one babies born in New York City (and thus one in every sixty-one women giving birth). Addiction to the new designer drug, crack, was said to be responsible for soaring levels of prostitution and sexually transmitted disease (including HIV) in the inner cities. The epidemic of HIV infection was said to be running out of control, both in America and elsewhere in the world. Several speakers attested that a vaccine was nowhere in sight.

The Zambian President, Kenneth Kaunda, summed up at the end of the conference by saying that AIDS had to be stopped at any price. Unless a cure could be found, he added, AIDS would be just like 'a soft nuclear bomb' – silent, and with no explosion, but with an effect just as devastating.

EPILOGUE

It was August Bank Holiday, and Sue and I decided to go on safari. We packed a picnic, got into the car, and ended up in the late afternoon sun on the pier at Weston-super-Mare. We were strolling happily among the other trippers and the candyfloss, when all of a sudden it clouded over, and then began to rain. We ran to take refuge in the pavilion at the far end, the one overhanging the sea.

Sue had to go to the toilet, and I was waiting for her outside when I realised that I was standing right beside an old favourite of mine. The logo, stretched across the glass display screen at the end, identified it as 'Sharpshooter', and it was constructed by Gameplan, one of the newer pinball manufacturers, who had only in the last fifteen years managed to break into the market once dominated by names like Gottlieb, Bally and Williams. I was half-way through the last ball by the time that Sue came out of the Ladies, but I knew it was her because of the flash of orange from her cagoule. I kept my eyes on the machine, but then shouted to her as she began to walk past. She came over and put her arms round my waist.

Seconds later I made the shot which gives this particular game its *raison d'être*: a late slice with the right-hand flipper which sends the ball screaming up the far left channel, over the rollover button, into a rubberised post, and straight back down the channel again. Each time that the ball touched the rollover, 50,000 points rang up, and a huge metallic whoop of celebration leapt forth from the back of the machine. This was no mere electronic burp, like that of the Space Invaders machines which have done just that in recent years: this was a real shrill yell of defiance. And we whooped as well – it was impossible not to. But even with the double whoop, and the 100,000 points, I just failed to make a replay. It didn't matter, and I turned back to Sue in triumph.

'Do you remember it?' I asked her.

'Do I remember what?'

'The pinball machine.'

'Oh yes,' she said, realisation dawning. 'Isn't it the one we used to play at Buffalo Bill's?'

'It is. But not only that. It's the one we were playing that first night when we met. It's playing our song, darling.'

We were driving back home through the rain when I suddenly recalled, quite clearly, another of the pinball machines in Buffalo Bill's, the one with the inverted horseshoe which, if you got the angle of the shot just right, whipped the ball around, and straight back down to the tip of the other flipper, while somewhere on the backboard a rodeo horse bucked and kicked a bell. Five horseshoes, and you had a replay. When you were really hot, you could just knock the ball from one flipper, through the loop, on to the other flipper, through the loop, and so on. When this happened, the horse kept bucking, the bell kept clanging, and the other people around the machine would begin to cheer.

Suddenly it struck me that the pinball machines at Buffalo Bill's had all been like this, had all had a wild west theme. Even when the manager replaced them, the new ones had all had cowboys and cowgirls spinning lassos, leaning on corral posts, and so forth. Then I remembered the massive T-bone steaks on their wooden platters, each with its own small pile of salt and coleslaw in the corner. And I recalled the rickety leather saddles that he had installed outside in the yard. He had tried, at least. He had really tried to make it into a fine little bar.

I'd always assumed that Buffalo Bill's had closed down, as planned, in October 1987. But it didn't, of course. The new owners knew a good business investment when they saw one. They very quickly forgot all about their plans for a Chinese restaurant, and instead kept the place operating just as before. The clientele, of both sexes, was overjoyed; the tills raked in the money. When I'd first heard that BB's was still open, I'd felt rather happy about it in a sentimental sort of way, but since then I'd heard that four of the regulars had died of Slim, and now I found myself feeling unaccountably angry, even ashamed. I began to wonder how many others would end up losing their lives because of meeting people in that fine little bar and places like it. It was meaningless, of course. People who wanted to would always find another bar just up the road.

'What was that?' asked Sue.

'Oh, was I talking? It was nothing.' I was quiet for the rest of the journey home.

*

Home is a huge, old, rented country house, in acres of fields and gardens: we just happened to arrive on the right doorstep, clutching the right advert, at the right time. I sit at the word processor, and Sue tends to the garden, or cooks, or paints, all of which she does with some skill. Many days she sits in the kitchen, which is the warmest room in the house, and struggles for hours with her English books. It's worth it, for her speaking and writing are improving all the while. I haven't yet learnt to speak Kinyarwanda. Maybe next year.

Other times she brings in bunches of flowers and arranges them, with outrageous panache, in pots and vases. Or she comes into the study where I sit staring at the computer screen, and quietly sets a cup of tea and a couple of biscuits down beside me, and kisses the top of my head. We still have our arguments, of course, but I think we're going to be OK.

We're hoping that our friends in Uganda and Kenya are going to be OK as well. We really hope it turns out all right for them too.

POSTSCRIPT

While this book was at the printers there were three significant developments in East Africa. The first, according to a report which appeared during September 1989 in the Kenyan *Sunday Times*, was that President Daniel Arap Moi instructed the Ministry of Health to ascertain how many Kenyans, and non-Kenyans resident in the country, were infected with HIV. He also ordered that AIDS patients in hospitals be isolated, and all HIV-infected prisoners segregated from their fellows. He cited instances of people deliberately infecting others, and said that these measures were designed to prevent the further spread of the virus. With this move, however, Kenya joined a growing list of countries – including the USA – which have renegued on previous declarations that discrimination against people with AIDS or HIV infection is counter-productive to both public health and human rights, and should therefore be avoided.

The second development came in November, when President Yoweri Museveni shocked the Ugandan nation by effectively dismissing the triumvirate of major-generals at the head of the NRA. Two of them, Elly Tumwiine and Fred Rwigyema, were sent away on courses, while the third, the President's half-brother Salim Saleh, who had been the army commander since early 1989, was assigned to special duties with the army reserve – a body which apparently does not exist. Whilst many observers commended these developments as an attempt to introduce greater ethnic balance to the NRA High Command, and as a bid to curb such recent army excesses as the suffocation of over one hundred young Itesot men who were detained for three days in an abandoned railway wagon, other more cynical commentators speculated that Museveni had merely demoted those figures who had built up a power-base which could conceivably rival his own. In addition, they pointed out that the new army commander, Colonel Mugisha-Muntu Oyera, was the very man who had headed NRA Military Intelligence from its inception up to early 1989.

There was, however, little such speculation concerning the President's half-brother. In Uganda these days it is common knowledge that Salim Saleh – an honourable man, who has always stressed the importance of maintaining discipline and good behaviour in the NRA – has been sick for almost two years with a wasting disease.

The third development was the most recent of all. As I was completing my final corrections to the proofs of this book, I received a phone call from Ros Widy-Wirski in Geneva. Ros, who is as concerned as I am that the data in *Slim* be accurate, told me that he had just received a faxed copy of an article which appeared in a Ugandan newspaper (believed to be *New Vision*) on World AIDS Day, 1 December 1989, containing the first official results from Uganda's national sero-survey of HIV. Below is part of the article, as transcribed from a tape recording of our phone call.

790,522 UGANDANS ARE HIV-POSITIVE: the estimated number of people in Uganda with HIV has risen to 790,522 [765,272 people over 15 years old, and 25,250 children]. Of this number, at least 10,000 have developed the AIDS disease. The [new] Minister of Health, Mr Zak Kaheru, disclosed this yesterday at a press conference at the Kampala International Conference Centre. The Minister said that the overall infection rate in Uganda was 6 per cent, and this meant that 94 per cent of the population was not infected at the beginning of 1988.

In a report on the national sero-survey for HIV in Uganda for 1988 done by the AIDS Control Programme (ACP), three regions were covered ... In rural areas, 12.1 per cent of the population in Central region [was] HIV-positive; in Western region 5.7 per cent; and in West Nile 6.6 per cent ... In the urban areas, 21.1 per cent of the population in Central region [was] HIV-positive; in Western region 29.1 per cent; and in West Nile 7.7 per cent. Kampala city [was] 17 per cent HIV-positive. [All the percentages in this paragraph apparently apply to adults only, rather than to the entire population of the regions.]

The Minister noted that in any given group, females were relatively more infected than males, in a 15.9 per cent to 12.2 per cent ratio. Infected females were on average five years younger than men. He added that the peak of infection for females was between 20 and 25 years, while males reached a peak between 25 and 30 years.

Mr Kaheru said that the samples of blood for the sero-survey were tested at Uganda's Virus Research Institute by ELISA technique, and were confirmed by Western blot tests. Sixty-eight villages and towns were visited across the country, and 11,000 samples of blood collected. Unfortunately, said the Minister, due to logistical problems the northern and eastern parts of the country were not done, except in West Nile.

The Minister said that the figures were based on very good technical grounds ... [He] estimated that the number of HIV-positive infections for 1989 could be close to one million ...

This report represents the first official confirmation of the scale of the catastrophe unfolding in Uganda. It is believed that the decision to disclose the results was indeed taken by President Museveni himself.

E. H., Somerset
5 December 1989

GLOSSARY OF ABBREVIATIONS

ACP – (national) AIDS Control Programme

AIDS – acquired immune deficiency syndrome, the collection of illnesses and symptoms resulting from infection with HIV

Antibody – a molecule produced by the bloodstream to combat an antigen such as a virus or bacterium

ARC – AIDS-related complex, a milder form of HIV-related disease that often precedes AIDS

BB's – Buffalo Bill's Wild West Bar and Eating House

BHC – British High Commission

CDC – Centers for Disease Control (Atlanta, Georgia, USA)

DA – District Administrator (leading district official in Uganda)

DHE – District Health Educator

DMO – District Medical Officer

DMS – Director of Medical Services

EIL – Experiment in International Living (US relief agency)

ELISA – enzyme-linked immunosorbent assay, the commonest blood screening test used to detect antibodies to HIV

FOBA – Force Obote Back Again; anti-Museveni rebel group

GPA – the WHO Global Programme on AIDS

GUD – genital ulcer disease

HE – health education

HIQ – *Health Information Quarterly* (Ugandan Ministry of Health publication)

HIV – human immunodeficiency virus, the retrovirus which causes AIDS, known prior to 1986 as HTLV-3 or LAV; the HIV discussed in this book is the more widespread form of the virus, HIV-1 and in 1985 another strain, HIV-2, was discovered in West Africa (the term HIV actually covers a range of slightly different viruses)

HIV-negative – displaying no antibodies to HIV; uninfected with HIV (in this book 'seronegative' is used interchangeably)

HIV-positive – displaying HIV antibodies, and therefore both infected with HIV and capable of transmitting the virus to others (in this book 'seropositive' is used interchangeably)

IMF – International Monetary Fund

KAP – knowledge, attitudes and practices (a type of survey)

KEMRI – Kenyan Medical Research Institute

KS – Kaposi's sarcoma, a rare cancer of the skin and internal organs; there is a new, aggressive form of KS which is one of the common presentations of AIDS

MI – Military Intelligence

NCPA – National Committee for the Prevention of AIDS (Uganda)

NRA – National Resistance Army, the former guerilla army which in 1986 helped Yoweri Museveni take power in Uganda

NRM – National Resistance Movement, the NRA's 'political parent'

PWA/PWAs – person/people with AIDS

RC – resistance committee, the basic elected unit of the NRM political system, from sub-parish level (RC1) through sub-county level (RC3) to district level (RC5)

Retrovirus – a type of virus that contains RNA instead of DNA, and which therefore evolves considerably faster than normal

SCF – Save the Children Fund

Seroconversion – the point at which an organism begins to display antibodies, and changes from seronegative to seropositive

SIV – simian immunodeficiency virus, varieties of which affect several different monkey species, causing an AIDS-like condition in some of them

Slim – the commonest presentation of AIDS in East and Central Africa, characterised by weight loss, weakness and chronic diarrhoea

SPA – the WHO Special Programme on AIDS, now known as the GPA

SPLA/M – Sudan People's Liberation Army/Movement, anti-government rebels based in southern Sudan

STD – sexually transmitted disease

TASO – The AIDS Support Organisation

TPDF – Tanzanian People's Defence Force, Tanzania's national army.

UFA/M – Uganda Freedom Army/Movement, former anti-Obote guerilla organisation led by Andrew Kayiira; sections of the UFA were incorporated into the NRA in 1986

UNICEF – United Nations Children's Fund

UNLA – Uganda National Liberation Army; the Ugandan army between April 1979 and January 1986, which supported the presidencies of Milton Obote and Tito Okello

UPC – Uganda People's Congress, Obote's political party

UPDA/UPDM – Uganda People's Democratic Army/Movement, a group of anti-Museveni rebels who began operations in the second half of 1986; mostly Acholi from the former UNLA

USAID – US Agency for International Development

Virus – one of the simplest organisms; having no independent life of its own, it can only reproduce by infecting a living cell

VRI – Virus Research Institute (Entebbe, Uganda)

Western blot – another blood-screening test for HIV antibodies; more complex, but also more accurate than ELISA

WHO – World Health Organisation

GLOSSARY OF AFRICAN TERMS

Banda – small, round African-style hut, designed especially for the use of foreign tourists

Baraza – front balcony of a house, often used for sitting and talking; by extension – a meeting-place or public meeting

Basuuti – woman's gown of cotton or satin; formal dress for Baganda women

Bhang/bhangi – marijuana

Biashara ya Kuma/'BK girls' – scurrilous nickname for Bahaya women from Bukoba; literally 'those who sell their vaginas'

Butiti – string of tiny beads worn around a woman's waist

Chai – tea; a bribe (colloquial)

Enkata – cushion of twisted grass or cloth, especially used for carrying heavy objects on the head, or supporting them on the ground

Endwadde enganda – 'complicated diseases', felt to be cured more easily by traditional medicine than by '*muzungu* medicine'

Galabea – long white gown worn by Moslem men

Guhamiriza – cattle-dance of the Batutsi

Jembe – two-sided African hoe

Juliana – a type of cloth popular with Baganda women; the Tanzanian nickname for AIDS

Kachabale – a technique for sexual arousal, involving the rapid rubbing of the penis between the vaginal lips

Kadogo – boy soldier, usually of the NRA

Kandooya – torture technique in which elbows and ankles are bound tightly behind the victim's back; also known as 'three-piece-tying'

Khanga – a rectangle of brightly coloured cotton used as a basic item of dress for both sexes across much of East and Central Africa; *khangas* bear a pattern or picture, and usually a Kiswahili epigram

Kitenge – a basic item of women's clothing, originating in Zaire, and consisting of lengths of brightly coloured and imaginatively designed cotton, usually sold in two or three pieces, for blouse, skirt and head-scarf

Magendo – middle-man dealing, usually on the black market; smuggling

Malaya – prostitute

Malwa – local beer, made from grain

Matatu – small public transport vehicle with a box-like structure on the back; the large number of passengers carried, and the high speeds attained, mean that *matatus* have a poor safety record

Matooke – green bananas, the staple food in Buganda

Mayembe – spirits, usually evil

Misada – (literally) economic aid; Kenyan nickname for AIDS

Mulokoli/balokoli – born-again Christian/s

Muzungu – white person; European

Mvule – African hardwood tree

Mzee – old man

Nyama muchomo – roasted meat, usually mutton or goat

Olubugo – Kiganda bark-cloth burial shroud

Oluja – forecourt; neatly swept patch of earth in front of a Kiganda house

'Radio Katwe' – rumour (colloquial)

Saba saba – heavy field artillery, as used in the Ugandan civil war of 1979

Sambusa – small deep-fried triangle of pastry, usually filled with mincemeat or peas

Shamba – garden; plot of agricultural land attached to house

Tonto – local beer, made from bananas

Toto – boy

Wabenzi – rich or powerful men; those who drive around in Mercedes

Waragi – strong liquor, especially popular in Uganda, and usually made from cassava, dates or bananas

Wazungu – Europeans

NB *Ba*ganda refers to the tribe, *Mu*ganda to an individual, *Bu*ganda to the home region, *Ki*ganda to customs and traditions, and *Lu*ganda to the language. The same prefixes apply to other Bantu groups.

On occasions, for ease of understanding in this book, African words have been pluralised by adding the letter 's'.